Core Connections, Course 2
Second Edition*, Version 5.0, Volume 1

Managing Editors / Authors

Leslie Dietiker, Ph.D., Director of Curriculum (Both Editions)
Boston University
Boston, MA

Evra Baldinger (First Edition)
University of California, Berkeley
Berkeley, CA

Michael Kassarjian (2nd Edition)
CPM Educational Program
Kensington, CA

Barbara Shreve (First Edition)
San Lorenzo High School
San Lorenzo, CA

Misty Nikula (2nd Edition)
CPM Educational Program
Bellingham, WA

Contributing Authors

Elizabeth Baker
Zane Middle School

Tara Bianchi
American Canyon Middle School

Bev Brockhoff
Glen Edwards Middle School

Clanci Chiu
Santa Barbara Junior High School

Mark Coté
Beaver Lake Middle School

Suzanne Cisco Cox
Turner Middle School

Kathleen Davies
Rincon Valley Middle School

Josea Eggink
Bloomington Public Schools

William Funkhouser
Zane Middle School

Lori Hamada
CPM Educational Program

Brian Hoey
CPM Educational Program

Janet Hollister
La Cumbre Jr. High School

Carol Jancsi
CPM Mentor Teacher

Rakesh Khanna
Hotmath, Inc.

Judy Kysh, Ph.D.
San Francisco State University

Sarah Maile
CPM Educational Program

Bruce Melhorn
International School Bangkok (ISB)

Chris Mikles
Post Falls Middle School

Bob Petersen
CPM Educational Program

Tom Sallee, Ph.D.
University of California, Davis

Lorna Thomas Vázquez
Neillsville, WI Math Consultant

Stephanie Whitney, Ph.D.
DePaul University

Program Directors

Elizabeth Coyner
Christian Brothers High School
Sacramento, CA

Leslie Dietiker, Ph.D.
Boston University
Boston, MA

Lori Hamada
CPM Educational Program
Fresno, CA

Brian Hoey
CPM Educational Program
Sacramento, CA

Michael Kassarjian
CPM Educational Program
Kensington, CA

Judy Kysh, Ph.D.
Departments of Education and
Mathematics San Francisco
State University, CA

Tom Sallee, Ph.D.
Department of Mathematics
University of California, Davis

Karen Wootton
CPM Educational Program
Odenton, MD

*Based on *Making Connections*: *Foundations for Algebra, Courses 1 and 2.*

e-book Manager
Carol Cho
Director of Technology
Martinez, CA

e-book Programmers
Rakesh Khanna
Daniel Kleinsinger
Kevin Stein

e-book Assistants
Debbie Dodd
Shirley Paulsen
Wendy Papciak
Anna Poehlmann
Jordan Wight

Assessment Manager
Karen Wootton
Director of Assessment
Odenton, MD

Assessment Assistants
Elizabeth Baker
Zane Middle School
Eureka, CA

William Funkhouser
Zane Middle School
Eureka, CA

Assessment Website
Elizabeth Fong
Michael Huang
Daniel Kleinsinger

Illustration
Kevin Coffey
San Francisco, CA

Jonathan Weast
Sacramento, CA

Homework Help Manager
Bob Petersen
CPM Educational Program

Homework Help Website
Carol Cho
Director of Technology

Parent Guide with Extra Practice
Elizabeth Coyner
Christian Brothers High School

Brian Hoey
CPM Educational Program

Bob Petersen
CPM Educational Program

Based on the Skill Builder materials created for Foundations for Algebra (2003), created by:
Heidi Ackley
Bev Brockhoff
Scott Coyner
Brian Hoey
Robert Petersen
Kristie Sallee

Steve Ackley
Ellen Cafferata
Sara Effenbeck
Judy Kysh
Edwin Reed
Tom Sallee

Elizabeth Baker
Elizabeth Coyner
William Funkhouser
Kris Petersen
Stacy Rocklein
Howard Webb

Technical Managers
Sarah Maile

Aubrie Maze

Technical Assistants
Stephanie Achondo
Rebecca Bobell
Hannah Coyner
Matthew Donahue
Leslie Lai
Eli Marable
Alexandra Murphy
Ryan Peabody
Anna Poehlmann
Ali Rivera
Claire Taylor
Sarah Wong

Robert Ainsworth
Delenn Breedlove
Mary Coyner
Bethany Firch
Michael Li
James McCardle
Wendy Papciak
Iris Perez
Eduardo Ramirez
Andrea Smith
Christy Van Beek
Alex Yu

Bethany Armstrong
Jason Cho
Carmen de la Cruz
Dana Kimball
Jerry Luo
Nyssa Muheim
Atlanta Parrott
Steven Pham
John Ramos
Rachel Smith
Megan Walters

4 5 6 7 8 9   20 19 18 17 16   Version 5.0

Printed in the United States of America   ISBN: 978-1-60328-082-2

A Note to Students:

Welcome to a new year of math! In this course, you will learn to use new models and methods to think about problems as well as solve them. You will be developing powerful mathematical tools and learning new ways of thinking about and investigating situations. You will be making connections, discovering relationships, figuring out what strategies can be used to solve problems, and explaining your thinking. Learning to think in these ways and communicate about your thinking is useful in mathematical contexts, other subjects in school, and situations outside the classroom. The mathematics you have learned in the past will be valuable for learning in this course. That work, and what you learn in this course, will prepare you for future courses.

In meeting the challenges of this course, you will not be learning alone. You will cooperate with other students as a member of a study team. Being a part of a team means speaking up and interacting with other people. You will explain your ideas, listen to what others have to say, and ask questions if there is something you do not understand. In this course, a single problem can often be solved several ways. You will see problems in different ways than your teammates do. Each of you has something to contribute while you work on the lessons in this course.

Together, your team will complete problems and activities that will help you discover mathematical ideas and develop solution methods. Your teacher will support you as you work, but will not take away your opportunity to think and investigate for yourself. Each topic will be revisited many times and will connect to other topics. If something is not clear to you the first time you work on it, you will have more chances to build your understanding as the course continues.

Learning math this way has an advantage: as long as you actively participate, make sure everyone in your study team is involved, and ask good questions, you will find yourself understanding mathematics at a deeper level than ever before. By the end of this course, you will have a powerful set of mathematical tools to use to solve new problems. With your teammates you will meet mathematical challenges you would not have known how to approach before.

In addition to the support provided by your teacher and your study team, CPM has also created online resources to help you, including help with homework, and a parent guide with extra practice. You will find these resources and more at www.cpm.org.

We wish you well and are confident that you will enjoy this next year of learning!

Sincerely,

The CPM Team

Core Connections, Course 2
Student Edition

Volume 1

Volume 2

Chapter 6 Solving Inequalities and Equations

Chapter 7 Proportions and Percents

Chapter 8 Statistics and Angle Relationships   435

Chapter 9 Circles and Volume   487

Checkpoint Materials

Introduction and Probability 1

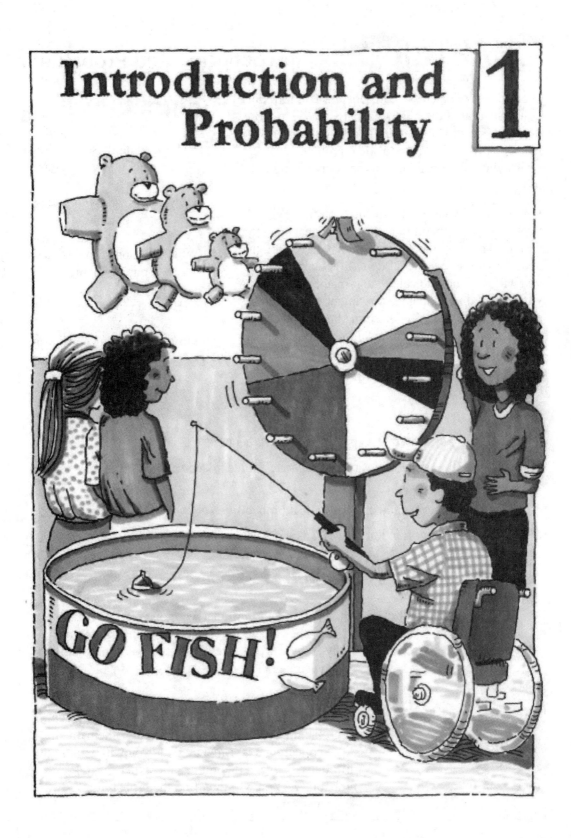

CHAPTER 1 Introduction and Probability

Welcome to math class! This chapter will introduce you to several of the big ideas that you will explore during this course. You will apply your current mathematical knowledge to solve problems, some of which you will revisit later in the course using new tools.

Later in the chapter, you will focus on finding **probability**. Probability is the chance that something will happen. It is something you may have thought about in various aspects of daily life, but in this chapter you will learn how to calculate it mathematically. As you work with fish tanks, experiment with spinners, and toss coins, you will determine how to find the theoretical and the experimental probability that an event will occur. You will also review or reinforce your understanding of working with fractions and other portions.

Guiding Questions

Think about these questions throughout this chapter:

How can I work with my team to figure it out?

What questions can I ask about this problem?

How can I represent this?

How can I organize my work?

In this chapter, you will:

➤ Find the likelihood that a specific event will occur.

➤ Calculate the probabilities of two separate events to decide which is more likely to happen.

➤ Find both experimental and theoretical probabilities of events.

➤ Add and subtract fractions, as well as write equivalent fractions.

Chapter Outline

Section 1.1 This section will introduce you to several of the big ideas of the course. Each problem will require your study team to work together using several problem-solving strategies.

Section 1.2 In this section, you will learn to find the probability of a specific event. You will also learn about the meaning of probability and how it is expressed mathematically. After collecting experimental data, you will explore the difference between theoretical and experimental probability. You will then find the probabilities of two separate events.

1.1.1 What do they have in common?

Finding Shared and Unique Characteristics

Have you ever tried to learn how to play a new game just by watching other people play it? You were probably watching for patterns in the game, such as what each player did to earn points or what actions earned penalties. If you were watching a game of soccer, for example, you might have figured out that kicking the ball into the goal earned the team one point. You might also have noticed that the goalkeeper is the only player on the field allowed to use his or her hands. Noticing the patterns could help you describe some of the rules of the game. This type of observation is also called *generalizing*. When you make an observation about what objects or actions have in common, like the actions that will *always* allow you to score a point in soccer, you are making a *generalization*.

Today you will be working in a team with the goal of making generalizations about various sets of objects. As you work, keep these questions in mind:

> What do the items have in common?
>
> What makes the items different?
>
> What are other characteristics that could describe the groups or sets?

1-1. MATH STARS

What do you have in common with your team members? What makes you unique? Today you will work with your teammates to discover some characteristics that you share and other characteristics that make each person in your team different.

Your Task: Get a copy of the Lesson 1.1.1A Resource Page and scissors. (Note: All resources pages can also be found at www.cpm.org.) Fold the resource page along the dotted lines and then cut along the solid lines. Unfold the cutout and glue it onto a piece of paper. Write each team member's name on a star.

- As a team, brainstorm something that all of you have in common that the rest of the class does not already know.

- List your team's common attribute on the paper in the center of the four stars.

- Find ways that each person in the team is unique from the others (things that are true about that person only), and write those things on each person's star.

To help you and your team members work together today, each team member has a specific job. Your job is assigned by your first name (or last name if team members have the same first name). Read the "Team Roles" information that follows and use it as a resource as you work with your team on this problem.

Team Roles

Resource Manager: If your name comes first alphabetically:

- Make sure your team has a Lesson 1.1.1A Resource Page, scissors, glue, and colored paper.

- Ask the teacher when the *entire* team has a question. *"No one has an idea? Should I ask the teacher?"*

- Make sure your team cleans up by delegating tasks. You could say, *"I will put away the _____ while you _____ ."*

Facilitator: If your name comes second alphabetically:

- Start the team's discussion of similarities and differences by asking, *"What might we have in common?"*

- Keep everyone discussing each part together by asking questions such as, *"Does anyone have ideas for what makes us each unique or different?" "What else might we have in common?"*

Recorder/Reporter: If your name comes third alphabetically:

- When your team is called on, share your team's ideas and reasons with the class.

- Help the team agree on an idea: *"Do we agree that this would not be obvious to the rest of the class?"*

Task Manager: If your name comes fourth alphabetically:

- Remind the team to stay on task and not to talk to students in other teams. You can suggest, *"Let's move on to the next part of the problem."*

- Listen for reasons and ask your teammates to justify their thinking. *"Why do you think that?"* or *"Would this be obvious to the rest of the class?"*

1-2. WHAT DO THEY HAVE IN COMMON?

In mathematics, it is sometimes useful to make general statements about sets of objects. In this problem, you will be given a set of cards (from the Lesson 1.1.1C Resource Page) with mathematical objects or information on them. With your team:

- Determine what each set has in common.
- On your paper, record what is written on the cards.
- On your paper, add two new examples that would belong to the set.
- Describe in words what all of the objects or information on the set of cards have in common.

When you are finished with a set of cards, call the teacher to your team. Explain your generalization to the teacher and get another set of cards.

1-3. **Mathography:** A mathography is a lot like your life history, except that it is focused on mathematics in your life.

a. Write a letter about yourself to your teacher. The letter will help your teacher get to know you as an individual. The letter should talk about these three general topics: you, you as a student, and you as a math student.

Remember to use complete sentences and make sure that it is neat enough for your teacher to read it easily. Start the letter with "Dear...." Make sure you sign your letter. This assignment should take 15 to 20 minutes to complete. Parts (b), (c), and (d) below have suggestions for what to write about each of the three topics.

b. **You:** Introduce yourself using the name you like to be called. Describe your hobbies, talents, and interests. State your goals or dreams. What are you proud of? What else would you like to share?

c. **You as a Student:** State the importance of school in your life. Describe yourself as a student. What kinds of classroom activities do you excel at most? What kinds of activities do you find frustrating? Explain which subjects are your favorites. Tell why you like them. How often do you finish in-class assignments? How faithfully do you do your homework?

d. **You as a Math Student:** Describe your most memorable moment in math and explain why you remember it. State your favorite math topic and name your least favorite. Explain how you feel about math this year.

1-4.   Decide what the shapes below have in common. Write your answer in a
        complete sentence. Then draw two more shapes that belong to the same set.

1-5.   According to the diagrams below, how long is each unknown piece?

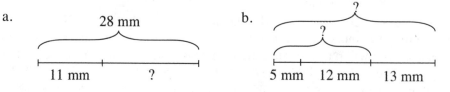

1-6.   Refer to the number line shown below. List two situations or problems for
        which you have used a number line in the past.

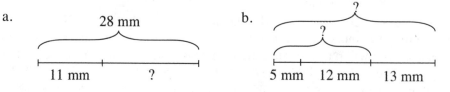

1.1.2   What is the best strategy?

Analyzing a Game

Have you ever watched someone win a game again and again? Do you think that person just has good luck? In many cases, winners have strategies that increase their chances of winning. How can you develop a winning strategy? Today you will start to answer this question. Later in this course, you will learn more about analyzing a game.

Throughout this course, it will be important for you to describe and explain your ideas. In this lesson, you will play a game called Color-Rama. As you play, describe any patterns that you notice. Also explain your thinking about why certain choices might be better than others. Paying close attention to what is happening as you play can give you ideas for developing a winning strategy.

1-7.   COLOR-RAMA

Your teacher will challenge your class to a game of Color-Rama! To play, a marker will be placed on the orange space on the board below. Your class will need to select *one* color for your class and *a different color* for your teacher. Then a volunteer will flip a coin three times. The coin has a "+" one side and a "–" on the other side. If the coin lands with the "+" showing, the marker will move one space to the right. If the "–" is showing, then the marker will move one space to the left. If the marker is on your class's color after three flips, your class wins. If it lands on a color no one picked, then no one wins. Which color do you think you should choose? Do you think that there is a way to predict which color the marker will land on after three moves?

Before you play, discuss the questions below with your team. When talking about strategies, be sure to describe your ideas and explain your reasoning. When your class has considered these questions, move on to problem 1-8.

Discussion Points

Does it matter which color is chosen?

Are all the colors equally likely to win? How can you decide?

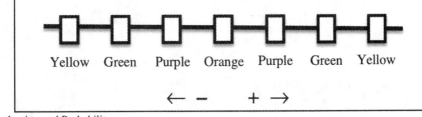

1-8.   LEARNING MORE ABOUT THE GAME

Do you think one color is a better choice than
the others if you want to win? Is there a color
that you should not pick? One way to answer
these questions is to play the game and keep
track of what happens.

Your teacher will give you and a partner a Lesson 1.1.2A Resource Page and a
coin with a "+" on one side and a "−" on the other side. You will need a small
object such as an eraser or paper clip to use as a marker. Once you have all of
your supplies, follow the directions below.

a.   Play the game several times and be sure to select a different color each
     time. Keep track of which colors win and lose each time, not just which
     partner wins. What do you notice?

b.   After you and your partner have played the game at least five times, join
     with another pair of students to form a team and discuss the following
     questions:

     • Does the color you choose seem to affect your chances of winning?

     • Is each color choice equally likely to result in a win? Explain why or
       why not in as many ways as you can.

c.   Play the game a few more times. Do your results agree with your answers
     from part (b) above? Why do your results make sense?

1-9.   PLAYING THE GAME

Now you get to play the game! As a class, choose two colors (one for your
class, one for your teacher) that you think will improve the class's chance of
winning.

a.   Is there any color you could choose that would guarantee your winning the
     game every time you play? Explain why or why not.

b.   Is there a color that would guarantee that you would *not* win? Explain why
     or why not.

Core Connections, Course 2

1-10.   In general, what makes a game fair? Discuss this question with your partner.
         Then think about whether there is a way to change the rules of Color-Rama to
         make it a fair game. Decide on any changes to the rules that you would
         recommend.

    a.   Play the game a few times with your new rules. Be prepared to describe the
         changes you made and explain your reasons for making the changes.

    b.   Is your new game fair? If not, could you make it fair? Work with your
         team to find a way to explain how you know your game is fair or why you
         cannot make it fair.

M ETHODS AND MEANINGS

Perimeter and Area

The **perimeter** of a shape is the total length of the boundary (around the shape) that encloses the interior (inside) region on a flat surface. See the examples at right.

Perimeter = 20 units

Perimeter = $5 + 8 + 4 + 6 = 23$

Area is a measure of the number of square units needed to cover a region on a flat surface. See the examples at right.

Area = 11 sq. units

The **area of a rectangle** is found by multiplying the lengths of the base and height. See the examples at right.

$$A = b \cdot h$$

Area = $5 \cdot 3 = 15$ m² (square meters)

The **area of a parallelogram** is equal to the area of a rectangle with the same base and height. If the base of the parallelogram is length b and the height is length h, then the area of the parallelogram is:

$$A = b \cdot h$$

The **area of a triangle** is half the area of a parallelogram with the same base and height. If the base of the triangle is length b and the height length h, then the area of the triangle is:
$$A = \tfrac{1}{2}b \cdot h$$

Finally, the **area of a trapezoid** is found by averaging the two bases and multiplying by the height. If the trapezoid has bases b_1 and b_2 and height h, then the area is:
$$A = \tfrac{1}{2}(b_1 + b_2)h$$

1-11. Find the perimeter and area of each figure below. Review the Math Notes box in this lesson for help. Be sure to include the correct units in your answers.

a.   8 in.   4 in.   5 in.   7.5 in.

b.   12 cm   13 cm   12 cm   13.4 cm   23 cm

c.   3 yds   7 yds   4 yds

1-12. Think about games that you can remember playing with your friends or family.

a. Talk with your family and/or friends and list as many games as you can think of.

b. Label each game on your list as "fair," "unfair," or "I'm not sure." For any game that you think is unfair, write down your reasons.

1-13. For each of the following pairs of events, predict which is more likely to happen and explain your reasoning.

a. Event 1: You will win more than $1,000,000 in a lottery sometime in your life.
Event 2: You will learn to speak a language that you do not already know.

b. Event 1: Your classmates will all wear the same kind of shoes on the same day.
Event 2: Your classmates will all eat the same thing for lunch on the same day.

1-14. Copy the number line below onto your paper. Place a point on the number line and label the point for each of the following numbers: −4 , 3, 0.5, −3.5 , 0, 1, −2, 5.

−5 −4 −3 −2 −1 0 1 2 3 4 5

1-15. Maria was playing a game with her brother. She said, *"I'm thinking of a number. When you multiply my number by six and add seven, you get twenty-five. What is my number?"*

a. Find Maria's number.

b. Explain how you figured out your answer to Maria's number puzzle.

1.1.3 What is my number?

Finding Unknowns

Today you will think about how to find a mystery number based on information given to you as part of a game. In the game, you will practice mental-math computations and will investigate ways to represent different situations. When you solve the number-game puzzles, you also might use a skill called *reversing* your thinking. Reversing is an important way of thinking mathematically. It means solving problems both backward and forward. As you work with your team, ask each other these questions:

How can we represent it?

What is the best approach for this problem?

Have we found all of the answers?

1-16. GUESS MY NUMBER

Today you will play the "Guess My Number" game. A pencil and a piece of paper may come in handy as you play the game. Each game below gives clues to a mystery number. Your task has two parts. First, figure out what the number is. Second, explain why you think it is the mystery number.

Game #1: *When I triple my number and add five, I get eleven. What is my number?*

Game #2: *When I add two to my number and then multiply it by five, I get thirty. What is my number?*

Game #3: *When I take half of my number and add two, I get twenty-four. What is my number?*

Game #4: *When I double my number and add eight, I get my number plus twelve. What is my number?*

Game #5: *When I double my number, add four, and then subtract my number and subtract three, I get my number plus one. What is my number?*

1-17.   Make up your own "Guess My Number" games with your
         team and be ready to share them with the class. Make at
         least one game that has only one answer. Also make one
         that works for all numbers. Can you create a game that
         does not work for any number?

MATH NOTES

METHODS AND MEANINGS

Mean

To understand a set of data, you often need to be able to describe
the approximate "center" of that data. One way to do this is to find the
mean of the data set, which is also called the **arithmetic average**.

To find the mean of a set of data, add the values of the data elements
(numbers) and then divide by the number of items of data. The
mean is a useful way to describe the data when the set of data does
not contain **outliers**. Outliers are numbers that are much smaller or
much larger than most of the other data in the set.

Suppose the following data set represents the number of home runs hit
by the best seven players on a Major League Baseball team during one
season:

$$16, 26, 21, 9, 13, 15, \text{ and } 9.$$

The mean is $\frac{16+26+21+9+13+15+9}{7} = \frac{109}{7} \approx 15.57$.

This number shows that a typical player among the best seven
home-run hitters on the team hits about 15 or 16 home runs each
season.

1-18.   Thu wants to play "Guess My Number." She states, "*When I triple my number
         and add five, I get twenty-six. What is my number?*" What is her number?
         Show how you know.

1-19.   One of the ideas that you have explored in previous courses is how to describe a set of data. One of the ways that you may have seen before is finding an **average** (also called a **mean**). Read the Math Notes box for this lesson to review what a mean is and how to find it. Then find the mean for each set of data below.

   a.   Jane's quiz scores: $82, 64, 73, 91, 85$

   b.   The number of cats your teammates have as pets: $0, 1, 3, 2$

   c.   The number of minutes Pam talked on the phone: $35, 40, 12, 16, 25, 10$

1-20.   Julio is an architect who designs skyscrapers. Assume that each story (also called a "floor" or "layer") of a new building is 15 feet high as you help Julio answer the following questions.

   a.   How high would a two-story building be? What about a 10-story building? What about a 30-story building?

   b.   If Julio had to design the building to be 750 feet tall, how many stories should the building have?

1-21.   Which is greater, $\frac{3}{4}$ or $\frac{11}{16}$? How can you be sure?

1-22.   Find the perimeter and area of each figure below.

1.1.4 How big is a million?

Investigating a Proportional Relationship

Can you imagine a tower built out of one million pennies? How tall would it be? In this lesson, you will work with your team to predict just how tall such a tower would be. To make sense of this question, you will measure some pennies and investigate the relationship between the height of a tower of pennies and the number of pennies in that tower. This is an example of a special relationship called a **proportional relationship**, which you will learn more about later in this course.

1-23.   How tall would a tower of a million pennies be? Would it be taller than your school building? Would it be taller than Mount Everest? (Mount Everest is approximately 8848 meters or 29,029 feet high.)

Discuss these questions with your team and make a prediction. Record your prediction on the table provided by your teacher.

1-24.   When you are working with your team to answer the "Penny Tower" questions, as well as other problems in this course, it is important to work effectively with other people. Effective math conversations are a valuable part of the learning process throughout this course. Choose a member of your team to read the "Collaborative Learning Expectations" below out loud.

COLLABORATIVE LEARNING EXPECTATIONS

Working with other students allows you to:
- Develop new ways of thinking about mathematics,
- Learn to communicate about math, and
- Understand ideas better by having to explain your thinking to others.

The following expectations will help you get the most out of working together.

T   Together, work to answer questions.

E   Explain and give reasons.

A   Ask questions and share ideas.

M   Members of your team are your first resource.

S   Smarter together than apart.

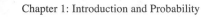

1-25. **TINY TOWERS**

To begin to investigate this question, start by collecting data. Parts (a) and (b) will lead you through the data-collection process.

a. How many pennies does it take to build a tower that is one centimeter tall? Use the tools provided by your teacher to answer this question.

b. On your own paper, create a table like the one at right. Work with your team to complete the missing information. Be prepared to explain your reasoning to the class.

Height of Tower (cm)	# of Pennies
1	
2	
3	
4	
5	
…	
10	
…	
20	
…	
30	
…	
100	

1-26. **THE HUNDRED-PENNY TOWER**

"I have an idea!" Carol said. *"If I know how tall a tower of one hundred pennies would be, maybe that can help me figure out how tall a tower of one million pennies would be."*

a. Discuss this idea with your team. How could Carol's idea work?

Height of Tower (cm)	# of Pennies
1	
2	
3	
4	
5	
…	…
	100

b. Work with your team to figure out how tall a tower of one hundred pennies would be. Can you find more than one way to figure this out? Be sure that each member of your team is prepared to explain your team's reasoning to the class.

1-27.   THE MILLION-PENNY TOWER

Now it is time to answer the big question: How tall would a tower of one million pennies be?

Your Task: Work with your team to calculate the height of a tower of one million pennies as accurately as you can. Can you find the height more than one way? Be prepared to explain your ideas to the class.

Discussion Points

Where would one million pennies belong in our table?

How can the height of the hundred-penny tower help us?

What is the relationship between the number of pennies and the height of the tower?

Further Guidance

1-28.   Carol said, *"To use my hundred-penny height to find the height of one million pennies, I have to know how many hundreds are in one million."*

a.   How many groups of 100 pennies are in 1000 pennies?

b.   How many 1000s are in 1,000,000? How do you know?

c.   Now work with your team to figure out how many towers of 100 pennies it would take to build a tower of 1,000,000 pennies. Be prepared to explain your reasoning to the class.

d.   Use this result along with the height of a hundred-penny tower that you found in problem 1-27 to find the height of a tower of one million pennies.

1-29.   Anouk was working with Carol. *"I have another way,"* she said. *"I can see in the table that the number of pennies is always seven times the number of centimeters. How can we reverse that to find the number of centimeters if we know the number of pennies?"*

a.   Discuss Anouk's question with your team. How can you find the height of the tower if you know the number of pennies in it?

b.   Find the height of a tower of 1,000,000 pennies using this method. Does it agree with the result you got in problem 1-28?

—————   *Further Guidance*   —————
           section ends here.

1-30.   Anouk wants to compare the million-penny
        tower to the height of Mount Everest. She
        read on the Internet that Mount Everest is
        approximately 8848 meters tall. Her
        calculation for the height of the million-
        penny tower is in centimeters.

        a. How can she change the units so that
            she can compare them? Discuss this
            with your team.

        b. Compare your own calculation for the million-penny tower to the height of
            Mount Everest.

        c. Look at the predictions made by your class at the beginning of this lesson
            and decide which team came closest to predicting the actual height.

1-31.   How accurate is your result? Is there any reason to believe that there may be
        some amount of error in your calculation? How much do you think this error
        would matter? Be prepared to share your ideas with the class.

1-32.   **Additional Challenge:** How many pennies would be in a tower that is 10 miles
        high?

1-33.   **Additional Challenge:** The Taipei-101 is the second-tallest building in the
        world. There is a staircase up to the 91st floor with an average of 22 steps from
        one floor to the next.

        a. How many steps would you have to climb to get from the 1st floor to the
            91st floor?

        b. When you are standing on the 91st floor, you are 1285 feet above the
            ground. How many stories are below you? About how many feet tall is
            each story of the building?

        c. About how high is each step?

18   *Core Connections, Course 2*

1-34. LEARNING LOG

Throughout this course, you will be asked to reflect about
your understanding of mathematical concepts in a Learning
Log. Your Learning Log will contain explanations and
examples to help you remember what you have learned
throughout the course. It is important to write each entry of the Learning Log in
your own words so that later you can use your Learning Log as a resource to
refresh your memory. Your teacher will tell you where to write your Learning
Log entries. Remember to label each entry with a title and a date so that it can
be referred to later.

For your first entry, consider what you know about proportional relationships.
The relationship between the number of pennies in a stack and the height of that
stack is an example of a proportional relationship. Talk with your team about
how you can describe this relationship.

Then record your ideas in your Learning Log, using numbers, words, and tables
to help show your thinking. Title this entry "Beginning to Think About
Proportional Relationships" and label it with today's date.

METHODS AND MEANINGS

MATH NOTES

Median

The mean is a useful way to find the center when data values are
close together or are evenly spaced. Another tool, the **median**, also
locates the approximate "center" of a set of data in a different way.

The **median** is the middle number in a set of data *arranged numerically*.
If there is an even number of values, the median is the mean of the two
middle numbers. The median is more accurate than the mean as a way to
find the center when there are outliers in the data set.

Suppose the following data set represents the number of home runs hit
by the best seven players on a Major League Baseball team:

$$16, 26, 21, 9, 13, 15, \text{ and } 9.$$

In this example, the median is 15. This is because when the data are
arranged in order (9, 9, 13, 15, 16, 21, 26), the middle number is 15.

Mean and median are called **measures of central tendency** because
they each describe the "center" of a set of data, but in different ways.

1-35.   Read the Math Notes box for this lesson and review the information about how
         to find the median of a data set. Then find the median for Andy's test scores:
         76, 84, 93, 67, 82, 87, and 76.

1-36.   Use the fact that there are 12 inches in a foot to answer the questions below.

         a.   How many inches tall is a 7-foot basketball player?

         b.   If a yard is 3 feet long, how many inches are in a yard?

1-37.   As you can tell from the examples of the number lines below, not all number
         lines change by one unit from mark to mark. Copy these number lines onto
         your paper and fill in the missing numbers.

1-38.   At the farmers' market, two pounds of peaches cost $4.20. How much will five
         pounds cost? Show all of your work or explain your reasoning.

1-39.   Janice's mother gave her a ten-dollar bill to buy five pounds each of bananas
         and apples at the grocery store. When she got there, she found that bananas
         were 80¢ per pound and apples were $1.40 per pound.

         Did Janice's mother give her enough money? If so, should she receive any
         change? If not, how much more money does she need? Show all of your work.

1.1.5 How can I rewrite it?

Investigating Number Patterns

In the past, you may have looked at number patterns to answer questions or to find the next part of a sequence. Have you ever taken a moment to consider how amazing the mathematics is in those patterns? Today you will investigate number patterns and learn about equivalent ways to write the same number. As a team, you will work to justify why two representations are the same and share your reasoning. In this course, you will often be asked to explain your reasons and justify your answers. When you are reasoning and justifying, you will focus on what makes a statement convincing or how you can explain your ideas. As you look at patterns today, ask your team these questions to help guide your conversations:

What can we predict about the next number in the pattern?

How can we justify our answer?

1-40. In this course, you will transition to using "x" as a variable, so this course will avoid using "x" as a multiplication sign. Instead, the symbol "$\cdot$" will be used to represent multiplication. Use a calculator to calculate the value of each expression below.

a. $1 \cdot 8 + 1$

b. $12 \cdot 8 + 2$

c. $123 \cdot 8 + 3$

d. $1234 \cdot 8 + 4$

e. What patterns do you see in parts (a) through (d) above? Discuss the patterns with your team. Be sure that when your team agrees on something, it is recorded on each person's paper.

f. Use the patterns you found to *predict* the next three expressions and their values. Do not calculate the answers yet. Instead, what do you *think* they will be?

g. Use your calculator to check the solution for each expression you wrote in part (f). Were your predictions correct? If not, look at the pattern again and figure out how it is changing.

1-41.　Sometimes patterns are not created with addition and multiplication, but with the numbers themselves. For example, when the fractions in the sequence below are changed to decimals, an interesting pattern develops.

$$\tfrac{1}{9}, \tfrac{2}{9}, \tfrac{3}{9}, \text{ and } \tfrac{4}{9}$$

a.　Use your calculator to change each of the fractions above to a decimal. Write each fraction and its equivalent decimal on your paper.

b.　Decimals like 0.3333... and the others you found in part (a) are called **repeating decimals** because the digits continue infinitely. Instead of using "..." to show that the numbers repeat, mathematicians write a bar over the digits that repeat, like this: $0.\overline{3}$. It is standard to write the repeating digits just once. For example, $0.2222... = 0.\overline{2}$.

List the next five fractions in the sequence $\tfrac{1}{9}, \tfrac{2}{9}, \tfrac{3}{9}$, and $\tfrac{4}{9}$. Predict how they will look if they are rewritten as decimals.

c.　Find the decimal equivalents of the five fractions you wrote in part (b) using your calculator. Do they match your predictions? Are there any that are different or that do not follow the pattern?

1-42.　Are 0.999..., $0.\overline{9}$, and 1 equal? How do you know? Discuss this with the class and justify your response. Help others understand what you mean as you explain your thinking.

1-43.　Decimal numbers that have only a finite number of digits such as 2.173 and 0.04 are called **terminating decimals**. Some fractions can be written as terminating decimals, such as the examples below.

$$\tfrac{1}{2} = 0.5 \qquad \tfrac{3}{4} = 0.75$$

Do the decimal equivalents of the numbers below terminate or repeat? Be ready to justify your answer.

a.　0.125

b.　$0.\overline{6}$

c.　$\tfrac{5}{6}$

d.　4

e.　$\tfrac{2}{5}$

f.　-0.33

1-44.   Representing numbers in multiple ways can help to show what those numbers mean. In problem 1-41, you saw that the fraction $\frac{9}{9}$ (or 1) can be represented as the decimal $0.\overline{9}$, and it can also be represented geometrically with a diagram. Portions can also be represented in words, such as "nine ninths," and as **percents**, which are portions of 100. The diagram at right is called a "portions web."

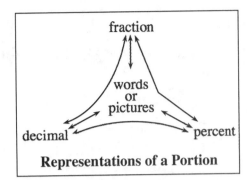

Representations of a Portion

Draw each of the portions webs below on your paper and complete them for the given fractions. In each part, determine if the decimal representation is terminating or repeating.

a. $\frac{2}{3}$ b. $\frac{5}{4}$

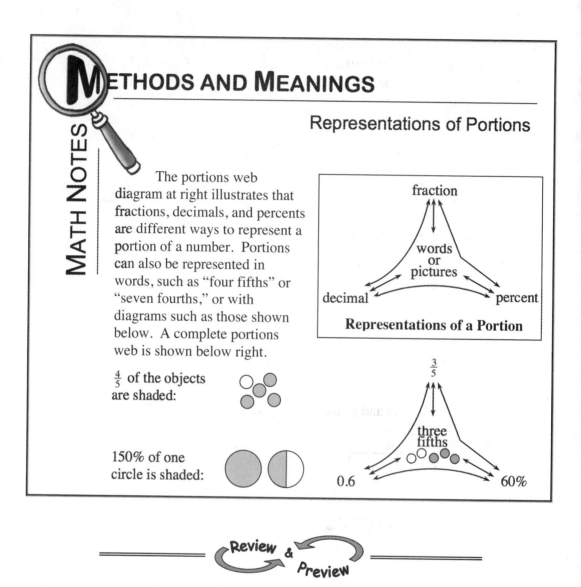

METHODS AND MEANINGS

Representations of Portions

The portions web diagram at right illustrates that fractions, decimals, and percents are different ways to represent a portion of a number. Portions can also be represented in words, such as "four fifths" or "seven fourths," or with diagrams such as those shown below. A complete portions web is shown below right.

Representations of a Portion

$\frac{4}{5}$ of the objects are shaded:

150% of one circle is shaded:

Review & Preview

1-45. Copy the rows of equations below and write what you predict will be the next five rows in the sequence.

$$1 \cdot 9 + 2 = 11$$

$$12 \cdot 9 + 3 = 111$$

$$123 \cdot 9 + 4 = 1111$$

$$1234 \cdot 9 + 5 = 11111$$

a. What patterns do you see?
Write your answer in complete sentences.

b. Use a calculator to discover whether your predictions were correct. If they were not correct, look at the pattern again and figure out how it is changing.

1-46.   Look at the representations shown in the Math Notes box for this lesson
         ("Representations of Portions"). Copy the diagrams below and write a fraction
         and a percent for the shaded portion of each one.

a.   b.   c.

1-47.   Represent each of the fractions below both with a diagram and with words.

a. $\frac{2}{3}$ b. $1\frac{1}{8}$ c. $\frac{6}{9}$

1-48.   If five notebooks cost $5.25, how much would three notebooks cost?

1-49.   Find the perimeter and area of each figure below.

a.   b.

1.2.1   What are the chances?

··

Introduction to Probability

You have probably heard a weather forecaster say that the chance of rain tomorrow is 40%. Have you thought about what that means? Does it mean that it will rain tomorrow for sure? What is the chance that it will not rain? In today's lesson, you will investigate the chance, or the **probability**, of something happening or not happening. As you do the activities, ask your team these questions:

> What is the probability that the event will occur?

> How can we record that probability?

1-50.   POSSIBLE OR IMPOSSIBLE?

With your team, make lists of three different types of events:
1. Events that you think are possible but not certain to happen.
2. Events that are certain to happen.
3. Events that would be impossible to happen.

Be ready to share your lists with the class. Then use your lists to complete the activities below.

a.   Draw a line segment on your paper and label the left end "Impossible" and the right end "Certain."

b.   At the "Impossible" end, write the events that your team decided could not happen. How could you label the possibility of these events occurring with a percentage?

c.   At the "Certain" end, write the events your team has decided are certain to happen. How could you label the possibility of these events occurring with a percentage?

d.   Along the line, write the events that you thought were possible. Place them along the line in order from closer to impossible, somewhere in the middle, or closer to certain.

1-51.   GO FISH

Mike wants to win a giant stuffed animal
at the carnival. He decided to play the
"Go Fish" game, which has three prizes: a
giant stuffed animal, a smaller stuffed
animal, and a plastic kazoo.

The game is set up with a tank containing
1 green fish, 3 blue fish, and 6 yellow
fish. To play, Mike must go fishing. The
game is set up so that every time a player
goes fishing, he or she will catch a fish.

To win the giant stuffed animal, Mike needs to catch a green fish.

a.   If *all* of the fish in the tank are green, how would you describe the
     probability of Mike's winning a giant stuffed animal?

b.   The way the tank is set up (with 1 green, 3 blue, and 6 yellow fish), what
     are the chances that Mike will catch a black fish?

c.   Given the information in the problem, what percent of the time would you
     expect Mike to catch a green fish and win the giant stuffed animal? Be
     ready to explain your thinking.

1-52.   In the game described in problem 1-51, you could expect Mike to win a giant
         stuffed animal 10% of the time. A percentage is one way to express the
         probability that a specific event will happen. You might also have said you
         expected Mike to win 1 out of every 10 attempts. So the **probability** that Mike
         will win is $\frac{1}{10}$, because the 1 represents the number of **desired outcomes** (*green*
         fish that Mike can catch) and the 10 represents the number of **possible
         outcomes** (*all* the fish that Mike could catch).

a.   What is the probability that Mike will catch a blue fish? A yellow fish?
     Write each of these probabilities as a fraction and a percent.

b.   Probabilities such as the ones you found in part (a) are called **theoretical
     probabilities** because they are calculated mathematically based on what is
     expected.

     What is the theoretical probability of getting a fish that is green, blue, *or*
     yellow (that is, a fish that is *any* of those three colors)? How do your
     answers for this problem compare to the probabilities you considered in
     problem 1-50?

1-53.   BUILDING A FISH TANK

The managers of the carnival
company have hired your team to
help them redesign the "Go Fish"
game. They want to control the
probability for winning to be sure
they make a profit. You can make
decisions about the total number of
fish in the tank and the colors of those fish to meet the carnival company's
requirements.

Work with your team to decide how many fish of each color you could put in
the tank so that the probability of catching a green fish will be each of the
following numbers. Be ready to explain your thinking to the class.

a. $\frac{2}{7}$ b. $\frac{5}{7}$

c. $\frac{8}{7}$ d. $\frac{7}{7}$

1-54.   SPINNERS – THEORY vs. REALITY, Part One

Your teacher will give your team a spinner.
You will need to decide how to color the spinner
so that it meets the following criteria.

   40% should be red. $\frac{1}{10}$ should be yellow.

   30% should be blue.   The rest should be green.

a.   Which color is the most likely result of a spin? How do you know?

b.   Which color is the least likely result of a spin? How do you know?

c.   Work with your team to determine the theoretical probability of the spinner
      landing on each of the four colors (red, yellow, blue, and green). Express
      your answers as fractions and percents.

d.   What is the probability of the spinner landing on purple? Explain.

e.   What is the probability of the spinner landing on either red or blue?

1-55.   SPINNERS – THEORY vs. REALITY, Part Two

Now you will use your new spinner to do an investigation.

a.   Each person in your team should spin the spinner 10 times while the other team members record the color resulting from each spin.

b.   Write the number of times the spinner landed on each color as the numerator of a fraction with the total number of spins as the denominator.

c.   Now combine your team's data with the results from the rest of your classmates. Use the class data to write similar fractions as you did in part (b) for each color.

d.   Recall that the numbers you calculated in part (c) of problem 1-54 are theoretical probabilities, because you calculated these numbers (before actually spinning the spinner) to predict what you expected to happen. The numbers you found in your investigation (when you actually spun the spinner) are called **experimental probabilities**, because they are based on the results from an actual experiment or event. Both theoretical and experimental probabilities can be written as a percent, a fraction, or a decimal.

   i.   Does it make sense that the theoretical probabilities and the experimental probabilities you calculated for the spinner might be different? Explain.

   ii. Does it make sense that the experimental probabilities that you found for the class are different from those found for just your team?

1-56.   LEARNING LOG

Write a Learning Log entry that explains how to find the probability of an event. Describe the difference between experimental and theoretical probability. Be sure to use examples to make your points clear. Title this entry "Probability" and label it with today's date.

1-57.   Joyce's dad packs her lunch and always packs a yogurt. Joyce knows that there
         are five yogurts in the refrigerator: one raspberry, two strawberry, one
         blueberry, and one vanilla. Her dad usually reaches into the refrigerator and
         randomly grabs a yogurt.

    a.   Which flavor is she most likely to have in her lunch today?

    b.   What are her chances of finding a vanilla yogurt in her lunch bag?

1-58.   Copy the number line below and place the following probabilities on it.

    a.   A $\frac{1}{4}$ chance that you will be the
         team member who gets supplies
         tomorrow.

    b.   A 25% chance of snow tomorrow.

    c.   A 0.8 probability of eating vegetables with dinner.

    d.   P(blue marble) $= \frac{5}{8}$.

    e.   A 0.01 probability that it will be 85° on Saturday.

1-59.   Write "theoretical" or "experimental" to describe the probabilities for each of
         the following situations.

    a.   The chance of getting tails when flipping a coin is $\frac{1}{2}$.

    b.   I flipped a coin eight times and got heads six times, so the probability is $\frac{6}{8}$.

    c.   My mom packed my lunch three of the past five days, so the probability
         that my mom will pack my lunch is $\frac{3}{5}$.

    d.   The chance of winning the state lottery is 1 in 98,000,000.

    e.   Based on mathematical models, the chance of rain today is 60%.

    f.   Lena got three hits in her last seven times at bat, so her chance of getting a
         hit is $\frac{3}{7}$.

1-60.   FRACTIONS AND PERCENTS

Marianna represented several percents as portions of 100 in the pictures below.

i.   *ii.*   *iii.*

a.   Write the percent represented in each picture.

b.   Write the portion represented in each picture as a fraction in at least two different ways.

1-61.   Find the mean and median for the lengths of the jumping frogs' bodies shown below (the length are in centimeters).

20.3, 12.5, 7.6, 13.9, 9.2, 21.7, 7.6, 17.5, 15.6, 14.1

1-62.   Craig is practicing his baseball pitching. He kept track of the speed of each of his throws yesterday, and made the histogram at right.

a.   Can you tell the speed of Craig's fastest pitch? Explain.

b.   Between what speeds does Craig usually pitch?

c.   Based on this data, what is the probability that Craig will pitch the ball between 70 and 75 miles per hour?

1.2.2 How can I use probability to make predictions?

Investigating Probability

Have you ever tried to predict which football team will win a big game? If so, you probably did not just pick the team with the coolest colors or the neatest mascot. You may have based your pick on statistics about win-loss records, player injuries, and other data. Knowing what has happened in the past can sometimes help you predict what will happen in the future. In this lesson, you will use data to make predictions.

As you work with your team to uncover a mystery spinner, keep the questions below in mind.

What is the probability or likelihood?

What do we expect to happen?

How does the actual event compare to our prediction?

What can we know for sure?

1-63.   THE MYSTERY SPINNER

Your teacher has a hidden spinner. Your challenge is to perform an experiment that will allow you to predict what the spinner looks like without ever seeing it.

Your Task: Your teacher will spin the spinner and announce each result. During the experiment, you will consider several questions about the results and about the hidden spinner. However, you will not be allowed to see it. Using the information you get, work with your team to figure out what the spinner looks like. When you think you know what it looks like, draw a diagram of the spinner.

1-64.   Use the data you collected in problem 1-63 to answer the following questions.

a.   Based on your data, how can you describe the likelihood of landing on each part of the spinner? How does the spinner that your team drew represent these likelihoods? Be prepared to share your ideas with the class.

b.   Use your data to write the experimental probability of each of the following results as a fraction, a decimal, and a percent.

   i.   The spinner lands on purple.

   ii. The spinner lands on green or orange.

c.   If your teacher were to spin the spinner 15 more times, how might this change your answers for part (b)?

d.   Do you know for sure that the spinner you drew in problem 1-63 looks exactly like your teacher's? Are you certain that the portions that you drew for each color are the same size as the portions on your teacher's spinner? Why or why not?

1-65.   Now your teacher will reveal the mystery spinner.

a.   How does your team's spinner compare to the actual spinner? Discuss the similarities and differences.

b.   Do your spinner and your teacher's spinner show the same likelihood for each section being spun? Explain why or why not.

1-66.   One way to compare your spinner and your teacher's spinner is to calculate the theoretical probability for each colored section of your teacher's spinner.

a.   What are some reasons the experimental probability and the theoretical probability for any section of the spinner could be different?

b.   Estimate the theoretical probability for getting each color on your teacher's spinner.

c.   How do the experimental probabilities (based on your class data) and the theoretical probabilities (based on the actual spinner) compare? How do you think they would compare if there were twice as many spins made? What about three times as many spins?

Problem continues on next page. →

1-66.   *Problem continued from previous page.*

  d. If you were to spin the spinner the number of times listed below, how many times would you expect it to land on orange? Explain how you found your answers.

   i.   6 times   *ii.*   48 times

  e. Approximately how many times would you expect to land on orange if you were to spin 100 times?

1-67.   Rachel and her little sister Christie often argue about who should wash the dishes at their house. Rachel suggests that they flip coins to solve their argument.

   "Flipping a coin is fair, since heads and tails each have an equal chance of happening. Each one has a probability of $\frac{1}{2}$," Rachel says. *"If the coin shows heads, then I do the dishes. If it shows tails, then you do them."*

  a. Is this system fair? That is, does each girl have an equal likelihood of washing the dishes each day? What is the theoretical probability for heads? For tails?

  b. Rachel and Christie flip a coin every evening for the first week. Christie has washed the dishes four times, and Rachel has washed the dishes three times. Christie tells Rachel that the system is not fair, because Christie has done the dishes more often than Rachel. Is Christie right?

  c. After the second week of coin flipping, Christie has washed the dishes ten times and Rachel has washed the dishes four times. Now Christie is really upset at Rachel because she has washed the dishes so many times.

   In light of this new information, do you think the system is fair or not fair? What would you recommend to Christie? Discuss your ideas with your team and be prepared to discuss this with the class.

1-68.   Flipping a coin has a theoretical probability of $\frac{1}{2}$ for heads and $\frac{1}{2}$ for tails, unless the coin is "rigged." Over the course of a large number of flips, each of the two outcomes will be closer to the theoretical probability ($\frac{1}{2}$) than they will for a few flips. But is it possible to determine the theoretical probability in other situations?

You will think about theoretical probability more in parts (a) through (e) below. It will help you to know that a standard deck of 52 playing cards has four suits: spades and clubs, which are black, and hearts and diamonds, which are red. Each suit has 13 cards: cards numbered 2 through 10, three "face" cards (a jack, a queen, and a king), and an ace. It will also be helpful to know that a standard number cube, also called a die (plural: dice), has six sides. Each side has a different number of dots, 1 through 6.

Look at the situations below and decide with your team if you can find a theoretical probability for each one. If you decide that you can find the theoretical probability, then do so.

a.   Picking an ace from a standard 52-card deck.

b.   *Not* rolling a 3 on a standard number cube.

c.   The chances of a thumbtack landing with its point up or on its side.

d.   Getting the one red crayon from a set of eight different-color crayons.

e.   The likelihood that you will run out of gas on a long car trip.

1-69.   **Additional Challenge:** Three friends join together and form a club. They want to select one of themselves randomly to be the club's leader. Describe how they can do this fairly using only a coin.

METHODS AND MEANINGS

Scaling Axes

The numbers on each axis of a graph or a number line show the **scaling** of the axes. The difference between consecutive markings tells the size of the **interval**. When you scale each axis, you must use equal intervals to represent the data accurately. For example, an interval of 5 creates a scale numbered $-15, -10, -5, 0, 5, 10, 15$, etc. Unequal intervals distort the relationship in the data.

Notice on the graph at right that 80 marks the end of the *fourth* interval from zero on the horizontal axis. If you divide 80 years by 4 you can see that the length of an interval on this graph is 20.

$$80 \div 4 = 20$$

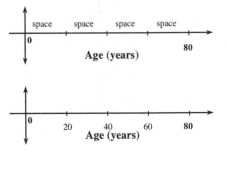

The second graph at right has each interval labeled. Labeling the graph this way is called "scaling the axis."

Review & Preview

1-70.   Imagine that you have a bag containing 10 marbles of different colors. You have drawn a marble, recorded its color, and replaced it fifty times, with the following results: 9 purple, 16 orange, 6 yellow, and 19 green marbles. Make a prediction for how many marbles of each color are in the bag. Show all of your work or explain your reasoning.

1-71.   A fair number cube with the numbers 1, 2, 3, 4, 5, and 6 is rolled.

a.   What is the probability of getting an even number?

b.   What is the probability of getting a factor of 6?

1-72.   Ramon is saving $7.75 per week to buy a new cell phone. The phone he wants costs $125.00. For how many weeks will he need to save his money? First, estimate your answer. Then figure out the actual number of weeks.

1-73.   If 18 inches is equal to $1\frac{1}{2}$ feet, how many feet long is a 36-inch board? A 72-inch board? A 144-inch board?

1-74.   Read this lesson's Math Notes box about scaling axes. Then, on your paper, copy the incomplete axes below and write the missing numbers on each one.

1.2.3 How can I change the chances?

Modifying the Sample Space

If you want to have the best chances of getting a red gumball from a gumball machine, is it better if the machine is full of gumballs or half empty? How do the chances of getting an ace in a deck of playing cards change if you have three or four decks of cards to choose from instead of only one deck? In this lesson, you will think about the size of the **sample space** (the collection of all possible outcomes of an event). Think about these questions as you work today:

How has the "whole" or total changed?

How has the "portion" or part we are interested in changed?

Has the event become more or less likely?

1-75.   Your team will be given a bag containing a set of colored blocks or counters. Each team will receive a bag that is identical to yours.

a.   Look at the blocks in your bag. If you were to reach into the bag and select one block without looking, what is the likelihood that it would be:

   i.   Red?   *ii.*   Green?

   iii. Blue?   *iv.*   Orange?

b.   Do your answers for part (a) represent theoretical or experimental probabilities? Justify your response.

1-76.   If you were to select one block from the bag 12 times, replacing the block you drew between each selection, how many of those times would you expect to have selected a blue block? What if you drew 24 times? Discuss both situations with your team and explain your answers.

Core Connections, Course 2

1-77.   DOUBLING BAGS

Now imagine that you and another team have combined the blocks from both of your bags into one bag.

a. Do you think the larger sample space will change the likelihood of drawing blocks of different colors? Discuss this with your team and be ready to explain your ideas to the class.

b. Get a second bag of blocks from your teacher and combine the contents of both bags. How many total blocks are there in the bag now? How many are there of each color?

c. Work with your team to find the theoretical probability for selecting each color of block in the combined bags.

d. Has the probability for drawing each different-colored block changed? How do your answers for part (c) above compare to the theoretical probabilities that you calculated for the original bag in problem 1-75? With your team, make sense of how the probability for drawing a blue block compares before and after combining the bags.

e. If you were to make 12 draws from the combined bag, replacing the block between draws, how many times would you expect to draw a blue block? Explain why your answer makes sense.

1-78.   In problems 1-75 through 1-77, even though you combined bags or changed the number of selections you made, the probability of drawing a blue block remained the same.

a. Do you think the probabilities would change if you combined three bags? Why or why not?

b. What change do you think you could make to increase the chances of choosing a blue block? Explain your reasoning.

1-79.   **Additional Challenge:** Use the spinner from the Lesson 1.2.2 Resource Page (available from your teacher or www.cpm.org). Play a game with the spinner while keeping score as follows:

● Every time you spin purple, you lose two points.

● Every time you spin green, you get one point.

● Every time you spin orange, you get three points.

If you play this game for a long time, do you think it is more likely that you will end up with a positive score or a negative score? Make a prediction and then try it out. You may want to keep score with counters.

Probability Vocabulary and Definitions

Outcome: Any possible or actual result of the action considered, such as rolling a 5 on a standard number cube or getting tails when flipping a coin.

Event: A desired (or successful) outcome or group of outcomes from an experiment, such as rolling an even number on a standard number cube.

Sample space: All possible outcomes of a situation. For example, the sample space for flipping a coin is heads and tails; rolling a standard number cube has six possible outcomes (1, 2, 3, 4, 5, and 6).

Probability: The likelihood that an event will occur. Probabilities may be written as fractions, decimals, or percents. An event that is guaranteed to happen has a probability of 1, or 100%. An event that has no chance of happening has a probability of 0, or 0%. Events that "might happen" have probabilities between 0 and 1 or between 0% and 100%. In general, the more likely an event is to happen, the greater its probability.

Experimental probability: The probability based on data collected in experiments.

$$\text{Experimental probability} = \frac{\text{number of successful outcomes in the experiment}}{\text{total number of outcomes in the experiment}}$$

Theoretical probability is a calculated probability based on the possible outcomes when they all have the same chance of occurring.

$$\text{Theoretical probability} = \frac{\text{number of successful outcomes (events)}}{\text{total number of possible outcomes}}$$

In the context of probability, "successful" usually means a desired or specified outcome (event), such as rolling a 2 on a number cube (probability of $\frac{1}{6}$). To calculate the probability of rolling a 2, first figure out how many possible outcomes there are. Since there are six faces on the number cube, the number of possible outcomes is 6. Of the six faces, only one of the faces has a 2 on it. Thus, to find the probability of rolling a 2, you would write:

$$P(2) = \frac{\text{number of ways to roll 2}}{\text{number of possible outcomes}} = \frac{1}{6}. \text{ or } 0.1\overline{6} \text{.or approximately } 16.7\%$$

1-80. Tom keeps all of his favorite marbles in a special leather bag. Right now, five red marbles, four blue marbles, and three yellow marbles are in the bag.

    a. If he randomly chooses one marble to give to a friend, what is the probability that it is blue?

    b. Tom does not really want to give away blue marbles and would like to change the probability that he chooses a blue marble to $\frac{1}{10}$. How many marbles that are not blue could he add to the bag so that the probability of choosing a blue marble becomes $\frac{1}{10}$?

1-81. Your team is in charge of games at the CPM Amusement Park. One of the games involves a robotic arm that randomly grabs a stuffed animal out of a large bin. You need to set up the game so that the probability of a customer's grabbing a teddy bear is exactly $\frac{1}{2}$.

    a. How would you set up the bin? Explain.

    b. What if you returned to check on the bin and found that there were 4 teddy bears left and 12 other animals? What could you add to or remove from the bin to return the probability of selecting a teddy bear to $\frac{1}{2}$?

1-82. Write four different fractions that are equal to 1. Use your calculator to check that you are correct.

1-83. A rectangular park is 150 yards on one side and 125 yards on the other.

    a. If Debbie walks around the park two times, how far does she walk? Sketch a figure and show your work.

    b. If Debbie wanted to walk 1,000,000 yards, how many times would she have to walk around the park?

1-84. Find the perimeter and area of each figure below.

    a.

    b.

1.2.4 How can I change fractions to percents?

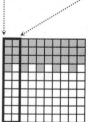

Expressing Fractions as Percents

In the last few lessons, you have been working with fractions and percents to represent probabilities. In this lesson, you will use geometric strategies to further your understanding of how to convert fractions to percents and to model the conversion. Learning the geometric strategies will give you a deeper conceptual knowledge of the connections between these different representations of portions.

1-85. After 25 flips of a fair coin, Lorraine and her partner recorded 14 heads ($\frac{14}{25}$ heads).

a. Is this more than, less than, or equal to 50%, the theoretical probability of flipping heads? Talk with your partner about how you know.

b. Percentages are one way to compare different portions of the total. If you have not already done so, work with your partner to calculate what percentage of Lorraine's flips were heads. Be prepared to share your strategy for finding the percentage with the class.

1-86. DaMarr also kept track of the number of heads he flipped. He wrote his experimental probability of flipping heads as the fraction $\frac{7}{20}$. He wants to rewrite $\frac{7}{20}$ as a percent. To do so, he knows that he needs to rewrite it as a portion of 100. He started by drawing the picture at right to represent $\frac{7}{20}$.

a. As he looked at his picture, DaMarr realized that he could adjust his drawing to show 100 parts instead of 20. DaMarr then drew a new diagram below his original picture. How many of the 100 parts are shaded? Explain your reasoning.

b. Explain how DaMarr can use his new picture to write $\frac{7}{20}$ as a percent.

c. Use a similar strategy to rewrite $\frac{3}{10}$ as a percent. Show your steps.

New diagram

1-87. Randy was playing "Double Heads," a game in which he would flip two coins at a time. He recorded the number of times he flipped two heads at the same time. He flipped the coins 50 times, and there were 20 times when both coins landed heads up, which he recorded as $\frac{20}{50}$.

    a.   How does $\frac{20}{50}$ compare to 50%?

    b.   Randy claims, " $\frac{20}{50}$ is equivalent to $\frac{70}{100}$ *because if I add 50 to the denominator to get 100 and add 50 to the numerator to get 70, the fraction becomes $\frac{70}{100}$.*" Explain to Randy why $\frac{20}{50}$ and $\frac{70}{100}$ are not equivalent portions.

> **Note:** This stoplight icon will appear periodically throughout the text. Problems with this icon display common errors that can be made. Be sure not to make the same mistakes yourself!

1-88. Three students invented a game in which they flip coins for one minute and then determine who flipped the highest percentage of heads. After their first round, each of them thinks that he or she was the winner of the game. Here is what they reported:

- "*I think I won,*" said Maria, "*Of my flips, $\frac{12}{25}$ were heads.*"

- Autymn said, "*I flipped my coin 40 times and had a total of 18 heads. Since both of my numbers are larger than yours, I must have won.*"

- Kumar reported, "*I recorded 44% of my flips as heads.*"

Help the students determine their percentage of heads. Justify your answer.

1-89. Change the fractions to percents using a strategy of your choice.

    a. $\frac{13}{20}$ b. $\frac{7}{10}$ c. $\frac{12}{25}$ d. $\frac{9}{30}$

1-90.　Rewrite each fraction as a percent and each percent as a fraction. Show your thinking with pictures or labeled calculations.

　　a.　$\frac{2}{5}$　　　　　b.　45%　　　　　c.　120%　　　　　d.　$\frac{21}{40}$

1-91.　Marissa is drawing coins from a bag that contains 5 pennies, 4 nickels, 5 dimes, and 2 quarters.

　　a.　What is the probability that she will draw a nickel? Write your answer as a fraction, as a decimal, and as a percent.

　　b.　If one penny, two dimes, and one quarter are added to the bag, what is the new probability that Marissa will draw a nickel? Write your answer as a fraction, as a decimal, and as a percent.

　　c.　In which situation is it more likely that Marissa will draw a nickel?

1-92.　Calculate the mean of each data set below. Can you find any shortcuts that allow you to find the mean without having to do much calculation?

　　a.　6, 10, 6, 10

　　b.　11, 12, 12, 13, 12

　　c.　0, 5, 4, 8, 0, 7

1-93.　If five slices of pizza cost $5.50, how much do two slices cost? Ten slices? Half a slice?

1-94.　Rewrite each expression as a single fraction.

　　a.　$\frac{3}{8}-\frac{1}{6}$　　　　　　b.　$\frac{4}{5}+\frac{3}{5}$　　　　　　c.　$\frac{5}{9}-\frac{1}{5}$

1.2.5 How can I represent it?

Rewriting Fractions

When probabilities and portions are expressed as fractions, they can sometimes be difficult to compare. For example, is a $\frac{2}{5}$ probability of winning a game greater than a $\frac{3}{7}$ probability?

In Lesson 1.1.5, you used different ways to represent a portion to help figure out whether $0.\overline{9}$ is equal to 1. In this lesson, you will develop strategies for rewriting fractions so you can compare different portions.

```
                    fraction
                      ↑↑↑
                       │
                       ↓
                     words
                       or
                    picture
         decimal  ↙        ↘  percent
```

Representations of a Portion

1-95. FRACTION TO PERCENT

Lila wants to rewrite $\frac{10}{25}$ as a percent. She decided to represent $\frac{10}{25}$ first in a picture.

a. How many sets of 25 will she need to make 100?

b. How many sets of shaded squares will she need? How many shaded squares is that in total?

c. Lila drew the picture below, and then she wrote the equation on the right to represent her work with the shapes.

$$\overset{\cdot\,4}{\overbrace{\frac{10}{25}}} = \frac{40}{100}$$
$$\underset{\cdot\,4}{\underbrace{\phantom{\frac{10}{25}}}}$$

When Lila multiplies the number of shaded squares by 4 and the number of total squares by 4, does the amount of shading compared to the total squares change? Explain how you know.

1-96. Multiplying any number by 1 does not change the value of the number. This is called the **Identity Property of Multiplication**. When the numerator (top number) and denominator (bottom number) of a fraction are multiplied by the same number, some people like to say that the fraction is multiplied by a **Giant One**. For example:

$$\tfrac{10}{25} \cdot \boxed{\tfrac{4}{4}} = \tfrac{40}{100}$$

a. Why is the fraction $\tfrac{4}{4}$ called a Giant One?

b. Each fraction below is shown next to a Giant One. Multiply the expressions to rewrite each fraction.

   i. $\tfrac{9}{25} \cdot \boxed{\tfrac{6}{6}}$ ii. $\tfrac{6}{15} \cdot \boxed{\tfrac{3}{3}}$

c. What if you do not know which numbers to use in a Giant One? Copy and complete each problem below on your paper.

   i. $\tfrac{5}{7} \cdot \boxed{} = \tfrac{40}{}$ ii. $\tfrac{5}{7} \cdot \boxed{} = \tfrac{}{70}$

1-97. Deanna is trying to compare $\tfrac{3}{7}$ to $\tfrac{2}{5}$. She started by representing $\tfrac{3}{7}$ in a picture. Then she divided the picture into five horizontal rows to rewrite the portion as $\tfrac{15}{35}$. Here is her work so far:

$$\tfrac{3}{7} \cdot \boxed{\tfrac{5}{5}} = \tfrac{15}{35}$$

5 sets of 7

5 sets of

a. Use a similar strategy to rewrite $\tfrac{2}{5}$ as a portion of 35. Is $\tfrac{2}{5}$ bigger or smaller than $\tfrac{3}{7}$?

b. Why does rewriting the fractions make it easier to compare the two fractions?

c. Why did Deanna choose 35 for her new denominator? Could she have chosen a different number?

1-98.   FAMILIES OF FRACTIONS

Using a Giant One, you can rewrite any fraction as a different fraction that represents the same portion of a whole. Fractions that are equal but that are written in different ways are called **equivalent fractions**.

For each fraction below, make three new fractions that are equivalent.

a. $\frac{7}{12}$ b. $\frac{3}{10}$ c. $\frac{9}{27}$

1-99.   Adele, Karla, and Lisa are reading the same book. Each has read a different number of pages, as described below.

Adele has read $\frac{5}{8}$ of the book.

Karla has read $\frac{12}{16}$ of the book.

Lisa has read $\frac{13}{24}$ of the book.

Help them decide who has the most left to read.

a.   What denominator could they use to compare the portions they have read?

b.   Which girl has the largest part left to read? Justify your ideas.

c.   How many pages could the book have? Be ready to explain your answer.

1-100.   Use the Giant One to rewrite each fraction as a part of 100. Then write the equivalent percent.

a. $\frac{3}{4} \cdot \boxed{} = \frac{}{100}$ b. $\frac{42}{200} \cdot \boxed{} = \frac{}{100}$ c. $\frac{7}{16} \cdot \boxed{} = \frac{}{100}$

d.   How do you decide which number to use in the Giant One?

1-101.   Which of the events below is most likely to happen? Justify your answer by rewriting the portion in a different form. In each case, show your thinking with pictures or with labeled calculations.

a.   A $\frac{4}{5}$ chance that the teacher will assign homework today.

b.   A 78% chance of a thunderstorm tomorrow.

c.   A $\frac{7}{10}$ probability of picking a green marble.

1-102.   LEARNING LOG

Think about the methods you have for comparing two probabilities to decide which is greater. In your Learning Log, create an example and explain two different strategies for comparing probabilities. Title this entry "Comparing Probabilities" and label it with today's date.

MATH NOTES

METHODS AND **M**EANINGS

Multiplicative Identity

If any number or expression is multiplied by the number 1, the number or expression does not change. The number 1 is called the **multiplicative identity**. So, for any number x:

$$1 \cdot x = x \cdot 1 = x$$

One way the multiplicative identity is used is to create equivalent fractions using a Giant One.

$$\frac{2}{3} \cdot \frac{2}{2} = \frac{4}{6}$$

By multiplying a fraction by a fraction equivalent to 1, a new, equivalent fraction is created.

1-103.   In problem 1-95, Lila rewrote $\frac{10}{25}$ as $\frac{40}{100}$ and represented it
with the picture at right. Tony thinks this fraction is also
equal to $\frac{2}{5}$.

   a.   Is Tony correct? Use the picture or calculations to explain
your reasoning. Write your answer in complete sentences.

   b.   How could Tony write an equivalent (equal) fraction using tenths? That is,
what fraction in the form $\frac{?}{10}$ can represent the diagram above?

1-104.   Zaria wants you to solve this puzzle: *"I am thinking of a number. If you divide
my number by 2 and subtract 4, you will get 2. What is my number?"* Show
how you know your answer is correct.

1-105.   Rewrite each fraction below as an equivalent fraction and as a percent.

   a. $\frac{5}{20}$ b. $\frac{9}{25}$ c. $\frac{9}{6}$

1-106.   Rewrite each expression as a single fraction.

   a. $\frac{3}{8}+\frac{1}{8}$ b. $\frac{4}{5}+\frac{3}{4}$ c. $\frac{6}{7}-\frac{2}{5}$

1-107.   What is the length of the marked portion of each line segment? Copy the
segment onto your paper before finding the missing length. Assume that the
entire line segment is subdivided into equal sections.

a.   ?   0   75

b.   ?   0   75

c.   ?   0   50

1.2.6 How do I add outcomes?

Fraction Addition

When finding probabilities, you often need to add fractions. Today you will investigate fraction addition.

1-108. Justin is working on a new problem: $\frac{1}{3}+\frac{1}{2}$. He drew the picture below to represent the problem.

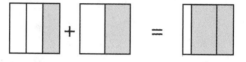

a. Could you name Justin's sum as a single fraction? Would he be correct to name it $\frac{2}{3}$?

b. Kermit sees Justin's work and says, *"You need to make all of the pieces the same size before you try to write the sum. You can use a Giant One to rewrite $\frac{1}{3}$ and $\frac{1}{2}$ each as sixths."* He writes:

$$\frac{1}{3} \cdot \boxed{\frac{}{}} = \frac{}{6} \qquad \frac{1}{2} \cdot \boxed{\frac{}{}} = \frac{}{6}$$

Finish Kermit's work to rewrite each fraction so that its denominator is 6.

c. What is the sum of the new fractions? Fix Justin's picture or draw a new diagram to explain why your answer makes sense.

d. Discuss with your team why Kermit might have chosen to rewrite each fraction as sixths. Could he have used a different number? Be ready to share your thinking.

1-109.   Before you can write the sum of two fractions, they must be rewritten so that both wholes have an equal number of parts. In other words, they must be rewritten to have a **common denominator**.

Three students were adding the fractions $\frac{1}{4}+\frac{5}{12}$ below. They each found a different common denominator:

Lily: $\frac{1}{4}+\frac{5}{12}$ Armando: $\frac{1}{4}+\frac{5}{12}$ Josue: $\frac{1}{4}+\frac{5}{12}$

$\frac{12}{48}+\frac{20}{48}$ $\frac{3}{12}+\frac{5}{12}$ $\frac{6}{24}+\frac{10}{24}$

$\frac{32}{48}$ $\frac{8}{12}$ $\frac{16}{24}$

a.   Who is correct? Can any number be a common denominator? Explain your reasoning.

b.   Which of their common denominators is easiest to work with? Why?

c.   Find at least three different common denominators you could use to add $\frac{3}{10}+\frac{1}{5}$.

1-110.   Vu needs to add $\frac{3}{8}+\frac{5}{6}$. He knows that he can rewrite each fraction as a portion of 48 because 6 and 8 are each factors of 48 in his multiplication table. *"Is there a smaller number that could work as a common denominator?"* he wonders.

a.   Where can you look in the multiplication table to see if 6 and 8 are each factors of a number less than 48?

b.   Use the multiplication table on the Lesson 1.2.6 Resource Page to find other number(s) you could use as a common denominator to add $\frac{3}{8}$ and $\frac{5}{6}$.

c.   Vu's next problem is to add $\frac{5}{4}+\frac{7}{10}$. Use the multiplication table to find the smallest number you could use as a common denominator. This number is called the **lowest common denominator**. After you find the lowest common denominator for Vu's problem, find the sum.

	1	2	3	4	5	6	7	8	9	10
1	1	2	3	4	5	6	7	8	9	10
2	2	4	6	8	10	12	14	16	18	20
3	3	6	9	12	15	18	21	24	27	30
4	4	8	12	16	20	24	28	32	36	40
5	5	10	15	20	25	30	35	40	45	50
6	6	12	18	24	30	36	42	(48)	54	60
7	7	14	21	28	35	42	49	56	63	70
8	8	16	24	32	40	(48)	56	64	72	80
9	9	18	27	36	45	54	63	72	81	90
10	10	20	30	40	50	60	70	80	90	100

1-111. One study team is trying to find the sum $\frac{5}{6} + \frac{3}{4} + \frac{1}{5}$.

   a. They first tried to use 24 as a common denominator. Why does 24 not work as a common denominator?

   b. Find a common denominator for this problem and explain how you found it.

   c. With your study team, describe how factors and multiples can help you find a common denominator.

1-112. With your team, find each sum. You may want to use the multiplication table to help you find common denominators.

   a. $\frac{1}{4} + \frac{5}{6}$ b. $\frac{2}{7} + \frac{2}{3}$ c. $\frac{5}{12} + \frac{1}{2}$ d. $\frac{3}{4} + \frac{1}{2} + \frac{1}{5}$

1-113. THE POWER OF PRIME NUMBERS

   Additional Challenge: A **prime number** is a number that has exactly two factors, namely, 1 and itself. Another way to explain this is that prime numbers can only be divided by themselves and by 1 without a remainder. (The only exception to this rule is the number 1, which is not prime.) Every number that is not prime can be rewritten as a product of **prime factors**. For example, $20 = 2 \cdot 2 \cdot 5$ or $36 = 2 \cdot 2 \cdot 3 \cdot 3$. Prime factors can also be used to build common denominators for fractions.

   a. What are the prime factors of each denominator in the sum $\frac{5}{6} + \frac{3}{4} + \frac{1}{5}$ (from problem 1-111)?

   b. What are the prime factors of the common denominator you found in part (b) of problem 1-111?

   c. What do the lists of factors you made in parts (a) and (b) have in common?

   d. How could the prime factors of each denominator in a pair of fractions help you find a common denominator for those fractions? Explain your thinking.

1-114.   For each part below, find a Giant One that will multiply the fraction on the left side of the equation to create the equivalent fraction on the right side of the equation. Then complete any other missing information.

a. $\frac{5}{6} \cdot \boxed{} = \frac{15}{}$

b. $\frac{}{3} \cdot \boxed{} = \frac{4}{6}$

c. $\frac{}{2} \cdot \boxed{} = \frac{8}{16}$

d. $\frac{}{4} \cdot \boxed{} = \frac{6}{24}$

1-115.   Fareed wants to add $\frac{1}{4} + \frac{5}{8}$.

a.   Add the fractions by using a Giant One to create a common denominator.

b.   How can factors help you find a common denominator?

1-116.   Mario was visiting the carnival when he noticed a few number relationships. He made them into brainteasers for you.

a.   If three tenths of the visitors were adults and there were 100 visitors, how many visitors were adults?

b.   Five eighths of the prizes at the Giant Spin were dolls. If there were 64 prizes, how many prizes were *not* dolls?

1-117.   Order these numbers from least to greatest:

$$\frac{1}{2} \quad 1.1 \quad \frac{5}{3} \quad 2 \quad 0 \quad 0.4 \quad -2 \quad \frac{5}{8}$$

1-118.   Find each sum.

a. $\frac{3}{5} + \frac{1}{3}$

b. $\frac{5}{7} + \frac{1}{2}$

c. $\frac{1}{6} + \frac{2}{8}$

1.2.7 What if there are multiple outcomes?

Compound Probability

So far in this section, you have worked with probabilities involving one specific desired outcome. Now you will investigate probabilities of **compound events**. Compound events are events with combinations of outcomes. In today's lesson, you will find the probability that *either* one of the events *or* the other event occurs. (In Chapter 5, you will consider the probability that *both* one event *and* another event occur.)

Think about these questions as you work with your study team:

How is this probability related to the probability of a single event?

Either what event *or* what other event are we interested in?

Does our answer make sense?

1-119. Thomas helps around the house by doing one chore after school. Each day, Thomas and his aunt use the spinner at right to decide which chore he will do. Here is what Thomas knows:

- The sections on the spinner for "rake leaves" and "do laundry" are the same size.

- The sections for "clean bathroom" and "vacuum" are equal in size and together make up half the spinner.

a. What is the probability that Thomas will spin "do laundry"?

b. Thomas hates to clean the bathroom. When he spins the spinner, what is the probability that it will not point to "clean bathroom"? Explain how you found your answer.

1-120. Thomas's aunt hopes that he will *either* spin "clean bedroom" *or* "rake leaves" today.

a. What is P(clean bedroom)? What is P(rake leaves)?

b. Spinning either chore in part (a) would make Thomas's aunt happy. With your study team, discuss the questions below and record your team's answers. Be sure to justify your conclusions.

- What is the probability that he will spin either one of the chores?

- How can you write the two outcomes as a single probability?

1-121.   Ms. Nguyen lets her students borrow pens and pencils on days when they have a quiz. She has a paper bag containing hundreds of wooden pencils, mechanical pencils, and blue pens.

Stuart forgot his pencil, and it is quiz day! Ms. Nguyen tells him that one out of every three students who reaches into the bag pulls out a wooden pencil. Two out of every five students pull out a mechanical pencil. The rest of the students pull out a blue pen.

    a.   If Stuart reaches into the bag without looking, is it more likely that he will choose a wooden pencil or a mechanical pencil? Justify your thinking.

    b.   How can you describe the probability that Stuart will pull out some kind of pencil—*either* a wooden pencil *or* a mechanical pencil—by using the probabilities that you already know? Consider what you know about adding and subtracting fractions and see if you already have a strategy to write this probability as a single number.

1-122.   Felicia was trying to find the probability that she would pull *either* a wooden pencil *or* a mechanical pencil out of Ms. Nguyen's bag from problem 1-121. *"I think I need to combine the probability that I will get a wooden pencil with the probability that I will get a mechanical pencil,"* she said. She set up this expression and drew a picture:

$$\tfrac{1}{3} + \tfrac{2}{5}$$

    a.   Felicia wondered if she could add the parts. Is the sum $\tfrac{3}{8}$? Why or why not?

    b.   Discuss with your team how Felicia could change the way she writes each fraction so that she can add them easily. Be ready to explain your reasoning. Then, find the sum.

1-123.   Steve shuffles a standard deck of 52 playing cards and starts to turn them over one at a time. The first three cards he turns over are an ace, a 4, and a jack.

    a.   How many cards are left in the deck?

    b.   How many of the remaining cards are aces?

    c.   What is the probability that the fourth card will be an ace?

    d.   Instead of getting an ace, he gets a 2 as the fourth card. The fifth card is a 5. What is the probability that the next card will be a king?

1-124.   What is the probability of getting either blue or green on a spinner that is $\frac{3}{10}$ green and $\frac{1}{5}$ blue? Show your work.

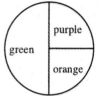

1-125.   If you were to spin the spinner at right, what would be the probability of landing on green or purple? Explain how you know.

1-126.   Find a value for x that will make each of the following equations true.

   a. $x + 8 = 21$ b. $x - 32 = 55$ c. $3x = 54$ d. $\frac{x}{5} = 10$

1-127.   Locate the coordinates of the three highlighted points on the graph of the triangle at right and write them as ordered pairs (x, y).

1-128.   Draw an example of each of the following shapes. Refer to the glossary in the back of the book if you need help.

   a.   rectangle   b.   square   c.   parallelogram

   d.   trapezoid   e.   scalene triangle   f.   right triangle

1-129.   Find the area and perimeter of each figure below.

   a.

   b.

1.2.8 What part is missing?

Subtracting Probabilities

In Lesson 1.2.7, you calculated probabilities for single events and combinations of events when *either* one outcome *or* the other is desirable. You have also compared those probabilities to decide which outcomes are most likely. In this lesson, you will work with your study team to apply your knowledge of fractions to represent and calculate the probabilities of a variety of events. As you work today, ask each other these questions to focus your discussion:

How can probabilities be combined?

How can the answer be rewritten in a different form?

1-130.   Eustice is adding fractions. Here is his work:

$$\frac{1}{2} + \frac{2}{4} = \frac{3}{6}$$

a.   How do you think Eustice got his answer? Does his answer make sense? Discuss Eustice's work with your team. Then explain your reasoning on your paper with diagrams and words.

b.   Help Eustice find the correct answer.

1-131.   Lindsay has a paper bag full of Fruiti Tutti Chews in three different fruit flavors. She says, *"If you reach into the bag, you have a $\frac{1}{3}$ chance of pulling out a Killer Kiwi. There is a $\frac{3}{5}$ chance that you will get Crazy Coconut."*

a.   If you reach into the bag, what is P(coconut or kiwi)?

b.   Does there have to be another flavor in the bag? How can you tell? If so, assuming that there is only one other flavor, what is the probability of getting that flavor?

c.   How many candies might Lindsay have in the bag? Is there more than one possibility? Assume that all candies in the bag are whole candies.

1-132.   Lyle asked for a challenge problem, and his teacher gave him this one:

There is a $\frac{2}{7}$ chance of drawing a red marble out of a bag of marbles. If the probability of drawing a red or a blue marble is $\frac{2}{3}$, what is the probability of drawing a blue marble?

When Lyle's teammates saw the challenge he was working on, they each had a different idea for how he should start.

- Mayra suggested that he start by rewriting $\frac{2}{3}$ and $\frac{2}{7}$ so that they have a common denominator.

- Kenessa disagreed. *"You want to set up a subtraction problem,"* she said. She wrote the expression $\frac{2}{3} - \frac{2}{7}$ to show the number Lyle needs to find.

- Darren had a different idea. *"The probability that you would draw either red or blue is the same as the probability of drawing red added to the probability of drawing blue,"* he said. He wrote this equation:

$$\frac{2}{7} + ? = \frac{2}{3}$$

a.   Which way would you suggest to Lyle as he starts working to find P(blue)?

- Discuss your ideas with your study team.

- Write a clear explanation of which method you recommend and why.

- Include your ideas about whether the other strategies will solve the problem and why you did not choose them.

b.   What is the probability of drawing a blue marble? Explain your reasoning.

1-133.   Louise is playing a game, but the spinner is incomplete. Each section of the spinner is labeled with the probability of spinning it. What fraction is missing?

1-134.   Charles found a spinner his teacher was making. He knew that if he put his problem-solving skills to use, he would be able to figure out the missing piece and finish the spinner for his teacher.

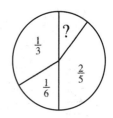

a.   Write an expression for the problem Charles needs to solve. Is there more than one way to do this?

b.   Find the solution.

1-135. Work with your study team to invent two new spinners with missing parts, like the spinners in problems 1-133 and 1-134. Then:

- Find the missing piece on your own paper.

- On a new sheet of paper, draw and label your spinner.

- Trade problems with another study team and find the missing parts of their spinners while they find yours.

1-136. LEARNING LOG

In your Learning Log, describe the process you use to add or subtract fractions when the probabilities have different denominators. Create an example and show your solution with pictures and number expressions. Then answer these questions:

- How do you rewrite the fractions to represent pieces that are the same size?

- How do you identify what common denominator to use?

Label these notes "Adding Probabilities with Unlike Denominators" and include today's date.

Ⓜ ETHODS AND MEANINGS

MATH NOTES

Equivalent Fractions

Fractions that are equal, but written in different forms, are called **equivalent fractions**. Rewriting a fraction in an equivalent form is useful when you want to compare two fractions or when you want to combine portions that are divided into pieces of different sizes.

A Giant One is a useful tool to create an equivalent fraction. To rewrite a fraction in a different form, multiply the original fraction by a fraction equivalent to 1. For example:

$$\frac{2}{3} \cdot \boxed{\frac{4}{4}} = \frac{2 \cdot 4}{3 \cdot 4} = \frac{8}{12}$$

A picture can also demonstrate that these two fractions are equivalent:

1-137.   Rewrite each fraction below in at least two different ways.

a. $\frac{6}{9}$ b. $\frac{11}{12}$ c. $\frac{3}{8}$ d. $\frac{10}{7}$

1-138.   Jonathan measured 2 cups of flour into a bowl on the counter. Then he spilled part of it, and now there is only $\frac{3}{8}$ cup left. How much did he spill?

1-139.   Maggie is making muffins with a recipe that yields 18 muffins.

a.   There are 12 people in Maggie's book club. If the muffins are divided evenly among each person, how much will each person get? Explain your thinking.

b.   If Maggie wanted to divide the muffins evenly between the 36 students in her class, how much muffin would each person get? Explain your thinking.

1-140.   **Multiple Choice:** If the probability of getting a particular result in an experiment is 75.3%, what is the probability of *not* getting that result? Explain your choice.

A. $75.3\% + 100\%$ B. $75.3\% - 100\%$

C. $100\% - 75.3\%$ D. $\frac{1}{75.3\%}$

1-141.   Throughout this book, key problems have been selected as "checkpoints." Each
checkpoint problem is marked with an icon like the one at left. These
checkpoint problems are provided so that you can check to be sure you are
building skills at the expected level. When you have trouble with checkpoint
problems, refer to the review materials and practice problems that are available
in the "Checkpoint Materials" section at the back of your book.

This problem is a checkpoint for area and perimeter of polygons. It will be
referred to as Checkpoint 1.

For each figure below, find the area and the perimeter.

a.

b.

c. Parallelogram

d. Trapezoid

Check your answers by referring to the Checkpoint 1 materials located at the
back of your book.

Ideally, at this point you are comfortable working with these types of problems
and can solve them correctly. If you feel that you need more confidence when
solving these types of problems, then review the Checkpoint 1 materials and try
the practice problems provided. From this point on, you will be expected to do
problems like these correctly and with confidence.

Chapter 1 Closure   What have I learned?

Reflection and Synthesis

The activities below offer you a chance to reflect
about what you have learned during this chapter.
As you work, look for concepts that you feel very
comfortable with, ideas that you would like to learn
more about, and topics you need more help with.

①   SUMMARIZING MY UNDERSTANDING

This section gives you an opportunity to show what you know about the main
math ideas in this chapter.

Candy Callipso, the CEO of the Moon &
Mercury Candy Company, has a crisis! She has
hired your team to help her solve a problem. A
customer ordered a thousand bubblegum
machines and specified that each one should have
a probability of exactly $\frac{1}{3}$ for getting a blue
gumball. The bubblegum machines were created
and sent out, but the customer has called,
claiming that the machines were filled
incorrectly. Candy's records show that each
machine was filled with 4 yellow gumballs, 8 red
gumballs, 16 green gumballs, and 20 blue gumballs.

Your Task: Work with your team to:

- Figure out whether the machines meet the customer's requirements.

    ○ If they do, find *at least two* other combinations of gumballs that
      would satisfy the picky customer.

    ○ If they do not, find *at least two* ways to adjust the contents of the
      machines so that the probability of getting a blue gumball is
      exactly $\frac{1}{3}$.

- Prepare a poster to report to Candy each of your proposed solutions. Be
  sure to explain how you know each solution will work.

②   **WHAT HAVE I LEARNED?**

Doing the problems in this section will help you to evaluate which types of problems you feel comfortable with and which ones you need more help with.

Solve each problem as completely as you can. The table at the end of this closure section provides answers to these problems. It also tells you where you can find additional help and where to find practice problems like them.

CL 1-142.   Vanson has a bunch of boxes that are all the same. He stacked four boxes, measured the stack, and found that it was three feet high.

a.   How high will a stack of 20 of these boxes be?

b.   The ceiling in the room where Vanson is working is just a little more than 9 feet high. He wants to stack boxes from the floor to the ceiling. How many boxes will fit in one stack?

CL 1-143.   Find the perimeter and area of Jacob's swimming pool shown in the diagram below. Be sure to show all of your work.

CL 1-144.   Tuan is playing a game, but the spinner is incomplete. If the numbers in the sections of the spinner represent the probabilities of spinning each section, help him figure out the fraction for the missing section of the spinner.

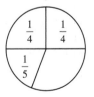

CL 1-145.   Complete each portions web.

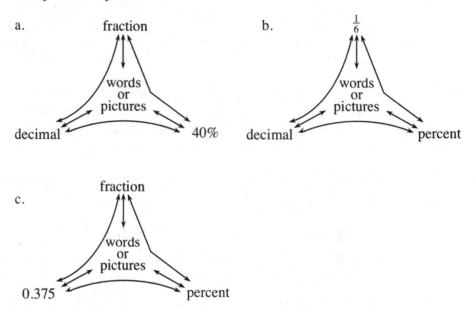

a.   fraction
     words or pictures
     decimal   40%

b. $\frac{1}{6}$
     words or pictures
     decimal   percent

c.   fraction
     words or pictures
     0.375   percent

CL 1-146.   Add $\frac{1}{6} + \frac{1}{2}$. Show all of your steps.

CL 1-147.   Write "theoretical" or "experimental" to describe the following situations.

   a.   The chance of rolling a sum of 3 with two number cubes is $\frac{1}{18}$.

   b.   I drew five cards out of a deck and got clubs three times.

   c.   I bought six raffle tickets and did not win anything.

   d.   Based on a mathematical model, the chance of a flood next year is 1.2%.

CL 1-148.   The county-fair prize wheel has equally spaced sections with the following colors: one is golden, two are silver, three are green, four are blue, six are red, and nine are yellow.

   a.   What is the probability of landing on gold? Give your answer as a fraction and as a percent.

   b.   If the probability of landing on yellow is 36%, what is the probability of not landing on yellow?

   c.   If the wheel is spun 100 times, how many times would you expect to land on silver?

CL 1-149. Kimberly is playing "Guess My Number." Her clue is, *"When I triple my number and subtract 7, I get 83."* Find Kimberly's number and explain how you know your answer is correct.

CL 1-150. For each of the problems above, do the following:

- Draw a bar or number line that represents 0 to 10.

- Color or shade in a portion of the bar that represents your level of understanding and comfort with completing that problem on your own.

If any of your bars are less than a 5, choose *one* of those problems and complete one of the following tasks:

- Write two questions that you would like to ask about that problem.
- Brainstorm two things that you DO know about that type of problem.

If all of your bars are a 5 or above, choose *one* of those problems and do one of these tasks:

- Write two questions you might ask or hints you might give to a student who was stuck on the problem.
- Make a new problem that is similar and more challenging than that problem and solve it.

③   WHAT TOOLS CAN I USE?

You have several tools and references available to help support your learning: your teacher, your study team, your math book, and your Toolkit, to name only a few. At the end of each chapter, you will have an opportunity to review your Toolkit for completeness. You will also revise or update it to reflect your current understanding of big ideas.

The main elements of your Toolkit should be your Learning Logs, Math Notes, and the vocabulary used in this chapter. Math words that are new appear in bold in the text. Refer to the lists provided below and follow your teacher's instructions to revise your Toolkit, which will help make it useful for you as you complete this chapter and as you work in future chapters.

Learning Log Entries
- Lesson 1.1.4 – Beginning to Think About Proportional Relationships
- Lesson 1.2.1 – Probability
- Lesson 1.2.5 – Comparing Probabilities
- Lesson 1.2.8 – Adding Probabilities with Unlike Denominators

Math Notes
- Lesson 1.1.2 – Perimeter and Area
- Lesson 1.1.3 – Mean
- Lesson 1.1.4 – Median
- Lesson 1.1.5 – Representations of Portions
- Lesson 1.2.2 – Scaling Axes
- Lesson 1.2.3 – Probability Vocabulary and Definitions
- Lesson 1.2.5 – Multiplicative Identity
- Lesson 1.2.8 – Equivalent Fractions

Mathematical Vocabulary

The following is a list of vocabulary found in this chapter. Make sure that you are familiar with the terms below and know what they mean. For the words you do not know, refer to the glossary or index. You might also add these words to your Toolkit so that you can reference them in the future.

area	compound events	desired outcomes
equivalent fractions	experimental probability	lowest common denominator
interval	mean	measure of central tendency
median	multiplicative identity	outcome
outliers	parallelogram	percent
perimeter	possible outcomes	probability
proportional relationship	rectangle	repeating decimal
sample space	scaling	terminating decimal
theoretical probability	trapezoid	triangle

Answers and Support for Closure Problems
What Have I Learned?

Note: MN = Math Note, LL = Learning Log

Problem	Solution	Need Help?	More Practice
CL 1-142.	a. 15 feet b. 12 boxes will fit in one stack.	Lesson 1.1.4	Problems 1-36 and 1-83
CL 1-143.	$P = 88$ m, $A = 369$ sq. m	MN: 1.1.2	Problems 1-11, 1-22, 1-49, 1-84, 1-129, and 1-141
CL 1-144.	$\frac{3}{10}$	Lessons 1.2.2 and 1.2.8 MN: 1.2.3	Problems 1-133 and 1-134
CL 1-145.	a. Two fifths, $\frac{2}{5}$, 0.4, 40% b. One sixth, $\frac{1}{6}$, $0.1\overline{6}$, 16.67% c. Three eighths, $\frac{3}{8}$, 0.375, 37.5%	MN: 1.1.5	Problems 1-44, 1-46, and 1-47
CL 1-146.	$\frac{8}{12}$, $\frac{4}{6}$, or $\frac{2}{3}$	Lesson 1.2.6 LL: 1.2.8	Problems 1-94, 1-106, 1-115, and 1-118
CL 1-147.	a. Theoretical b. Experimental c. Experimental d. Theoretical	Lessons 1.2.1 and 1.2.2 MN: 1.2.3 LL: 1.2.1	Problems 1-59 and 1-75
CL 1-148.	a. $\frac{1}{25} = 4\%$ b. 64% c. 8	Lessons 1.2.1 and 1.2.2 MN: 1.2.3 LL: 1.2.1	Problems 1-57, 1-71, 1-80, 1-124, and 1-125
CL 1-149.	Kimberly's number is 30. $30 \cdot 3 - 7 = 83$	Lesson 1.1.3	Problems 1-16, 1-17, 1-18, and 1-104

2

Fractions and Integer Addition

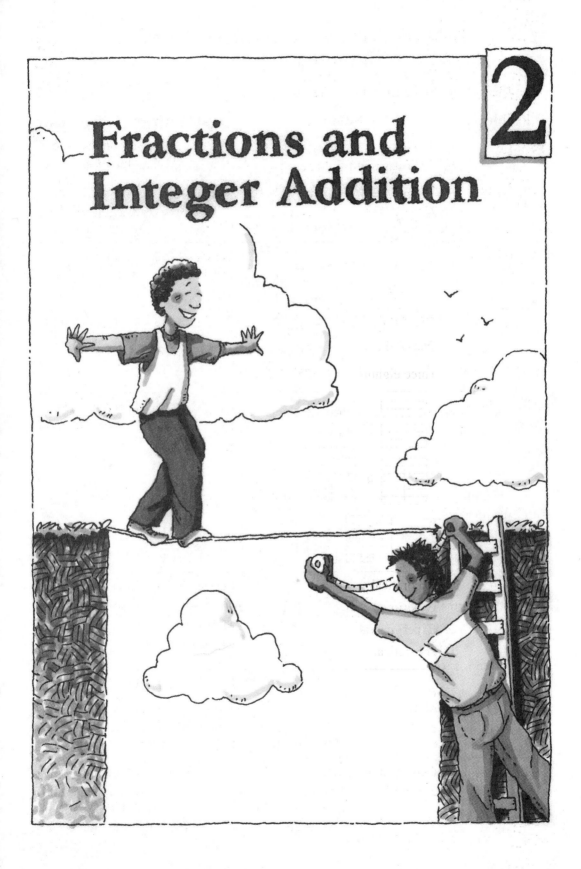

CHAPTER 2 Fractions and Integer Addition

In Chapter 2 you will work to deepen your understanding about various types of numbers. In Section 2.1, you will look carefully at relationships between fractions, decimals, and percents to rewrite numbers in different forms and to compare them to each other.

In Section 2.2, you will direct an acrobat to move back and forth on a tightrope as you learn about adding and multiplying **integers** (positive and negative whole numbers, and zero). You will also learn how to add and multiply numbers containing fractions and decimals (called **rational numbers**). Then you will represent and combine positive and negative values using pictures. Finally, you will learn ways to make calculations without having to write anything down or use a calculator.

Guiding Questions

Think about these questions throughout this chapter:

How can the number be rewritten?

Are the numbers equal?

How can I visualize it?

How can I describe the motion?

In Section 2.3, you will look at coordinate graphs and learn how to scale axes to make the graphs the most useful for different purposes.

In this chapter, you will learn how to:

➢ Rewrite numbers in different forms in order to compare them.

➢ Determine whether a fraction can be rewritten as a repeating or terminating decimal.

➢ Build (compose) and take apart (decompose) numbers and lengths.

➢ Add and multiply positive and negative integers and rational numbers.

➢ Choose appropriate scales and set up useful graphs for data.

Chapter Outline

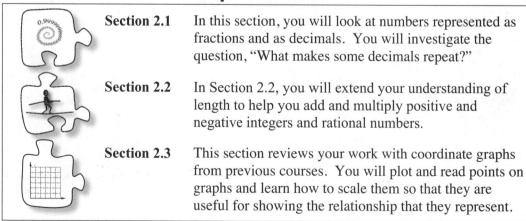

Section 2.1   In this section, you will look at numbers represented as fractions and as decimals. You will investigate the question, "What makes some decimals repeat?"

Section 2.2   In Section 2.2, you will extend your understanding of length to help you add and multiply positive and negative integers and rational numbers.

Section 2.3   This section reviews your work with coordinate graphs from previous courses. You will plot and read points on graphs and learn how to scale them so that they are useful for showing the relationship that they represent.

2.1.1 When do decimals repeat?

Fraction-to-Decimal Conversions

In previous lessons, you explored different representations of portions (parts) of wholes. You looked at portions represented as fractions and as decimals, and you went back and forth between the representations. While fractions are written in a common format, that is, as the quotient $\frac{a}{b}$ where a and b are integers, their decimal representations have two types, terminating and repeating. Why does this happen? In this lesson, you will work with your team to determine what makes some decimals terminate (end) and some repeat.

2-1. Compare the portions in each picture below.

Portion A: Portion B: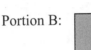

a. Represent each portion as a fraction and as a decimal.

b. The pictures and fractions for each representation are similar, but the decimals look very different. With your team, discuss how the two decimals look different and why they might look this way. Be ready to share your ideas.

2-2. In Lesson 1.1.5, you rewrote fractions like $\frac{1}{9}$ as decimals by dividing on your calculator. Looking at how division works can help explain why fractions can look so different when written as decimals.

$$\frac{1}{9} = 1 \div 9 = 0.111... = 0.\overline{1}$$

Imagine that you have 13 cheese sticks that you need to divide evenly among 5 people. You can write this relationship as 13 cheese sticks ÷ 5 people or $\frac{13}{5}$ or $5\overline{)13}$. The problem is represented with the pictures and symbols below.

13 cheese sticks

$$\begin{array}{r} 2 \\ 5\overline{)13} \\ \underline{10} \\ 3 \end{array}$$

5 groups of 2 pieces

Problem continues on next page. →

2-2.   *Problem continued from previous page.*

a. Talk with your team about how this diagram represents dividing 13 by 5, or
    $\frac{13}{5}$. Why are there five groups of two pieces?

b. What does the 2 above the division symbol represent? What does the
    10 represent?

c. Where are the three leftover pieces shown in the symbols?

d. Our number system is based on powers of ten, so to share the three leftover
    pieces between the 5 people, we would divide the pieces into tenths. Add a
    decimal point in the dividend to show that the three wholes are being
    rewritten as thirty tenths (3.0), as shown below.

    3 pieces = $\frac{30}{10}$ pieces

    $$\begin{array}{r} 2. \\ 5\overline{)13.0} \\ \underline{10}\downarrow \\ 30 \end{array}$$

    Determine how many tenths each person gets. Then show where this is
    written in the problem, and complete the division process.

e. How much cheese will each person receive? Write your answer as a
    fraction and as a decimal.

2-3.   You know that $\frac{3}{4}$ can be written decimally as 0.75. To see why
        this is so, set up your own division problem to rewrite $\frac{3}{4}$ as a
        decimal. Use the Lesson 2.1.1 Resource Page, but *do not use a
        calculator*. Show your work on the diagram and in symbols.

a. Each bold line in the diagram represents one piece. Are there enough
    whole pieces to put some in each of four groups? Explain.

b. Divide each of the whole pieces into tenths and then divide these into four
    groups. How many tenths are in each group? How many tenths are left
    over?

c. If you divide each tenth that is left over into 10 pieces again, what fraction
    of the original is each new piece? How many are there? You may need to
    visualize these pieces instead of drawing them.

d. How many of these new, smaller pieces will be in each of the four groups?
    How many will be left over?

e. How can you tell that the decimal has terminated (ended)?

2-4.   To see why $\frac{2}{3}$ does not terminate, use the Lesson 2.1.1 Resource
        Page to rewrite it as a decimal. Follow the same procedure used
        in problem 2-3, and be sure not to use a calculator.

   a.   As you continue to divide the pieces into three groups,
        what happens?

   b.   How is the process of dividing $\frac{2}{3}$ the same as dividing $\frac{3}{4}$, and how is it
        different? Why does one decimal terminate, but the other does not?

2-5.   Katrina works at the Fraction Factory. Her job is to sort
        all of the customer orders into two groups: terminating
        decimals and repeating decimals.

   a.   Katrina's boss wants her to write $\frac{20}{33}$ as a decimal
        without using a calculator. Katrina's work so far is
        shown at right. What results did she get each time
        she subtracted?

   b.   Will the decimal for $\frac{20}{33}$ terminate or repeat? How
        do you know? To be sure, how far should Katrina
        continue with her division?

$$
\begin{array}{r}
0.60 \\
33\overline{)20.000} \\
198\downarrow \\
\hline
20 \\
0 \\
\hline
200
\end{array}
$$

2-6.   **Additional Challenge:** Represent $\frac{1}{7}$ as a
        decimal without using your calculator.
        When does it repeat? How do you know?

2-7.   THE ROLE OF THE DENOMINATOR

        Additional Challenge: Both $\frac{1}{3}$ and $\frac{2}{3}$ can be rewritten as repeating decimals,
        $0.\overline{3}$ and $0.\overline{6}$, respectively. Does the number in the denominator cause the
        fraction to repeat? For example, will every fraction with a denominator of 15
        be equivalent to a repeating decimal? (Ignore fractions that are equal to whole
        numbers, like $\frac{15}{15} = 1$ or $\frac{45}{15} = 3$.)

   a.   With your team, investigate fractions with a denominator of 15, including
        $\frac{5}{15}$ and $\frac{10}{15}$. Can you find a fraction with 15 in the denominator that does
        not repeat and that is not equal to a whole number? Are you able to find
        one? More than one?

   b.   Why do some numbers with a denominator of 15 repeat and others do not?
        Discuss this with your team. Write down an idea and test it.

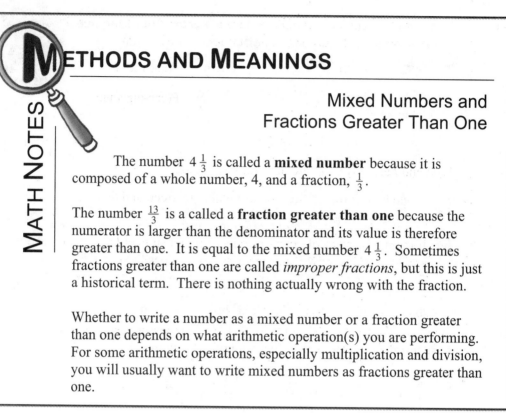

METHODS AND **M**EANINGS

MATH NOTES

Mixed Numbers and Fractions Greater Than One

The number $4\frac{1}{3}$ is called a **mixed number** because it is composed of a whole number, 4, and a fraction, $\frac{1}{3}$.

The number $\frac{13}{3}$ is a called a **fraction greater than one** because the numerator is larger than the denominator and its value is therefore greater than one. It is equal to the mixed number $4\frac{1}{3}$. Sometimes fractions greater than one are called *improper fractions*, but this is just a historical term. There is nothing actually wrong with the fraction.

Whether to write a number as a mixed number or a fraction greater than one depends on what arithmetic operation(s) you are performing. For some arithmetic operations, especially multiplication and division, you will usually want to write mixed numbers as fractions greater than one.

Review & Preview

2-8.   How many tenths are in one whole? How many hundredths?

2-9.   Convert the following fractions to decimals. Show your work.

a. $\frac{2}{5}$

b. $\frac{3}{8}$

c. $\frac{30}{20}$

2-10.   Mario ordered a pizza for dinner. When it arrived, Mario quickly ate $\frac{1}{8}$ of the pizza. While Mario was getting napkins, his pet poodle ate $\frac{1}{3}$ of the pizza.

a. Draw a model of the pizza that shows the portion that has been eaten.

b. Write a numerical expression to show the fraction of the pizza that is left.

c. About what percent of the pizza is left?

Core Connections, Course 2

2-11.   Nicole has a machine that will produce a number from 1 through 50 when she pushes a button. If she pushes the button, what is:

a.   P(multiple of 10)?

b.   P(not 100)?

c.   P(not a multiple of 4)?

d.   P(one-digit number)?

2-12.   Lyle and his study team are designing spinners.

a.   If one half of the sections on a spinner are green and there are 14 sections, how many are green?

b.   If three fourths of the sections on a different spinner have stripes and there are 24 sections, how many sections have stripes?

2-13.   Which of the fractions listed below will have repeating decimals and which will have terminating decimals? Explain how you know.

a. $\frac{2}{5}$

b. $\frac{7}{45}$

c. $\frac{5}{99}$

d. $\frac{27}{250}$

2-14.   Here are the lengths (in inches) of snakes in a reptile display at the zoo: $10, 31, 36, 36, 38, 42, 47, 48, 49,$ and 52. Find the mean and median of the lengths.

2-15.   Thomas has a bag with 7 green marbles, 5 blue marbles, and 4 red marbles. For each part below, if the marble selected is replaced before the next marble is drawn, find the probability for the given draw. Write your answer as a fraction, as a decimal, and as a percent.

a.   A red marble?

b.   A red or a green marble?

c.   An orange marble?

2-16.   Finding patterns is an important problem-solving skill used in mathematics. You will use the patterns in Diamond Problems to solve other problems later in the course. Can you discover a pattern for the numbers in each of the four diamonds below?

Copy the Diamond Problems below and use the pattern you discovered to complete each of them.

2-17.   Read the Math Notes box for this lesson. Then rewrite each number below as a single fraction greater than one.

a. $1\frac{1}{11}$

b. $3\frac{2}{5}$

c. $2\frac{4}{15}$

2.1.2 How can I rewrite a decimal?

Rewriting Decimals as Fractions

In Lesson 2.1.1, you worked with different fractions and found ways to rewrite those fractions as repeating and terminating decimals. In this lesson, you will reverse your thinking and will instead represent decimals as fractions.

As you work with your team today, ask each other these questions to focus your discussion:

How else can I describe the portion?

How many pieces are in the whole?

fraction

words
or
pictures

decimal   percent

Representations of a Portion

2-18.   Complete the Representations of a Portion web for each number below. An example for $\frac{2}{3}$ is shown at right.

a. $\frac{7}{10}$

b.   0.75

c.   Three fifths

d. $\frac{5}{8}$

$\frac{2}{3}$

two
thirds

$0.\overline{6}$ $66\frac{2}{3}\%$

Representations of a Portion

e.   With your team, explain how you rewrote 0.75 as a fraction in part (b). Is there more than one way? Be as specific as possible.

2-19.   Since 0.7 is described in words as "seven tenths," it is not a surprise that the equivalent fraction is $\frac{7}{10}$. Obtain a set of decimal cards from your teacher or use the list below to complete the following tasks:

• Use the names of fractions (like "twenty-three hundredths") to rewrite each terminating decimal as a fraction. First try to use what you know about place value to write the fraction.

• With your calculator, check to be sure the fraction is equal to the decimal.

a.   0.19   b.   0.391   c.   0.001

d.   0.019   e.   0.3   f.   0.524

2-20.   Jerome works at the Fraction Factory in the department that
         changes decimals into fractions. He has just received an order to
         rewrite $0.\overline{73}$ as a fraction. He started to rewrite it as $\frac{73}{100}$, but he is
         not sure that he is correct. Is $\frac{73}{100}$ equal to $0.\overline{73}$? Be ready to
         justify your answer.

2-21.   Katrina is now responsible for finding the decimal
         equivalent for each of the numbers below. She
         thinks these fractions have something to do with the
         decimals and fractions in problem 2-19, but she is
         not sure.

         Get a set of the fractions in parts (a) through (f)
         below on cards from your teacher, and use your
         calculator to change each fraction into a decimal.
         Add the decimal information to the card. Can you
         find a pattern?

         a. $\frac{19}{99}$ b. $\frac{391}{999}$ c. $\frac{3}{9}$

         d. $\frac{1}{999}$ e. $\frac{524}{999}$ f. $\frac{19}{999}$

         g. What connections do these fractions have with those you found in problem
             2-19? Be ready to share your observations with the class.

         h. Use your pattern to predict the fraction equivalent for $0.\overline{24}$. Then test your
             guess with a calculator.

         i. Use your pattern to predict the decimal equivalent for $\frac{65}{99}$. Check your
             answer with your calculator.

2-22.   REWRITING REPEATING DECIMALS AS FRACTIONS

Jerome wants to figure out why his pattern from problem 2-21 works. He noticed that he could eliminate the repeating digits by subtracting, as he did in the work at right. This gave him an idea. *"What if I multiply by something before I subtract, so that I'm left with more than zero?"* he wondered. He wrote:

$$0.\overline{73} = 0.737373....$$
$$-0.\overline{73} = -0.737373....$$
$$0 = 0$$

$$10(0.\overline{73}) = 7.373737...$$
$$- (0.\overline{73}) = -0.737373...$$

"The repeating decimals do not make zero in this problem. But if I multiply by 100 instead, I think it will work!" He tried again:

$$100(0.\overline{73}) = 73.737373...$$
$$- (0.\overline{73}) = - 0.737373....$$
$$99(0.\overline{73}) = 73.0$$

a. Discuss Jerome's work with your team. Why did he multiply by 100? How did he get 99 sets of $0.\overline{73}$? What happened to the repeating decimals when he subtracted?

b. *"I know that 99 sets of $0.\overline{73}$ are equal to 73 from my equation,"* Jerome said. *"So to find what just one set of $0.\overline{73}$ is equal to, I will need to divide 73 into 99 equal parts."* Represent Jerome's idea as a fraction.

c. Use Jerome's strategy to rewrite $0.\overline{85}$ as a fraction. Be prepared to explain your reasoning.

2-23.   DESIGN A DECIMAL DEPARTMENT

Congratulations! Because of your new skills with rewriting fractions and decimals, you have been put in charge of the Designer Decimals Department of the Fraction Factory. People write to your department and order their favorite fractions rewritten as beautiful decimals.

Recently, your department has received some strange orders. Review each order below and decide if you can complete it. If possible, find the new fraction or decimal. If it is not possible to complete the order, write to the customer and explain why the order cannot be completed.

Order 1:   "I'd like a terminating decimal to represent $\frac{44}{99}$."

Order 2:   "Could you send me 0.208 as two different fractions, one with 3000 in the denominator and one with 125 in the denominator?"

Order 3:   "Please send me $0.\overline{43}$ written as a fraction."

2-24.   **Additional Challenge:**
A strange order has arrived in the Designer Decimals Department. The order requests a new kind of decimal to be written as a fraction.

> *Please send me the decimal*
> *0.01001000100001...*
> *rewritten as a fraction.*

The order is reprinted at right. With your team, rewrite the decimal as an equivalent fraction or explain why you cannot rewrite it.

2-25.   LEARNING LOG

Make an entry in your Learning Log that summarizes what you have learned in the past two lessons. For example, how can you tell if a decimal is repeating or terminating? How can you change a decimal to a fraction, especially if it is repeating? Can every fraction be represented as a decimal, and can every decimal be represented as a fraction?

Title your entry "Repeating and Terminating Decimals" and include today's date.

METHODS AND MEANINGS

Fraction ⇔ Decimal ⇔ Percent

The **Representations of a Portion web** diagram at right illustrates that fractions, decimals, and percents are different ways to represent a portion of a number. Portions can also be represented in words, such as "four fifths" or "twelve fifteenths," or with diagrams.

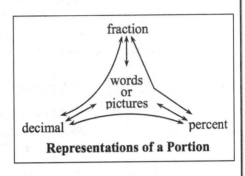

Representations of a Portion

The examples below show how to convert from one form to another.

Decimal to percent:
Multiply the decimal by 100.

$$(0.34)(100) = 34\%$$

Percent to decimal:
Divide the percent by 100.

$$78.6\% = 78.6 \div 100 = 0.786$$

Fraction to percent:
Set up an equivalent fraction using 100 as the denominator. The numerator is the percent.

$$\tfrac{4}{5} \cdot \boxed{\tfrac{20}{20}} = \tfrac{80}{100} = 80\%$$

Percent to fraction:
Use 100 as the denominator. Use the digits in the percent as the numerator. Simplify as needed.

$$22\% = \tfrac{22}{100} \cdot \boxed{\tfrac{1/2}{1/2}} = \tfrac{11}{50}$$

Terminating decimal to fraction:
Make the digits the numerator. Use the decimal place value as the denominator. Simplify as needed.

$$0.2 = \tfrac{2}{10} = \tfrac{1}{5}$$

Fraction to decimal:
Divide the numerator by the denominator. If sets of digits repeat, then write just one of the repeating sets and place a "bar" over it.

$$\tfrac{3}{8} = 3 \div 8 = 0.375$$

$$\tfrac{70}{99} = 70 \div 99 = 0.70707... = 0.\overline{70}$$

Repeating decimal to fraction:
Count the number of decimal places in the repeating block. Write the repeating block as the numerator. Then, write the power of 10 for the number of places in the block, less 1, as the denominator. Below, the repeating block (713) has 3 decimal places so 713 is the numerator and 1000 − 1 is the denominator.

$$0.\overline{713} = \tfrac{713}{1000-1} = \tfrac{713}{999}$$

2-26. Which of the following fractions are repeating decimals and which are terminating? Show how you made your decisions.

a. $\frac{2}{15}$ b. $\frac{11}{20}$ c. $\frac{17}{40}$ d. $\frac{1}{12}$

2-27. Copy the portions webs below and fill in the missing parts.

a.

Representations of a Portion

b.

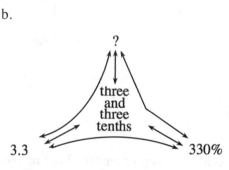

Representations of a Portion

2-28. Lila is making a spinner game for her cousins to play. She has divided it into 8 equal sections and has labeled each section with a symbol. When the spinner lands on a flower (✿), her cousins will win a prize.

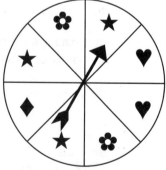

a. What is P(★)? Express your answer as a fraction, as a decimal, and as a percent.

b. What is the probability of not getting ♦? Write your answer as a fraction, as a decimal, and as a percent.

c. What is P(✿)? Write your answer as a fraction, as a decimal, and as a percent.

d. If Lila's cousins spin 100 times, about how many times would you expect them to spin a heart (♥)?

2-29.   Copy the graphs below onto your paper. Then complete the scale by labeling
         the remaining tick marks.

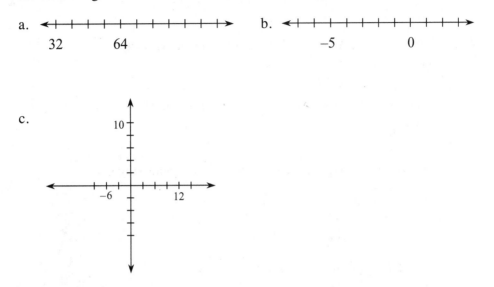

a.
      32   64

b.
                                        −5   0

c.
      10

   −6   12

2-30.   Approximately 3 out of every 25 Americans live in California. About 3 out of
         every 50 Americans live in New York, and about 2 out of every 25 Americans
         live in Texas.

         a.   Which state has the largest population?

         b.   Which state has the smallest population?

         c.   About what percentage of Americans do *not* live in California, New York,
              or Texas?

2.2.1 How can I build it?

Composing Integers

Units of length can be placed one after another in a line to find a measure of an object's length. Today you will look at how to compose (put together) different lengths to create a new total length.

2-31.   CROSSING THE TIGHTROPE

Cecil is an acrobat in a local circus. His job is to move across a tightrope from point A to point B while blindfolded! He can only move using the distances that you tell him to move in your instructions. He needs to reach the end of the tightrope (point B) to take his bow and go down a ladder. Assume the platforms on both sides of the tightrope extend infinitely (have no end). Cecil may go past the ladder. However, if he does, make sure he turns around and goes back toward the ladder.

Your Task: Work with your team to find different combinations of the lengths given in parts (a) through (e) below that will allow Cecil to move from point A and end at point B (the end of the tightrope). You may use each length as many times as you like.

For each crossing, look for at least three different ways to get the acrobat across. For each solution, draw a diagram on your paper that shows how the available lengths were combined to get Cecil across the tightrope.

You can find a digital version of this activity at cpm.org. The length strips from the Lesson 2.2.1A Resource Page might also be helpful.

a.   Span of tightrope: 24 feet   Given lengths: 2, 4, 8, 10 feet

b.   Span of tightrope: 17 feet   Given lengths: 2, 3, 10 feet

c.   Span of tightrope: 15 feet   Given lengths: 3, 4, 6, 11 feet

d.   Span of tightrope: 27 feet   Given lengths: 4, 8, 12, 19 feet

e.   Span of tightrope: 23 feet   Given lengths: 7, 11, 13 feet

2-32.   To represent the way that the acrobat could move across a span of 17 feet, Mara wrote the expressions shown below. If each number represents a length in feet, check that each expression would get Cecil exactly to point B. Be prepared to defend each conclusion with a diagram.

a. $7+3+7$ b. $7+10$

c. $10+7$ d. $10+10+(-3)$

e.   What does the -3 in part (d) represent as a movement for Cecil?

2-33.   Write numerical expressions (similar to those in problem 2-32) for each of your solutions to part (c) of problem 2-31.

2-34.   When combining lengths to make a new length (like you did to get the acrobat across the rope), does the order of the numbers (or lengths) matter? Discuss this with your team or partner and decide whether it matters or not. Be ready to explain why your answer makes sense.

2-35.   DESIGNING A TIGHTROPE

In problem 2-31, you found multiple ways to combine lengths to get an acrobat to the end of the tightrope.

a.   This time, you are given lengths of 2, 5, and 9 feet. With your team, decide if the acrobat could cross a tightrope of length 1, 2, 3, 4, 5, 6, 7, 8, 9, or 10 feet. For each length that you think is possible, write an expression to represent the acrobat's movements. Remember that you can combine rope lengths going forward (in the positive direction) or backward (in the negative direction). For each length that you think is not possible, explain why it is not possible.

b.   Could you combine lengths of 2, 6, and 8 feet to cross a tightrope 15 feet long? Explain why or why not.

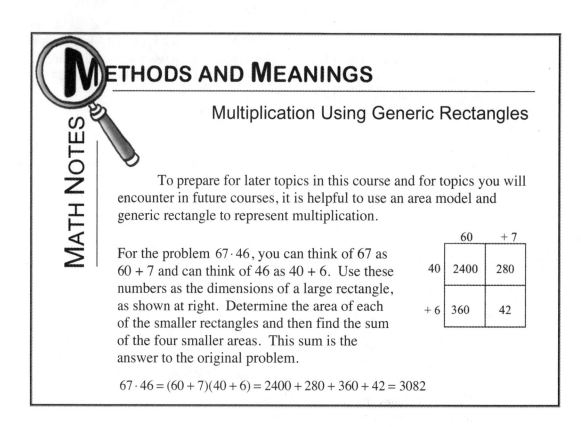

METHODS AND MEANINGS

Multiplication Using Generic Rectangles

MATH NOTES

To prepare for later topics in this course and for topics you will encounter in future courses, it is helpful to use an area model and generic rectangle to represent multiplication.

For the problem $67 \cdot 46$, you can think of 67 as $60 + 7$ and can think of 46 as $40 + 6$. Use these numbers as the dimensions of a large rectangle, as shown at right. Determine the area of each of the smaller rectangles and then find the sum of the four smaller areas. This sum is the answer to the original problem.

	60	+ 7
40	2400	280
+ 6	360	42

$$67 \cdot 46 = (60 + 7)(40 + 6) = 2400 + 280 + 360 + 42 = 3082$$

Review & Preview

2-36.   Read the Math Notes box in this lesson. Then use generic rectangles to complete the following multiplication problems.

    a. $54 \cdot 32$ b. $91 \cdot 78$

2-37.   Below are some new distances with given lengths to help Cecil cross the tightrope. Find at least two ways to get Cecil across. Write your solutions as numerical expressions.

    a.   Span of tightrope: 6 feet   Given lengths: $1, 3, 4$ feet

    b.   Span of tightrope: 8 feet   Given lengths: $2, 5, 7$ feet

2-38.   Simplify each of the following expressions to find the length of the tightrope.

    a. $5 + 2 + 8$ b. $4 + 9 + 3$

    c. $7 + 3 + 2 + (-4)$ d. $8 + 6 + 2 + (-5)$

2-39.   Copy these incomplete number lines. Label the missing numbers on each of them.

a.   50, 20, 0   Length (cm)

b.   32.4, 0   Length (cm)

c.   8.8, 0   Time (min)

d.   10, 0   Time (min)

2-40.   One of the topics you will review in this course is reading graphs. Look at the graph at right. This graph shows positive and negative values on both axes. It divides the flat surface into four parts, or quadrants, and is therefore called a **four-quadrant** graph.

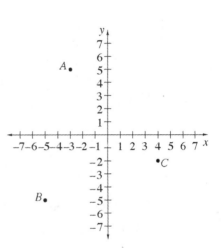

a.   The coordinates (the *x*- and *y*-values) for point *A* are $(-3, 5)$. Explain how these numbers tell you the position of point *A* using the graph.

b.   Name the coordinates (x, y) for points *B* and *C*.

c.   If Samantha moved point *A* 9 units down and 6 units to the right, at what point would she end up?

2-41.   Gracie loves to talk on the phone, but her parents try to limit the amount of time she talks. They decided to keep a record of the number of minutes that she spends on the phone each day. Here are the data for the past nine days: 120, 60, 0, 30, 15, 0, 0, 10, and 20.

a.   Find the mean and median for the information.

b.   Which of the two measures in part (a) would give Gracie's parents the most accurate information about her phone use? Why do you think so?

2.2.2 How can I find the length?

. . . .

Adding Integers and Rational Numbers

Today you will continue to explore how to combine integer (positive and negative whole numbers and zero) and rational number (fraction and decimal) lengths in multiple ways to find a new length. You will also continue to learn how different combinations can be written with numerical expressions, such as $3+3+(-2)+11$.

2-42.   Find the length of the tightrope if each expression for rope lengths below starts Cecil at point A and has him end at point B. Assume the numbers represent lengths in feet.

    a. $8+(-3)+2$
    b. $12.25+7.5+(-1.75)$

    c. $6.1+(-3.05)+(-2.05)$
    d. $-1\frac{1}{4}+8\frac{1}{2}$

    e. $14.14+10.325+(-13.6)$
    f. $26\frac{1}{3}+(-12\frac{1}{2})+3\frac{1}{6}$

2-43.   For Cecil's new act, his tightrope is 5 feet long.

    a.   If he begins at point A, write two expressions that will make him end at point B. What do these expressions have in common?

    b.   Explain why $5+2+(-2)$ is **equivalent** to (the same as) telling Cecil to move 5 feet to the right.

    c.   Will $5+2+(-2)+2+(-2)$ get Cecil to point B? Will $5+2+(-2)+3+(-3)$? How would you describe his movements in these cases?

2-44.   What if Cecil's tightrope was a number line like the one shown below?

a.   On your paper, sketch the number line above.

b.   How can you represent $-2 + 3$ using the number line? Discuss your ideas with your team and use the number line to represent Cecil's movements and your answer.

c.   On the same number line, start at 3 and represent $3 + 2$ and $3 + (-2)$. How are these two computations similar and how are they different?

d.   Describe how the two computations $8 + (-5)$ and $8 + 5$ would be related if you represented them on a number line.

2-45.   In parts (c) and (d) of problem 2-44, you may have discovered that for each of the pairs of computations, the distance that you moved on the number line from each starting value was the same. This was true even though in one case the number added was positive and in the other case it was negative. The *sign* of the number added told you in which *direction* to move, while the *size* of the number told you how *far* to move.

The amount that you moved is one way to describe the absolute value of the number. In a previous course, you may have learned that **absolute value** is the value of a number without regard to its sign, or the distance a number is from 0 on a number line (in either direction) and that the symbol $|x|$ is used to indicate the absolute value of any number x.

Evaluate each absolute value expression below.

a. $|-20 - 5.3|$ b. $|45 + 7.7|$ c. $-|8 + 81|$ d. $-|0 - 3|$

2-46.   MAKING ZEROS

For Cecil's newest act, he starts at point A on the left end of his tightrope, walks on the tightrope, turns around, sometimes many times, and then ends up back at point A on the left end of his tightrope.

a.   Work with your team to write at least three expressions that show how Cecil could move and still start and end at point A.

b.   Build three more expressions similar to the expressions you wrote in part (a). For your three expressions, do one with two numbers, one with three numbers, and one with eight numbers. What do all of your expressions have in common?

2-47.   Sally lives in North Dakota, where the winter temperature is often below zero. One day, the thermometer read 10 degrees below zero, but it rapidly rose 15 degrees in one hour as a warm front moved in. Then it dropped 15 degrees as night fell. What is the resulting temperature? Draw a diagram to represent this scenario.

2-48.   Gina was working on the previous problems when she had a new idea.

"Look," she boasted, *"I can use these ideas to add large integers quickly without even picking up a pencil."*

She wrote down each of the following expressions and calculated each answer in less than 5 seconds. Talk with your team about how she could have done this.

a. $583.6 + 212.72 + (-583.6)$

b. $313\frac{6}{11} + (-300)$

c. $212 + (-150.75)$

2-49.   Consider Cecil's movements on the tightrope as you answer the questions below.

   a.   What happens when Cecil goes forward 5 feet and then goes back 5 feet? Where does he end up?

   b.   Chad decided to record Cecil's moves with the diagram at right. Explain what you think his drawing means.

   c.   Using the same strategy, Chad recorded a different set of instructions for Cecil with the diagram shown at right. What could this diagram represent? How long is the tightrope if these moves end at point B?

2-50.   LEARNING LOG

   How can you describe two numbers that add to zero? Discuss this question with your team and then write your ideas in your Learning Log. Use as many real-world contexts as you can to provide examples. Label this entry "Making Zeros" and label it with today's date.

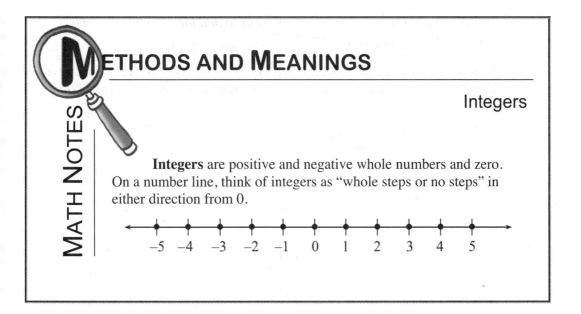

MATH NOTES

METHODS AND MEANINGS

Integers

Integers are positive and negative whole numbers and zero. On a number line, think of integers as "whole steps or no steps" in either direction from 0.

$$\begin{array}{ccccccccccc} & -5 & -4 & -3 & -2 & -1 & 0 & 1 & 2 & 3 & 4 & 5 \end{array}$$

2-51. Write an expression to represent each of the following sketches. Then give the value of each sketch.

a.
$$+ \; + \; -$$
$$+ + \frac{-}{+}$$
$$- \; +$$

b. A number line from -5 to 5 with an arrow pointing left.

c.
$$- + + -$$
$$+ - - +$$

d. A number line from -5 to 5 with an arrow pointing right.

2-52. Use the numbers $5, 6$, and 7 and the operations of addition, subtraction, multiplication, and/or division to create three different number expressions with three different values. One of the expressions should have a value of 37.

2-53. Use a number line to show your work as you find the value of each expression.

a. $-5 + 3.25$

b. $3.18 + (-7)$

2-54. Rewrite the following fractions as decimals and decide if they are terminating or repeating decimals. Show your work and explain how you made your decision.

a. $\frac{7}{8}$

b. $\frac{2}{9}$

c. $\frac{4}{7}$

d. $\frac{11}{22}$

2-55. Evan's uncle gave him money for his birthday.

a. Evan plans to put half of the money in his savings account, spend $\frac{1}{5}$ of the money on bubble gum to share with his friends, and buy comic books with the money he has left. What portion of the money will he spend on comic books?

b. Evan uses some of his comic-book money to buy a magazine for $4. If Evan's uncle gave him $30, what fraction of this money did he spend on the magazine?

2.2.3 How can I add signed numbers?

More Addition of Integers and Rational Numbers

In Lesson 2.2.2, you used integers to represent lengths in two directions. You began to think about using "+" and "−" tiles to represent this forward and backward movement. Today, you will use + and − tiles to model expressions with integers, assigning the + tile a value of one (+1) and the − tile a value of negative one (−1). In your teams, think about these questions as you work:

Can we show what an integer represents in more than one way?

What can we do if the numbers are very large?

2-56.   WHO HAS MORE?

With a partner, get a bag of + and − tiles from your teacher. Reach into the bag, get a small handful, and put them on your desk. Each person should have his or her own bunch of + and − tiles.

a.   Write what you got on your paper.

b.   Whose pile has the greatest value? Find the value of each pile to justify your answer.

c.   If you took a bigger handful of tiles, would you have a better chance of having a higher value? Discuss this with your partner and decide why or why not.

2-57.   WIN-A-ROW

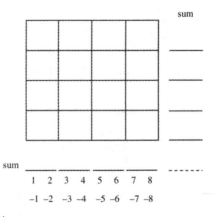

Obtain a Lesson 2.2.3B Resource Page
from your teacher. Read the directions
for scoring in the game below and play
Win-A-Row against a partner.

Scoring: When all the boxes in the table
        have been filled in, calculate the
        sum of each row and the sum of
        each column. Every positive sum
        means one point for Player 1.
        Every negative sum means one point
        for Player 2.

How to Play the Game:
1. Play one round of rock-paper-scissors to determine who plays first.
2. Player 1 places one of the numbers 1, 2, 3, 4, 5, 6, 7, or 8 in the square he or she chooses and then crosses that number from the list.
3. Player 2 places one of the numbers $-1, -2, -3, -4, -5, -6, -7,$ or -8 in another square and then crosses that number from the list.
4. Alternate play until all squares are full and all of the numbers have been crossed off the list.
5. Add the numbers in each row and write each row's sum on the appropriate blank in the "Sum" column. Give the winner of each row one point.
6. Add the numbers in each column and write each column's sum on the appropriate blank in the "Sum" row. Give the winner of each column one point.
7. If the two players tie after adding the rows and columns, find the sum of the diagonal (from top to bottom and left to right) to decide the final winner.
8. If the two players' sums are still tied, find the sum of the other diagonal (from bottom to top and left to right) to decide the final winner.
9. If the game is still tied at this point, both players win!

Ending the Game: The game ends when all squares are full and all sums have
        been found.

Core Connections, Course 2

2-58.   For each expression below:

- Build each expression with + and − tiles.

- Sketch each collection of + and − tiles and find the value of the expression.

- Write the solution as an equation.

For example, in part (a) below, you might draw the figure at right and record $-8 + 2 = -6$.

a. $-8 + 2$ b. $-5 + (-3)$ c. $2 + (-4)$ d. $-7 + (-7)$

e. $-4 + 3$ f. $-4 + 8 + (-2)$ g. $-3 + 5 + 3$ h. $-6 + 6$

2-59.   Think about the problems you have worked on involving positive and negative numbers. How would you find the answer to $-200 + 14$? Without using your calculator, find the sum. Explain your reasoning to your teammates and be prepared to describe your strategy.

2-60.   Using the method you discussed with your teammates, simplify the expressions below.

a. $-100 + 50$

b. $-30\frac{5}{8} + (-60\frac{1}{4})$

c. $-25.63 + (-30.59)$

d. $75 + (-30) + 160 + (-29)$

2-61.   **Additional Challenge:** Can you put together any number of + and − tiles to get any value? Consider this question with your team as you answer the following questions.

a.   To start, consider the number –3. Can –3 be represented by a pile containing a total of 19 tiles? Of 22 tiles?

b.   Write a general description of the total number of + and − tiles that could be in a pile represented by –3.

c.   Choose another number and describe the number of + and − tiles in the piles it could represent.

d.   Can any number be represented with any number of + and − tiles? Explain.

METHODS AND MEANINGS

Additive Inverse and Additive Identity

The **additive identity** is the number zero (0). When you add zero to any number, you get the same number you started with. For example, $3 + 0 = 3$. In general, $x + 0 = x$.

The **additive inverse** of a number is its opposite. For example, the additive inverse of 7 is –7 and the additive inverse of –2 is 2. The additive inverse "undoes" addition. Suppose you have the number 3 and you want to add a number to it to get zero (the additive identity). Then adding –3 gives you $3 + (-3) = 0$. Thus, –3 is the additive inverse of 3, and 3 is the additive inverse of –3. In general, $x + (-x) = 0$.

Review & Preview

2-62.   Sketch each expression using + and – tiles or draw it on a number line. Then find the simplified value of each expression.

a. $-5 + 6 + 4$

b. $7 + (-3) + (-4)$

c. $8 + |(-2) + (-3)|$

d. $|-5| + 3 + 6$

2-63.   What happens if Cecil goes any number of feet in one direction and then goes the same number of feet the other direction? Where does he end up? How do you know?

2-64.   John has a bag of marbles that contains 12 red marbles, 20 green marbles, and 17 blue marbles.

a.   If John pulls one marble out of the bag, what is the probability that it will not be red? That is, P(not red)?

b.   What is the probability that he will draw a purple marble? That is, P(purple)?

Core Connections, Course 2

2-65.   Find the missing lengths in the problems below. Assume each line segment is
          subdivided into equal segments. Show your work.

a.

   0   20

b.

   0   60

2-66.   On Saturday, Stella worked for two hours helping
          her mother around the house. She spent $\frac{1}{3}$ of her
          time doing laundry, $\frac{1}{4}$ of her time cleaning, and the
          rest of her time working in the yard. How much of
          her time was spent in the yard? Show all of your
          work. Use a diagram if it helps.

2.2.4 Can I show it another way?

Multiplication as Repeated Addition

In previous lessons, you created expressions to help Cecil cross a tightrope. For example, when the tightrope was 16 feet long, you could have written an expression such as $7 + 7 + 7 + 7 + 7 + 7 + 7 + 7 + (-5) + (-5) + (-5) + (-5) + (-5) + (-5) + (-5) + (-5)$. When a calculation involves adding the same number over and over, as this one does, is there a shorter way to write the expression? Today, you will consider this as you continue to write and simplify expressions.

2-67. Cecil, the tightrope walker introduced in problem 2-31, still needs your help. He wants to cross a rope that is 6 feet long. Using only the lengths of 5 and 8 feet, find *at least two ways* Cecil can move to reach the end of the rope at the ladder. For each solution, draw a diagram and write an expression.

2-68. Cecil moved across the rope as shown at right. Show two ways to represent his moves with number expressions. Do both ways get him to the same endpoint?

$$\overset{\displaystyle 6 \quad\quad 6 \quad\quad 6 \quad\quad 6}{A \xrightarrow{\hspace{6cm}} B}$$

2-69. Cecil is now so good at crossing the tightrope that he can make a leap of 7 feet at a time. He crossed the rope in these leaps as shown below. Record his moves two ways. Which way is easier to record?

2-70. When adding the same number several times, multiplication can help. For example, if the tightrope walker moved to the right 3 feet, 3 feet, 3 feet, and then 3 feet, it is shorter to write $4(3)$ instead of $3 + 3 + 3 + 3$. Note that parentheses are another way to show multiplication. Use multiplication to write $2 + 2 + 2 + 2 + 2$.

2-71.   How did Cecil, the tightrope walker, move if he started at point A and his moves were recorded as the expression $3(6.2)+2$? Draw a diagram and record how far along his rope he was when he finished.

2-72.   Imagine that Cecil, the tightrope walker, starts at point B and walks on the rope toward point A as shown at right.

a.   How should this be written? Is there more than one way?

b.   Where does he end up?

2-73.   To represent $2(3)$, Chad drew the diagram at right. How do you predict Chad would draw $5(-3)$? What is the value of this expression?

2-74.   The two equal expressions $2(3)$ and 6 can be represented with the diagram at right. Draw similar diagrams for each of the expressions in parts (a) through (c) below.

a.   What does $2(3+5)$ mean? What is the value of this expression? Describe it with words and a diagram.

b.   What does $2(3)+5$ mean? What is the value of this expression? Describe it with words and a diagram.

c.   Compare $2(3+5)$ with $2(3)+5$. How are these movements the same or different? Explain your thinking and draw a diagram.

2-75.   Draw a diagram to represent the expression $3(-2.5)+(-4)$. Is this the same as $3(-2.5+(-4))$? Use diagrams to justify your decision.

2-76.   MENTAL MATH

Work with your team to find strategies for figuring out
mentally (without using a calculator or writing anything
down) how far Cecil moved in parts (a) and (b) below.
Then write a number expression for each set of moves
along with its result.

a.   Cecil traveled 105 feet to the left 7 times. How far did he end up from his
     starting point?

b.   Cecil repeated the following pattern 12 times: He traveled to the right
     198 feet and then to the left 198 feet. How far did he end up from his
     starting point?

2-77.   When you need to multiply mentally, it is often useful to use the **Distributive
Property**. The Distributive Property states that when you multiply a sum by a
number, you must multiply each part of the sum by that number. For example,
part (a) of problem 2-76 can be seen as $7(-105) = 7(-100 + (-5))$. The
Distributive Property tells us that this is equal to $7(-100) + 7(-5)$ or
$-700 + (-35)$. You will explore the Distributive Property further in Chapter 4.

Use the Distributive Property to rewrite and calculate each product shown
below.

a. $6(12 + (-4))$ b. $7(300 + (-10))$

c. $4 \cdot 302$ d. $5(871)$

2-78.   LEARNING LOG

In your Learning Log, describe what you have learned
about adding and multiplying positive and negative
integers. Be sure to include examples and diagrams or
other representations that explain your thinking. Title this
entry "Adding and Multiplying Integers" and label it with
today's date.

MᴇᴛʜODS AND Mᴇᴀɴɪɴɢꜱ

MATH NOTES

Addition of Integers

Recall that **integers** are positive and negative whole numbers and zero, that is, $\dots -3, -2, -1, 0, 1, 2, 3, \dots$.

You have been introduced to two ways to think about addition. Both of them involve figuring out which, if any, parts of the numbers combine to form zero. One way to think about this concept is to think about the tightrope walker from problem 2-31. If Cecil travels one foot to the right (+1) and one foot to the left (−1), he will end up where he started, so the sum of (+1) and (−1) is zero.

$$\xrightarrow{1}$$
$$\xleftarrow{-1}$$

Another useful strategy for finding zero is to use + and − tiles. The diagram at right can be represented by the equation $-1 + 1 = 0$. You can use this same idea for **adding any two integers**. Use + and − tiles to build the first integer, add the tiles for the second integer, and then eliminate zeros. Study the examples shown in the diagrams below.

Example 1: $5 + (-3)$ $\left(\frac{+}{-}\right)\left(\frac{+}{-}\right)\left(\frac{+}{-}\right)$ + + $5 + (-3) = 2$

Example 2: $-5 + (2)$ $\left(\frac{-}{+}\right)\left(\frac{-}{+}\right)$ − − − $-5 + (2) = -3$

Example 3: $-6 + (-2)$ − − − − − − $-6 + (-2) = -8$
                 − −

With practice, zeros can be visualized. This helps you determine how many remaining positive or negative tiles show the simplified expression.

2-79. Find the value of each of the following expressions. Use a tile diagram or a number line to help you, if you need it.

a. 3(4)

b. 4 + 11 + (−4)

c. 3.2(2)

d. |(−2) + (−2) + (−2)|

e. |2(−7.5)|

f. $\left(10\frac{1}{5}\right)(−5)$

2-80. Use the Distributive Property to rewrite each of the following products as sums, and then calculate the value, as shown in the example below.

Example: $4(307) = 4(300) + 4(7) = 1200 + 28 = 1228$

a. 9(410)

b. 6(592)

2-81. Copy and complete each of the Diamond Problems below. The pattern used in the Diamond Problems is shown at right.

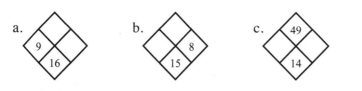

2-82. Copy and complete each of the portions webs below.

a.

b.

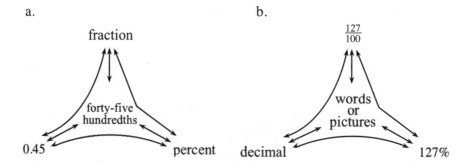

2-83.   Camille had a very fun birthday party with lots of friends and family attending. The party lasted for 3 hours. She and her friends played games for $\frac{3}{8}$ of the time, ate pizza and cake for 50% of the time, and spent the remainder of the time opening presents. Draw a diagram and make calculations to show the amount of time spent opening presents.

2-84.   Jahna measured the heights of the sunflowers growing in her backyard. Here are the heights that she found (in inches): 34, 48, 52, 61, 76, 76, 61, 84, 61, 39, 83, 61, 79, 81, 56, and 88.

   a.   Find the mean and median of the heights.

   b.   Create a histogram to represent this data. Your histogram should have four bins, each with a width of 15.

2.2.5 How big is part of a part?

Multiplication of Portions

You have seen how Cecil's repeated integer-sized moves can be represented with addition or multiplication. But what if you need to calculate part of a whole? For example, if 200 people enter a competition and $\frac{1}{4}$ of them are chosen for the final round, how do you calculate how many were chosen? Sometimes you may even need to calculate a part of a part. For example, if Cameron sprinted $\frac{2}{3}$ of the $\frac{1}{4}$-mile track, how would you calculate how far Cameron sprinted? Today you will use different models to help you answer these kinds of questions.

2-85. Cecil has just created a spectacular routine. (A routine is a sequence of moves to get from start to finish.) His routine has two parts. The first part consists of a series of creative leaps followed by a somersault. The first part ends with Cecil's doing an elaborate bow while balancing on one toe. Then he moves into the second part of the routine, which includes several back flips and spins. When performed perfectly, the routine moves Cecil exactly to the other end of his tightrope. The routine can be represented by the following expressions. First,

Part I: $3(2) + 3(3) + (-5) + 4$

Then he pauses to take a bow in place. And then,

Part II: $5 + 3 + 4(1 + -1) + (-3) + (-5) + 3(5 + (-2)) + 1$

Work with your team to draw an accurate diagram (drawn to scale) to represent Cecil's routine. Then answer the following questions and be ready to share your reasoning. Assume that the numbers used to describe the routine represent feet.

a. How long is Cecil's tightrope? How far from the starting point is Cecil when he takes his bow after Part I?

b. What portion of the tightrope length does Cecil travel in each part of the routine?

c. Cecil had only completed two thirds of his routine when a rather violent sneeze caused him to fall. How far from the starting point was Cecil when he sneezed and fell?

2-86.   Garden Road Middle School is planning a field trip for students to attend a conference about careers in mathematics. Half of the students signed up to go on the field trip, but only three fourths of those students brought back their permission slips to attend the field trip. Explore what fraction of students in the school will be able to go on the field trip.

   a.   Discuss this problem with your team. Do you have to know how many students go to Garden Road Middle School to be able to answer this question? Why or why not? Once you have reached agreement on this issue, ask your teacher for a Lesson 2.2.5 Resource Page, called "Unit Rectangles," or draw eight identical rectangles on a full sheet of paper. Then follow the steps below to answer the question.

   b.   The entire school's enrollment—no matter what it is—can be represented with an unshaded unit rectangle, as shown at right.

   Garden Road Middle School Students

   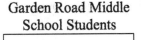

   Half of the school plans to attend. To show this, divide your rectangle into two equal pieces, as shown below. Then lightly shade and label one of the halves to show the half of the school that is planning to attend.

   Label the other half with an appropriate label.

   ½ of the school plans to attend

   c.   Three fourths of the students planning to attend brought back their permission slips to go to the conference. Represent this portion on your rectangle.

   d.   What fraction of the whole school will attend the conference?

   e.   If the total school population is 120 students, how many would attend?

   f.   **Additional Challenge:** How do you know that the total school population cannot be either 125 or 250?

2-87.   Howie has $\frac{5}{8}$ of a pizza left over from last night's dinner. He loves pizza and eats half of the remaining pizza the next day for breakfast.

   a.   Draw your own diagram or use your unit rectangle resource page to determine what portion of the original pizza Howie ate for breakfast.

   b.   Write an equation to show $\frac{1}{2}$ of $\frac{5}{8}$.

2-88.   Joe Dominguez has decided to plant a
         rectangular flower garden. Joe loves red
         carnations. He wants 50% of the garden to
         be planted with carnations, and one third of
         the carnations must be red.

   a.   On a unit rectangle, label and shade the
        fraction of the garden that must be
        carnations.

   b.   Now label and shade the fraction of the
        carnations that must be red.

   c.   What fraction of the whole garden must be red carnations?

   d.   What fraction of the garden is not carnations?

   e.   Express the number of red carnations with a number sentence.

2-89.   For each of the four diagrams below, write an equation that represents the
         darkly shaded portion and a sentence that describes that section.

Example: $\frac{1}{2}$ of the
           school is
           girls

$\frac{3}{4}$ of $\frac{1}{2}$ is $\frac{3}{8}$

$\frac{3}{4}$ returned their
permission slips

$\frac{3}{8}$ of the students at the school are girls who returned their permission slips.

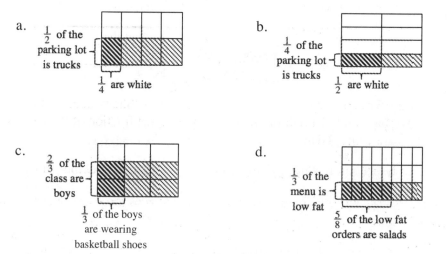

   a. $\frac{1}{2}$ of the
        parking lot
        is trucks

        $\frac{1}{4}$ are white

   b. $\frac{1}{4}$ of the
        parking lot
        is trucks

        $\frac{1}{2}$ are white

   c. $\frac{2}{3}$ of the
        class are
        boys

        $\frac{1}{3}$ of the boys
        are wearing
        basketball shoes

   d. $\frac{1}{3}$ of the
        menu is
        low fat

        $\frac{5}{8}$ of the low fat
        orders are salads

METHODS AND **M**EANINGS

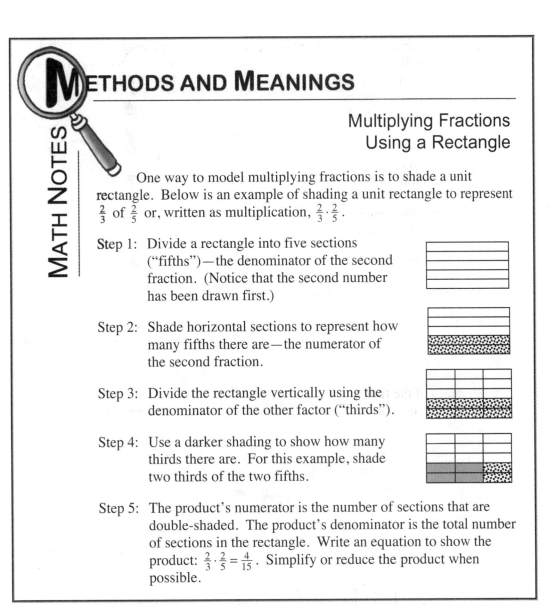

MATH NOTES

Multiplying Fractions
Using a Rectangle

One way to model multiplying fractions is to shade a unit rectangle. Below is an example of shading a unit rectangle to represent $\frac{2}{3}$ of $\frac{2}{5}$ or, written as multiplication, $\frac{2}{3} \cdot \frac{2}{5}$.

Step 1: Divide a rectangle into five sections ("fifths")—the denominator of the second fraction. (Notice that the second number has been drawn first.)

Step 2: Shade horizontal sections to represent how many fifths there are—the numerator of the second fraction.

Step 3: Divide the rectangle vertically using the denominator of the other factor ("thirds").

Step 4: Use a darker shading to show how many thirds there are. For this example, shade two thirds of the two fifths.

Step 5: The product's numerator is the number of sections that are double-shaded. The product's denominator is the total number of sections in the rectangle. Write an equation to show the product: $\frac{2}{3} \cdot \frac{2}{5} = \frac{4}{15}$. Simplify or reduce the product when possible.

Review & Preview

2-90.   Frieda Friendly works for a local car dealership. She noticed that $\frac{3}{4}$ of the cars are sedans and that half of them are white. What fraction of the dealership's cars are white sedans?

a.   Use a unit rectangle to represent this situation. Label the parts carefully.

b.   Write an equation or a sentence that describes the situation, and answer the question.

c.   Write your answer from part (b) as a decimal and as a percent.

2-91.   In parts (a) and (b) of problem 2-89, the rectangular models for $\frac{1}{2}$ of $\frac{1}{4}$ and $\frac{1}{4}$ of $\frac{1}{2}$ looked different, but the answers were the same. Read the steps for the example given in the Math Notes box in this lesson for how to calculate $\frac{2}{3}$ of $\frac{2}{5}$. Then follow the steps and draw a similar rectangle to show $\frac{2}{5}$ of $\frac{2}{3}$. Are the answers the same? Why or why not?

2-92.   Simplify each expression.

   a. $-32 + |10 + 2|$ b. $17\frac{1}{3} + (-50\frac{1}{3}) - 5\frac{1}{2}$ c. $-5.37 + 8.14 - 1.89$

2-93.   Do you think it matters what order you follow when performing math operations? Investigate this by doing the following problems.

   a.   For the problem $9 + 2(3)$, do you get the same final answer if you add first as you do if you multiply first?

   b.   For the problem $(2 \cdot 4) \cdot 7$, do you get the same final answer if you start with the first two numbers as you do if you start with the last two numbers?

2-94.   **Multiple Choice:** Which of the following numbers could not represent a probability? Write a sentence explaining why they could not.

   A. $-\frac{1}{10}$ B.   1   C.   1%   D.   0.1

2.2.6 Is there an easier way?

Multiplying Mixed Numbers

Mathematics is a powerful tool for solving many problems you encounter in the real world. But real-world problems worth solving often involve "messy" numbers and many steps. Fortunately, the operations you know (addition, subtraction, multiplication and division) can be applied to all the different kinds of numbers you might encounter. Today you will review multiplication of simple fractions. Then you will extend what you know to working with fractions greater than one, mixed numbers, and decimals. As you work with your team, keep the following question in mind:

> Would using a different form of this number make the problem easier?

2-95. While working in class, Stephanie had to do the problem $\frac{3}{5} \cdot \frac{6}{7}$. She started to draw rectangles to solve the problem. Stephanie looked over at Audrey's work and saw that Audrey was way ahead of her.

"How did you get so far ahead of me? Why aren't you drawing rectangles for these problems?" Stephanie asked.

"I remembered a shortcut," Audrey said. *"Didn't you notice that when we drew the rectangles, we got the same thing as if we had multiplied the numerators and then multiplied the denominators? I just did 3 · 6 = 18 and 5 · 7 = 35 and got $\frac{18}{35}$. It was a lot faster. So when I saw these problems, I decided I wasn't going to draw the rectangles with all those little pieces."*

a. Check Audrey's method using a rectangle model.

b. What information does multiplying 5 · 7 tell you about the model?

c. What information does multiplying 3 · 6 tell you about the model?

2-96. Multiply the following pairs of fractions using rectangles or Audrey's method.

a. $\frac{7}{8} \cdot \frac{5}{6}$

b. $\frac{2}{13} \cdot \frac{4}{5}$

c. $\frac{6}{7} \cdot \frac{6}{7}$

d. $\frac{4}{7} \cdot \frac{3}{8}$

e. $\frac{6}{11} \cdot \frac{1}{2}$

f. $\frac{8}{3} \cdot \frac{9}{14}$

2-97.　Ronna is making a small flowerbed that is $3\frac{1}{2}$ feet by $1\frac{1}{2}$ feet. She needs to find the area so she can add the correct amount of fertilizer to the soil.

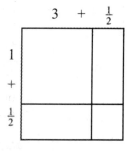

On your paper, draw the rectangle shown at right. Then complete parts (a) through (c) below.

a.　Write the area in each of the four parts of the drawing. Then find the total area.

b.　Write an equation that represents the sum of the four areas.

c.　What multiplication problem could you use to solve this problem?

2-98.　Using the process shown in the previous problem, find the area of Ronna's flowerbed if the dimensions are $1\frac{1}{2}$ feet by $5\frac{1}{3}$ feet. Clearly label all dimensions. Write the multiplication problem that can be used to solve this problem.

2-99.　CHANGE CAN BE GOOD

As Jonique was working in class, she had to do the problem $2\frac{1}{2}\cdot 3\frac{1}{4}$. She did not want to draw rectangles. However, she thinks that she has figured out a shortcut for multiplying mixed numbers.

"I know how to change mixed numbers into fractions. That will make the problem much easier," she boasted.

Look at Jonique's work shown at right.

$$2\tfrac{1}{2}\cdot 3\tfrac{1}{4}$$
$$\tfrac{5}{2}\cdot\tfrac{13}{4}$$
$$\tfrac{65}{8}$$
$$8\tfrac{1}{8}$$

Try Jonique's shortcut on the following problems. Show each step.

a.　$3\frac{1}{2}\cdot 1\frac{1}{2}$　　　　b.　$1\frac{1}{3}\cdot 2\frac{1}{2}$　　　　c.　$1\frac{1}{3}\cdot 3\frac{1}{3}$

d.　Compare part (a) with the generic rectangle method in problem 2-97. Which method do you prefer? Why?

2-100. Have you heard people say, "You can't mix apples and oranges?" Anyone who has made fruit salad might disagree. However, you do have to pay attention to what a number represents when you are using it to solve a problem. To add or multiply two quantities, you may need to convert not only the numbers to some other form (like fractions to decimals), but also the quantities they represent.

For example, to add $\frac{1}{2}$ foot to 3 inches, you need to first convert them to the same units, either feet or inches. You could change $\frac{1}{2}$ foot to 6 inches and then add it to 3 inches to get 9 inches. On the other hand, you could change 3 inches to $\frac{1}{4}$ foot and then add it to $\frac{1}{2}$ foot to get $\frac{3}{4}$ foot.

Complete the specified operations for the following quantities, making sure that you are working with like parts, that is, the same units of measure. Each answer can be expressed with one number, although there are multiple ways to represent each one. Be sure you label your answer.

a. $2\frac{1}{2}$ feet + 8 inches

b. $\frac{3}{8}$ of a day + $\frac{1}{2}$ of a day + 6 hours

c. 12.5 meters + 14 kilometers

d. Cecil performing a routine three times that consists of a 5-foot leap and a 3-yard skip. That is, 3(5 feet + 3 yards).

2-101.   Multiply the mixed numbers.

a. $1\frac{1}{3} \cdot 1\frac{1}{2}$ b. $3\frac{1}{3} \cdot 2\frac{1}{2}$

c. $2\frac{1}{2} \cdot 2\frac{1}{2}$ d. $2\frac{1}{2} \cdot 1\frac{1}{4}$

2-102.   Below is a fast mental-math technique to find $\frac{5}{6} \cdot 24$. Remember that
$\frac{5}{6} \cdot 24 = 5 \cdot \frac{1}{6} \cdot 24$.

a.   What is one sixth of 24?

b.   What is five times that quantity?

c.   What is $\frac{5}{6} \cdot 24$?

2-103.   Use the above method to calculate mentally each product below. Write an
equation for each problem.

a. $\frac{3}{4} \cdot 24$ b. $\frac{3}{8} \cdot 32$ c. $\frac{4}{7} \cdot 35$

2-104.   While going on a field trip, a busload of 54 students
will have to be split up into three groups. Two thirds
will go to lunch first, and one third will go visit the
exhibits. How many will go to lunch first? Write an
equation to represent the problem.

2-105.   Draw a coordinate grid. Make both the x-axis and y-axis go from −10 to 10.
Then plot the following points. Label each point with its letter.

a.   (−2.2, 4.64)   b.   (8.2, 7.59)

c. $(-3\frac{4}{7}, -9\frac{3}{10})$ d.   (0.62, −5.1)

2.3.1   How can I make a useful graph?

Choosing a Scale and Graphing Data

Graphs can be useful tools for finding relationships and making predictions. In this lesson, you will work with your team to make choices about how to set up a graph in the most useful way, depending on its purpose. As you work, use the questions below to help focus your discussion.

Does our data fit? Can we see it clearly?

How can we make it clearer?

How can we make a prediction?

Will a different choice make it easier to predict?

2-106.   PAYTON'S BATS

Payton loves bats. She wants to know if she can predict the wingspan of a bat by knowing the length of its body.

Payton looked up measurements for five species of bats. For each species, she found the typical body length (from the head to the tail) and the wingspan (from the tip of one wing to the tip of the other). She organized the information in the table below.

Bats in Tennessee – Typical Body Measurements

Type of Bat	Length (inches)	Wingspan (inches)
Big Brown Bat	5	14
Little Brown Bat	3.5	10
Brazilian Free-Tailed Bat	4.25	12
Evening Bat	4	11
Indiana Bat	3	10

Work with your team to decide how Payton can use the data in the table to predict the wingspan of a bat if she knows its body length. Explain how she would do this.

2-107.   Payton has started a graph. Her work is shown at
          right and on the Lesson 2.3.1A Resource Page.

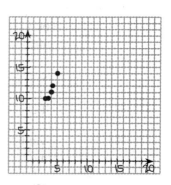

    a.   Which axis represents the length of a bat?
          Which axis represents the wingspan? How
          can you tell? When you are sure, label each
          axis.

    b.   What is the **scale** on the horizontal axis? In
          other words, what is the length of each single
          unit on the horizontal axis? What is the scale on the vertical axis? Is this
          scale appropriate for graphing this data? Discuss this question with your
          team and write down your ideas.

    c.   Payton wants her data to be spread out so that she can see relationships
          clearly. Does this graph allow her to do that? Are there any changes she
          could make to her graph that might make it clearer? Be prepared to explain
          your ideas to the class.

2-108.   Payton has an idea. *"I will make the numbers on the horizontal axis bigger,"*
          she says. *"That way, the points will be more spread out and easier to see."*

    a.   Payton's new axes are drawn on the
          resource page, also shown at right. How has
          Payton changed the scale? Will all of her
          data fit on this new graph?

    b.   Will Payton's new graph be more useful?
          Discuss this with your team and then test
          your ideas by plotting Payton's data points
          on the new set of axes.

2-109.   Payton has come to your team for help.

          Use the resource page with a set of axes such as
          the ones at right to complete the following
          problems.

    •   Work with your team to decide on a scale for
          each axis that will make Payton's data (from
          problem 2-106) easy to see.

    •   Then, on your own paper, draw axes, mark
          your scales, and plot Payton's data points.

2-110.   Payton found more information about bats. In parts (a) and (b) below, you will use the information she found to make predictions about the bats.

   a.   The common vampire bat is native to northern Mexico and Central and South America. It feeds on the blood of sleeping cows by making very small cuts into their skin and then licking the wounds.

        Use your graph of bat length and wingspan to predict the wingspan of the common vampire bat if it typically has a length of about 2.75 inches.

   b.   The Kitti's hog-nosed bat, also called the bumblebee bat, is the world's smallest bat and also the world's smallest mammal! It lives in Thailand and Myanmar. It weighs less than a tenth of an ounce (less than a penny) and is only about one inch long!

        Make a prediction for the wingspan of the Kitti's hog-nosed bat. Be prepared to explain your thinking to the class.

2-111.   Paul's movie studio is advertising *Invasion of the Bats*. He is designing a cardboard cutout of a giant bat (four feet long) in flight.

        Work with your team to quickly sketch a graph of Payton's data (from problem 2-106) that will also fit the data for Paul's giant bat. Estimate the wingspan Paul should use for his cutout.

2-112.   Now compare the graphs that you made in problems 2-106 through 2-111.

   a.   Which graph would be most useful for making predictions about bats in Tennessee?

   b.   Which graph would be most useful for making predictions about bats around the world?

2-113.   Look at the graphs that your team made in this lesson and compare them to those made by other teams. Work with your team to brainstorm a complete list of information that should go on a graph to make it useful. Be sure to consider each of the questions below.

- What information tells you what is shown on each axis?
- What information tells you the exact coordinates of a point on the graph?
- What information tells you what the graph is about?

Be ready to contribute your team's ideas to a class discussion.

2-114.   LEARNING LOG

In your Learning Log, describe the elements needed for a complete graph. Include a sketch of a graph that shows where each of these elements should be located. Title this entry "Making Complete Graphs" and label it with today's date.

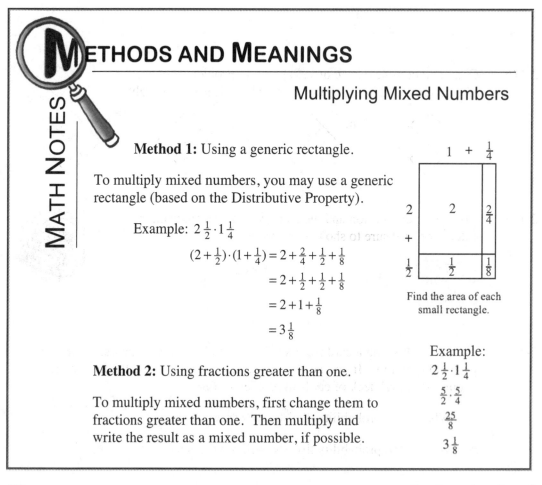

MATH NOTES

METHODS AND MEANINGS

Multiplying Mixed Numbers

Method 1: Using a generic rectangle.

To multiply mixed numbers, you may use a generic rectangle (based on the Distributive Property).

Example: $2\frac{1}{2} \cdot 1\frac{1}{4}$

$$(2+\tfrac{1}{2}) \cdot (1+\tfrac{1}{4}) = 2 + \tfrac{2}{4} + \tfrac{1}{2} + \tfrac{1}{8}$$
$$= 2 + \tfrac{1}{2} + \tfrac{1}{2} + \tfrac{1}{8}$$
$$= 2 + 1 + \tfrac{1}{8}$$
$$= 3\tfrac{1}{8}$$

Find the area of each small rectangle.

Example:
$2\frac{1}{2} \cdot 1\frac{1}{4}$

$\frac{5}{2} \cdot \frac{5}{4}$

$\frac{25}{8}$

$3\frac{1}{8}$

Method 2: Using fractions greater than one.

To multiply mixed numbers, first change them to fractions greater than one. Then multiply and write the result as a mixed number, if possible.

2-115. Complete the scaling for each number line or set of axes.

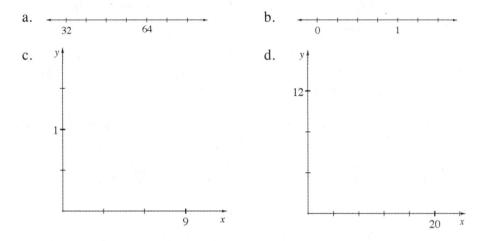

2-116. Copy and complete each of the Diamond Problems below. The pattern used in the Diamond Problems is shown at right.

2-117. Copy each expression and then simplify it without using a calculator. Be sure to show all steps.

a. $7\frac{5}{8} + 2\frac{9}{16}$

b. $2\frac{7}{8} + 6\frac{1}{6}$

c. $8 - 6\frac{2}{5}$

2-118. Carmen is drawing a card from a standard deck of playing cards. Find each probability below. If you need a reminder, you may reread the information about a standard deck of cards in problem 1-68.

a. What is the probability that she will draw a heart?

b. What is the probability that she will *not* draw a club?

2-119.   Christina collected information about the ages of the players on her softball team. The ages were 10, 12, 14, 13, 12, 11, 13, 12, 11, 12, 12, and 13. Christina wants to describe the players' ages in an article for the school newspaper. She does not want to list all of the ages, so should she use the range (difference between the highest and lowest values) or a measure of central tendency (mean, median) to describe them? Justify your choice.

2-120.   This problem is a checkpoint for multiple representations of portions. It will be referred to as Checkpoint 2.

For each portion of a whole, write it as a percent, as a fraction, and as a decimal.

a. 0.43   b. nine tenths

c. 39%   d. $\frac{16}{25}$

Check your answers by referring to the Checkpoint 2 materials located at the back of your book.

Ideally, at this point you are comfortable working with these types of problems and can solve them correctly. If you feel that you need more confidence when solving these types of problems, then review the Checkpoint 2 materials and try the practice problems provided. From this point on, you will be expected to do problems like these correctly and with confidence.

2.3.2 How can I make the data fit?

More Graph Scaling

In this lesson, you will use all that you know about graphs to solve challenging graphing problems. Each of the situations in this lesson will require you to think hard about what a graph tells you and what the best way is to show it. As you work together to solve these problems, think about what makes the task challenging. Focus with your team on how you can get yourselves "unstuck" if your teacher is not immediately available.

2-121.   Andre works in his family's juice shop. He has invented the new Mathberry Madness smoothie, and word is getting around. He wants a graph showing how many new smoothies have been sold throughout the first month. He has gone through the cash-register records and gathered the data for some of the first 12 days, shown in the table at right.

Day	Smoothies Sold
3	3
4	5
6	10
9	20
10	28
12	38

He wants to graph his data and use it to predict approximately how many Mathberry Madness smoothies he can expect to sell by Day 20. He has started the graph below right.

Your Task:

- Examine Andre's graph. Can you use it to predict how many smoothies would be sold by Day 20? Why or why not?

- Contribute your ideas to a team discussion and then work with your team to decide how to scale the axes so that you can graph Andre's data accurately and make a prediction.

- Then, on your own paper, graph Andre's data.

- Show where on the graph you would expect to place a data point for Day 20 and explain how many smoothies are likely to be sold by then.

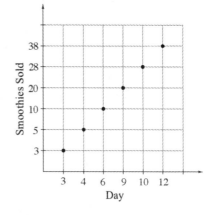

2-122.   GRAPHING CHALLENGES

Your teacher will assign your team one of the graphing challenges shown below. Work with your team to plan an appropriate scale for each axis. Then create a graph and place the data on the graph. Be prepared to explain to the class how you created your graph and why it is accurate and easy to read.

Challenge A: The table at right shows the time it took five different students to get to the mall and how far they traveled to get there.

Distance (miles)	Travel Time (minutes)
4.1	13
1.7	7
3.0	10
2.2	20
0.5	9

Challenge B: To use the pool at the Columbus Recreation Center, guests must pay one annual membership fee and then another small fee each time they swim. Jeff and his five friends kept track of how many times they visited the pool in one year and how much money they each spent.

Number of Visits	Cost (dollars)
18	$53
29	$65
100	$135
84	$119
62	$97
114	$149

2-123.   Jackson heard that baseball pitchers are getting taller and taller. He found the data shown in the table at right.

a.   Jackson thought a graph might help him see how the heights are changing, but he thinks that this data will be really hard to graph. Discuss this with your team. Do you agree? What, if anything, makes this data hard to graph? Explain.

b.   Jackson has an idea! He decided to change the way he wrote the data and started the table shown on the next page. How did Jackson figure out what numbers to put in the table? Discuss this with your team and then copy and complete the table on your own paper.

Average Heights of Pitchers

Year	Height (in.)
1870	69.3
1900	71.4
1930	72.5
1960	73.5
1970	73.9
1990	74.3
2000	74.4

Problem continues on next page. →

Core Connections, Course 2

2-123.   *Problem continued from previous page.*

	Average Heights of Pitchers

c.   On your paper, graph Jackson's data. Be sure to choose an appropriate scale and label the axes so that it is a complete graph.

d.   Help Jackson predict how tall pitchers might be on average in the year 2020.

Years after 1870	Height above 60 inches (in.)
0	9.3
30	11.4

MATH NOTES

METHODS AND MEANINGS

Intervals and Scaling

The numbers on the axes of a graph show the **scaling** of the axes. The difference between consecutive markings tells the size of the **interval**. When you scale each axis, you must use equal intervals to represent the data accurately. For example, an interval of 5 creates a scale numbered 0, 5, 10, 15, etc. Unequal intervals distort the relationship in the data. It is important to note that horizontal and vertical axes *do not* need the same scaling. In fact, it is often convenient to choose different scales for the two axes.

Notice on the graph at right that 80 marks the end of the *fourth* interval. If you divide 80 years by 4, you can see that the length of an interval on this graph is 20.

$$(80 \div 4 = 20)$$

The second graph at right has each interval labeled. This is called "scaling the axis."

years old

years old

Review & Preview

2-124.   Troy is a fan of baseball, and his favorite player is Moe Jauer of the Minnesota Triplets. Troy made a table displaying how many home runs Jauer hit during his first five seasons. Graph Troy's data.

Season	Home Runs
1	6
2	9
3	13
4	7
5	9

2-125. Sara turned in the two graphs below for homework, but her teacher marked them wrong. Explain to Sara what mistakes she made. Then choose one of her graphs to correct, copy it on your paper, and correct it.

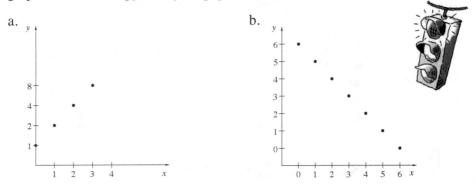

a.

b.

2-126. If a set of *xy*-axes has 20 grid units in each direction and the greatest value of the data to be placed on the horizontal axis is 132, what would be an appropriate and convenient scale to use for this axis? Explain.

2-127. Simplify each expression.

a. $\frac{2}{3}(0.8)$ b. $\frac{4}{3} \cdot \frac{3}{7}$ c. $-\frac{5}{6} \cdot \frac{4}{7}$ d. $-\frac{4}{5} \cdot (-1\frac{1}{3})$

2-128. For each of the experimental results described, write the indicated probability.

a. A coin is flipped 80 times. It lands tails 47 times. What is the P(heads)?

b. A bag contains purple and orange marbles. Sam randomly takes out one marble and then returns it to the bag. He does this 18 times, and 12 of those times an orange marble is pulled out. What is P(green)?

c. Sarah pulls a card from a standard deck and then replaces it. She does this 30 times, and 40% of the time it is hearts. What is the probability that she does *not* get hearts? (Note: For more information on standard card decks, refer to problem 1-68.)

2-129. Use your reasoning about numbers to answer the following questions.

a. If multiplying by $\frac{1}{4}$ makes a positive number smaller, then what does dividing by $\frac{1}{4}$ do to the value of the number? Explain your reasoning.

b. If multiplying by 1 does not change the value of a number, then what effect does multiplying by $\frac{2}{2}$ have? Explain your reasoning.

c. If you find 80% of a number, do you expect the answer to be greater or less than the number? What if you find 120%? Explain your reasoning.

Core Connections, Course 2

Chapter 2 Closure What have I learned?

Reflection and Synthesis

The activities below offer you a chance to reflect about what you have learned during this chapter. As you work, look for concepts that you feel very comfortable with, ideas that you would like to learn more about, and topics you need more help with.

① SUMMARIZING MY UNDERSTANDING

This section gives you an opportunity to show what you know the main math ideas in this chapter.

Cecil Steps Up to the Challenge

Cecil has entered the World Tightrope Championships and needs your help to design a winning routine for the competition. After reading the rules handbook, he has learned that the competition will involve a 23-foot long tightrope and that there are four requirements for his routine:

- All moves must be 3 feet, 4 feet, or 5 feet in length.

- Acrobats must cross the center of the rope at least 5 times.

- The routine must include a move of traveling 3 feet six times in a row, a dazzling move known as the Tres Por Seis.

- The routine must include a series of moves that result in traveling backward 11 feet, also referred to as the Gyara.

- Cecil will also get extra points for other creative movements that he adds to his routine, but his total routine must be able to be performed within the 3-minute time limit.

There are ladders at both ends of the tightrope. Cecil must begin his routine at the left side of the tightrope, but he may finish his routine at either end of the tightrope and then climb down the ladder.

Your Task: With your team, design a routine for Cecil. Then create a poster that shows Cecil's movements both as a diagram and as a numerical expression. Lastly, color-code the parts of the routine to show how the diagram and expression are connected.

WHAT HAVE I LEARNED?

Doing the problems in this section will help you to evaluate which types of problems you feel comfortable with and which ones you need more help with.

Solve each problem as completely as you can. The table at the end of this closure section provides answers to these problems. It also tells you where you can find additional help and where to find practice problems like them.

CL 2-130.   Convert the following fractions to decimals and the decimals to fractions.

a. $\frac{13}{9}$ b. $\frac{7}{8}$ c.   0.204   d.   0.47

CL 2-131.   Suppose that Cecil, the tightrope walker, can only travel lengths of 5 feet, 6 feet, and 8 feet. He can travel forward or backward and can go farther than his ladder and come back. Show two number expressions that represent a way for Cecil to cross a tightrope of the following lengths. Make at least one of your expressions for each length include a backward movement.

a.   16 feet   b.   19 feet   c.   13 feet   d.   3 feet

CL 2-132.   Cecil started from Point A and moved according to the expression $8+(-5)+7+6+(-7)+5+(-8)$. What one additional step does Cecil need in order to return to the starting point?

CL 2-133.   Rewrite each of these products as an addition problem and then state the number that the expression represents.

a.   5(3)   b.   3(−2)

CL 2-134.   George is playing a game, but the spinner is incomplete. Help him figure out what fraction is missing.

CL 2-135.   Multiply $\frac{2}{3} \cdot \frac{1}{2}$. You may want to copy and complete the diagram at right to show your work.

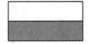

Core Connections, Course 2

CL 2-136. Mary has a bag of colored tiles. There are 8 red tiles, 7 blue tiles, 9 yellow tiles, and 12 green tiles. If she reaches into the bag, what is the probability of picking a:

a. Yellow tile?   b. Green tile?   c. Purple tile?

CL 2-137. Copy the incomplete axes and fill in the missing numbers so that the scaling is consistent.

a. 0   16   b. 0   50

CL 2-138. Use the numbers $0, 1, 2, 2\frac{1}{2}, 3, 7, 7\frac{1}{2}, 9$, and 10 to answer each of the following questions. Note that you may use each number as many times as you like.

a. List five numbers with a mean of 5.

b. List five numbers with a mean of 5 and a median of $2\frac{1}{2}$.

c. If a list of five numbers has a mean of 5, what is the largest median that this set of data can have?

CL 2-139. For each of the problems above, do the following:

- Draw a bar or number line that represents 0 to 10.

- Color or shade in a portion of the bar that represents your level of understanding and comfort with completing that problem on your own.

If any of your bars show than a 5, choose *one* of those problems and do one of the following tasks:
- Write two questions that you would like to ask about that problem.
- Brainstorm two things that you DO know about that type of problem.

If all of your bars are at 5 or above, choose one problem and do one of these tasks:
- Write two questions you might ask or hints you might give to a student who was stuck on the problem.
- Make a new problem that is similar and more challenging than that problem and solve it.

WHAT TOOLS CAN I USE?

You have several tools and references available to help support your learning: your teacher, your study team, your math book, and your Toolkit, to name only a few. At the end of each chapter, you will have an opportunity to review your Toolkit for completeness. You will also revise or update it to reflect your current understanding of big ideas.

The main elements of your Toolkit should be your Learning Logs, Math Notes, and the vocabulary used in this chapter. Math words that are new appear in bold in the text. Refer to the lists provided below and follow your teacher's instructions to revise your Toolkit, which will help make it useful for you as you complete this chapter and as you work in future chapters.

Learning Log Entries

- Lesson 2.1.2 – Repeating and Terminating Decimals
- Lesson 2.2.2 – Making Zeros
- Lesson 2.2.4 – Adding and Multiplying Integers
- Lesson 2.3.1 – Making Complete Graphs

Math Notes

- Lesson 2.1.1 – Mixed Numbers and Fractions Greater Than One
- Lesson 2.1.2 – Fraction ⇔ Decimal ⇔ Percent
- Lesson 2.2.1 – Multiplication Using Generic Rectangles
- Lesson 2.2.2 – Integers
- Lesson 2.2.3 – Additive Inverse and Additive Identity
- Lesson 2.2.4 – Addition of Integers
- Lesson 2.2.5 – Multiplying Fractions Using a Rectangle
- Lesson 2.3.1 – Multiplying Mixed Numbers
- Lesson 2.3.2 – Intervals and Scaling

Mathematical Vocabulary

The following is a list of vocabulary found in this chapter. Some of the words have been seen in the previous chapter. The words in bold are words that are new to this chapter. Make sure that you are familiar with the terms below and know what they mean. For the words you do not know, refer to the glossary or index. You might also add these words to your Toolkit so that you can reference them in the future.

absolute value	**additive identity**	**additive inverse**
Distributive Property	**equivalent**	fraction greater than one
four-quadrant graph	**integers**	interval
mixed number	**rational numbers**	repeating decimal
scaling	terminating decimal	

Core Connections, Course 2

Answers and Support for Closure Activity #2
What Have I Learned?

Note: MN = Math Note, LL = Learning Log

Problem	Solution	Need Help?	More Practice
CL 2-130.	a. $1.\overline{4}$ b. 0.875 c. $\frac{51}{250}$ d. $\frac{47}{100}$	Lessons 2.1.1 and 2.1.2 MN: 2.1.1 and 2.1.2	Problems 2-9, 2-54, 2-82, and 2-120
CL 2-131.	Answers vary. Sample answers: a. $5+5+6$, $8+8$, $3(8)+(-8)$ b. $5+6+8$, $5(5)+(-6)$ c. $6+6+6+(-5)$, $3(5)+6+(-8)$ d. $5+6+(-8)$, $8+(-5)$	Lessons 2.2.1 and 2.2.2 MN: 2.2.2 and 2.2.4 LL: 2.2.4	Problems 2-37, 2-38, 2-52, 2-58, and 2-62
CL 2-132.	The total is 6, so -6 will return to start.	Lessons 2.2.1 and 2.2.2 MN: 2.2.2 and 2.2.3 LL: 2.2.2 and 2.2.4	Problems 2-48, 2-49, and 2-58
CL 2-133.	a. $3+3+3+3+3=15$ b. $(-2)+(-2)+(-2)=-6$	Lesson 2.2.4 MN: 2.2.4 LL: 2.2.4	Problems 2-67, 2-68, 2-69, 2-70, 2-71, 2-72, 2-75, and 2-79
CL 2-134.	$\frac{4}{15}$	Lessons 1.2.2 and 1.2.8 MN: 1.2.3	Problems CL 1-144, 2-10, 2-55, and 2-66
CL 2-135.	$\frac{2}{6}$ or $\frac{1}{3}$	Lesson 2.2.5 MN: 2.2.5	Problems 2-90 and 2-127
CL 2-136.	a. $\frac{9}{36}$ or $\frac{1}{4}$ b. $\frac{12}{36}$ or $\frac{1}{3}$ c. 0: There are no purple tiles; impossible	Lessons 1.2.1 and 1.2.2 MN: 1.2.3 LL: 1.2.1	Problems CL 1-148, 2-15, 2-28, 2-64, and 2-118

Problem	Solution	Need Help?	More Practice
CL 2-137.	Only the missing numbers are listed. a. 4, 8, 12, 20 b. 25, 75, 100, 125, 150	Lessons 2.3.1 and 2.3.2 MN: 1.2.2 and 2.3.2	Problems 2-29, 2-39, 2-65, 2-115, and 2-126
CL 2-138.	a. Possible responses include: $0, 2\frac{1}{2}, 2\frac{1}{2}, 10, 10$ or $1,2,2,10,10$ or $1,3,7,7,7$ b. Possible responses include: $0, 2\frac{1}{2}, 2\frac{1}{2}, 10, 10$ or $1, 2\frac{1}{2}, 2\frac{1}{2}, 9, 10$ c. The sum of the numbers should be 25; the largest median to achieve that with is $7\frac{1}{2}$, using the list $0, 2\frac{1}{2}, 7\frac{1}{2}, 7\frac{1}{2}, 7\frac{1}{2}$.	MN: 1.1.3 and 1.1.4	Problems 2-14, 2-41, 2-84, and 2-119

Arithmetic Properties

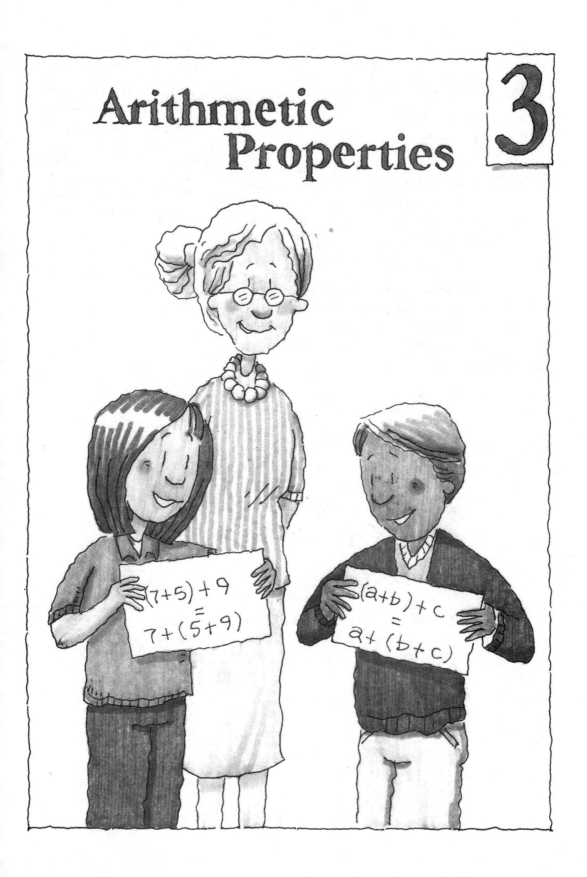

CHAPTER 3

Arithmetic Properties

The acrobat from Chapter 2 has somersaulted into Chapter 3, where you will continue to use the acrobat's routines as you work with integers. Specifically, you will learn about grouping mathematical operations so that you can simplify expressions accurately. In the first section of this chapter, you will also begin to think about how to figure out unknown amounts, a skill that is essential for algebraic thinking.

In the second section of this chapter, you will revisit integers as you investigate subtraction of positive and negative numbers and think more deeply about multiplication.

Section 3.3 extends your previous understanding of operating with portions to include division with fractions, mixed numbers, and decimals.

In this chapter, you will learn how to:

➢ Simplify expressions with multiple operations by identifying and evaluating groups.

➢ Subtract and multiply positive and negative numbers.

➢ Divide with fractions, mixed numbers, and decimals.

Guiding Questions

Think about these questions throughout this chapter:

What strategy can I use?

How can I calculate it?

What is another way to show it?

Chapter Outline

Section 3.1 In this section, you will find strategies for grouping operations within number expressions so you can simplify them accurately.

Section 3.2 Section 3.2 connects subtraction of integers to your earlier work with adding and multiplying integers. You will expand your knowledge of how to find differences and products.

Section 3.3 In this section, you will extend your understanding of operations with fractions and decimals to include division.

3.1.1 How can I simplify it?

· ·

Grouping Expressions

In previous lessons you have worked with expressions, combinations of numbers, variables, and operation symbols, that involve either adding integers or multiplying integers. Today you will examine expressions that involve *both* operations. By the end of this lesson, you will be expected to be able to answer these target questions:

> How can expressions with the same numbers and operations
> have different meanings?

> Does the order in which we do each operation matter?

3-1.   Katrina wrote the following set of instructions for Cecil:
$4 \cdot 2.5 + 1$.

a.   If Cecil the acrobat follows Katrina's instructions, how far will he go? Draw a diagram of Cecil's movements and show how far he will move.

b.   Katrina drew the diagram at right. How was she thinking about Cecil's moves? Write an expression to represent Katrina's diagram.

$$\underset{2.5}{\longrightarrow} \underset{1}{\longrightarrow} \underset{2.5}{\longrightarrow} \underset{1}{\longrightarrow} \underset{2.5}{\longrightarrow} \underset{1}{\longrightarrow} \underset{2.5}{\longrightarrow} \underset{1}{\longrightarrow}$$

c.   Explain why Katrina's diagram in part (b) will not give her the correct length for $4 \cdot 2.5 + 1$.

d.   Cecil changed Katrina's set of instructions so that the length of 1 foot came first, as shown in the diagram at right. Write an expression to represent this new diagram. How far does Cecil move here? Does this give the same length as $4 \cdot 2.5 + 1$?

$$\underset{1}{\longrightarrow} \underset{2.5}{\longrightarrow} \underset{2.5}{\longrightarrow} \underset{2.5}{\longrightarrow} \underset{2.5}{\longrightarrow}$$

3-2. Cecil's trainers proposed each of the following movements. Which one requires the longest rope? Draw diagrams to justify your answer.

a. $8 + 2(6.48)$ feet

b. $2 + 8(6.48)$ feet

c. $(8 + 2)6.48$ feet

3-3. The expression $5 + 3 \cdot 4 + 2$ can be used to represent the group of + tiles shown at right.

```
                    + + + +
          + + +              +
          + +      + + + +   +
                   + + + +
```

a. Work with your team to explain how each part of the expression connects with the groups of + tiles. How many tiles are there?

b. Each group of + tiles is represented by a different part of the expression, also called a **numerical term**. Numerical terms are single numbers or products of numbers. It is often useful to circle terms in an expression to keep track of separate calculations. For example, each term circled in the expression below represents a separate part of the collection of + tiles above.

$$⑤ + ③\cdot④ + ②$$

Circle the terms in the expression shown below. Then explain what each term could describe about collections of + or − tiles.
$$4 \cdot 5 + 1 + 3(-2) + 6$$

3-4. Circle the terms and simplify each expression shown below. **Simplify** means to write an expression in its simplest form. In the case of numerical expressions, the simplest form is a single number.

a. $7.08 + 2.51 + (-3.84)$

b. $7.8 + 2.1(-3)$

c. $5(-\frac{3}{5}) + 2 \cdot 1.5$

d. $4.35 \cdot 2 + 5 + \left(3\frac{1}{4}\right)(-1) + (-10)$

3-5. GROUPING CHALLENGE

Work with your team to add parentheses to $1 + 3 \cdot 2 + 8 + (-4)$ so that the resulting expression has the smallest possible value. Then find a different way to add parentheses to the same expression so that it has the largest possible value. For each expression, draw a diagram of how Cecil would move.

3-6.   LEARNING LOG

In your Learning Log, answer the target questions for
this lesson, which are reprinted below. Be sure to
include examples to support your ideas. Title this entry
"Grouping Integers" and label it with today's date.

How can expressions with the same numbers and operations have different
meanings?

Does it matter in which order we do each operation?

3-7.   Consider the expression $7 + 3 \cdot 4 + 2$.

a.   What movements does this represent for Cecil walking on his tightrope?
Draw a diagram to show his movements and the length of his walk.

b.   How many different answers can you get by grouping differently? Add
parentheses to the expression $7 + 3 \cdot 4 + 2$ to create new expressions with as
many different values as possible.

3-8.   Find the distance between each pair of points if they were graphed on a number
line. Represent your work using absolute value symbols.

a.   −27.1 and 53.2   b.   71.54 and −28.3   c.   −38.9 and −7.3

3-9.   Find the missing information from the following relationships.

a.   Mark has downloaded four times as many
songs on his music player as Chloe. If
Mark has 440 songs, how many songs
does Chloe have?

b.   Cici likes to collect shoes, but she only has
half the number of pairs of shoes that her
friend Aubree has. If Cici has 42 pairs of
shoes, how many pairs of shoes does
Aubree have?

c.   Tito walked three more miles than Danielle. If Danielle walked 2 miles,
how far did Tito walk?

3-10.   After a pizza party, Julia has parts of five pizzas left over, as shown below. Each pizza was originally cut into 12 pieces, and the shaded areas represent the slices that were not eaten.

pizza A   pizza B   pizza C   pizza D   pizza E

a.   What fraction of pizza A is left?

b.   If all of the pieces were put together, how many whole pizzas could Julia make? How many extra pieces would she have?

c.   Julia wants to write the amount of leftover pizza as a single fraction. How could she do this?

3-11.   Copy and complete the generic rectangle below. What multiplication problem does it represent and what is the product?

	___	+ 5
___	200	100
+ 7	___	___

3.1.2 What if they are complicated?

Identifying Terms in Expressions

In today's lesson, you will continue to simplify expressions using the correct Order of Operations. You will also learn how to identify terms in expressions that are more complicated.

3-12. For each of the following expressions:

- Draw a diagram that could represent the expression.

- Simplify the expression.

a. $-3 + 4(-2)^3 + 5$ b. $-3^2 + 4(-2 + 5)$

3-13. Katrina and Madeline were working on problem 3-12 when Madeline noticed, *"These two expressions look almost the same, except that one has two terms, while the other has three!"*

Discuss Madeline's observation with your team. Explain which expression has two terms and which has three. **Terms** in expressions are separated by addition (+) and subtraction (−) signs unless the sum or difference is inside parentheses.

3-14. Consider the expression $3(5 + 2 \cdot 4) + 2(-3)$.

a. Work with your team to draw a diagram representing this expression. Your diagram could show Cecil's movements, for example, or it could show + and − tiles that could be represented by this expression.

b. Simplify the expression.

c. Discuss with your team how you might circle terms in this expression. Be ready to explain your ideas to the class.

3-15.   For each of the following expressions, visualize them as Cecil's movements on a tightrope or as groups of $+$ and $-$ tiles. Then:

- Describe to your team members how you see each expression.

- Circle the terms and simplify each expression.

    a. $3(8.63)+1$ b. $1+3(8.63)$

    c. $4\frac{1}{3}+2\left(3\frac{2}{5}\right)+5$ d. $4\frac{1}{3}+2(3\frac{2}{5}+5)$

    e. $4+(-2)+3(5)$ f. $2(-4+3+5)$

    g. $2.68(20)+4+3(-5)$ h. $4(-7.6)+3\frac{1}{2}(100+5)$

3-16.   **AIM FOR 16**

In this game, you and the other players will create expressions that contain the same four numbers. Then you will compare the numbers that your expressions represent to see whose number is closest to 16.

Your teacher will roll four number cubes to determine the four numbers you can use in your expression. You may use each number as either a positive or negative integer, and each number must appear exactly once in your expression. For example, if a number cube lands on 5, you can use either 5 or −5 in your expression. Try to make an expression that represents a number that is as close to 16 as possible.

Your score is how far your expression's value is from 16. For example, for an expression that represents 20, the score would be 4, and for an expression that represents 13, the score would be 3. Compare your expression with your opponent's. Whoever has the lowest score wins that round. As you continue playing more rounds, keep track of your total score and try to keep it as low as you can.

3-17.   **Additional Challenge:** Simplify each of the expressions below. For each one, be sure to show your work or explain your reasoning.

    a. $\left(4+2(-5)+3\left(2+(-3)\right)+2\right)6+(-2)$

    b. $\left(9+3(-2+4)\right)+\left(6+2\left(5+(-7)\right)+1\right)$

3-18. LEARNING LOG

In your Learning Log, summarize what you have learned in this section about simplifying expressions with multiplication and addition. Be sure to include examples to demonstrate your thinking. Title this entry "Simplifying Expressions with Multiplication and Addition" and label it with today's date.

METHODS AND **M**EANINGS

Expressions, Terms, and Order of Operations

A mathematical **expression** is a combination of numbers, variables, and operation symbols. Addition and subtraction separate expressions into parts called **terms**. For example, $4x^2 - 3x + 6$ is an expression. It has three terms: $4x^2$, $3x$, and 6.

A more complex expression is $2x + 3(5 - 2x) + 8$, which also has three terms: $2x$, $3(5 - 2x)$, and 8. But the term $3(5 - 2x)$ has another expression, $5 - 2x$, inside the parentheses. The terms of this expression are 5 and $2x$.

Mathematicians have agreed on an **Order of Operations** for simplifying expressions.

Original expression:
$$(10 - 3 \cdot 2) \cdot 2^2 - \tfrac{13 - 3^2}{2} + 6$$

Circle expressions that are grouped within parentheses or by a fraction bar:
$$\boxed{(10 - 3 \cdot 2)} \cdot 2^2 - \frac{\boxed{(13 - 3^2)}}{2} + 6$$

Simplify *within* circled terms using the Order of Operations:
$$\boxed{(10 - 3 \cdot 2)} \cdot 2^2 - \frac{\boxed{(13 - 3 \cdot 3)}}{2} + 6$$

- Evaluate exponents.
$$\boxed{(10 - 6)} \cdot 2^2 - \frac{\boxed{(13 - 9)}}{2} + 6$$

- Multiply and divide from left to right.

- Combine terms by adding and subtracting from left to right.
$$(4) \cdot 2^2 - \frac{4}{2} + 6$$

Circle the remaining terms:
$$\boxed{4 \cdot 2^2} - \boxed{\frac{4}{2}} + \boxed{6}$$

Simplify *within* circled terms using the Order of Operations as described above:
$$\boxed{4 \cdot 2 \cdot 2} - \boxed{\frac{4}{2}} + \boxed{6}$$
$$16 - 2 + 6$$
$$20$$

3-19.   Show the numbers of + and − tiles represented by each expression below. Sketch each model and state the number that it represents.

a. $(-2)+(-6)$ b. $(-2)+4+(-2)$ c. $5+(-8)$

3-20.   Copy each expression below and circle each term. Then simplify each expression.

a. $-8+2(-5)$ b. $3(7.5+2)+4.6$

c. $4\frac{1}{2}(-2+1+7)$ d. $5(6+2)+4+2(-5+8)$

3-21.   Justin is working with the integer tiles shown in the diagram at right.

$$\begin{array}{c} + + + + + + \\ - - - - - - \end{array}$$

a.   What is the value of Justin's diagram?

b.   If Justin removes three positive tiles, what will the value be?

c.   If Justin starts with the original diagram and removes three negative tiles, what will the value be?

d.   Justin has a new arrangement of tiles shown at right. If he removes four positive tiles, what will the value be?

$$\begin{array}{c} + + + + \\ - - - - - - \end{array}$$

3-22.   Linh has a bag of beads that contains 10 glass beads, 7 metal beads, 15 plastic beads, and 3 clay beads. For each part below, if the bead selected is replaced before the next draw, what is the probability that Linh will pull out a:

a.   Metal bead?   b.   Bead that is not plastic?   c.   Glass or plastic bead?

3-23.   Copy each portions web below and fill in the missing parts.

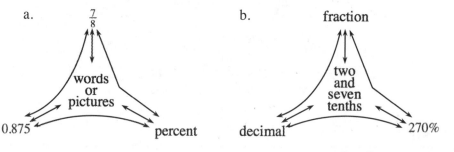

a. $\frac{7}{8}$ b.   fraction

words or pictures   two and seven tenths

0.875   percent   decimal   270%

3.2.1 How can I subtract?

....

Subtraction of Integers

In Chapter 2, you worked with adding and multiplying **integers** (positive and negative whole numbers and zero). In this lesson, you will use + and − tiles to learn about subtraction of integers. Keep the following questions in mind as you work with your team today. At the end of the lesson, you will discuss your conclusions about them.

How can we remove negative tiles when the collection has only positive tiles?

How can we think about subtraction when there are not enough to "take away"?

When does subtracting make the result larger?

3-24. Examine the assortment of positive and negative tiles at right. What integer does this assortment represent?

a. What happens if three + tiles are removed? How can you use numbers and symbols to represent this action and the resulting value?

b. What happens if three − tiles are removed from the original set of tiles? Again, how can you represent this action and the result using numbers and symbols?

3-25. It is often useful to represent operations and expressions in multiple ways. These ways include:

- A diagram (for example, using + and − tiles or with a number line)
- A numerical expression
- A situation described in words
- The total value

In each part labeled (a) through (c) below, one representation is given. Work with your team to create each of the other representations.

a. Start with: $+ + + +$ $+ +$ Then: $+ + + +$
        $+ + + +$ $- -$ $+ + + +$

b. $-8 - (-3)$

c. It is cold! The first time I looked at the thermometer today, it said it was 0 degrees Fahrenheit. Then it dropped 5 degrees! How cold is it now?

3-26.   Note: Before you start this problem, you may want to review the Math Notes box in Lesson 2.2.4. It will remind you of how to use + and − tiles to represent integer addition.

For each of the expressions below:
- **Build** an assortment of tiles that represents the first integer.
- **Explain** how to subtract using words.
- Find a way to **draw** the process on your paper.
- **Record** the expression and result as a number sentence.

a. $7-5$ b. $0-4$ c. $-6-2$

d. $3-(-4)$ e. $-8-(-5)$ f. $-1-(-9)$

3-27.   Subtraction can also be represented on the number line model.

$$-8 \quad -7 \quad -6 \quad -5 \quad -4 \quad -3 \quad -2 \quad -1 \quad 0 \quad 1 \quad 2 \quad 3 \quad 4 \quad 5 \quad 6 \quad 7 \quad 8$$

a.   Sketch the number line above on your paper.

b.   How can you represent $2-7$ using the number line? Discuss your ideas with your team and use the number line to represent your answer.

c.   How can you represent $1-(-2)$ using the number line? Again, discuss your ideas with your team and use the number line to represent your answer.

3-28.   The Deep Submergence Vehicle, Alvin, can dive to a maximum depth of
         14,764 ft. If sea level is 0, then this depth can be written as –14,764 ft. The
         deepest point in the Pacific Ocean, as well as the world, is a location called
         Challenger Deep in the Mariana Trench. It has a depth of –35,840 ft. Tory and
         Nina wanted to know the distance from the bottom of the trench to Alvin when
         the submarine was at its maximum dive depth.

         Tory knew that they needed to subtract to find the difference between the two
         depths, so she did $-35,840-(-14,764)$. Nina, on the other hand, did
         $-14,764-(-35,840)$.

         a.   Complete both computations. What do you notice about the solutions?

         b.   If you want to find the distance between the two depths, what could you do
               with the computations to get a positive value? Write both expressions to
               show this.

         c.   Use your work from part (b) to find the distance between Alvin at its
               deepest dive depth and the following points. For each calculation, write an
               equation and your solution.

               i.   The Puerto Rico Trench in the Atlantic Ocean, –28,374 ft.

               ii.   The Eurasia Basin in the Arctic Ocean, –17,881 ft.

               iii. The Java Trench in the Indian Ocean, –23,376 ft.

3-29.   Absolute value can be thought of as the distance between a number and zero,
         but it can be thought of as the distance between two non-zero numbers, as well.
         Use your number line model from problem 3-27 to answer the following
         questions.

         a.   Place points at 8.6 and 3.4 on your number line. What is the absolute value
               (distance) between 8.6 and 3.4? How can you tell?

         b.   Use the number line to find the absolute value (distance) between –6.72
               and 4.13.

3-30.   Represent the distance between each pair of points below in two ways using the
         absolute value symbol. For example, the distance between 8 and 3 can be
         written $|8-3|=|5|=5$ as well as $|3-8|=|-5|=5$.

         a. $-2\frac{1}{6}$ and 1   b.   2.38 and 7.49   c. $9\frac{3}{10}$ and –6.55

3-31.   Zariah drew the diagram at right to show Cecil the
         acrobat's movements on a tightrope.

         a.   Her expression is $8+(-3)+2$. Discuss with your team how
              the numbers in her expression are related to the diagram.

         b.   Zariah decided to change the length of the acrobat's sequence by *removing*
              the 2-foot arrow. How does this change the length of the sequence? How
              can this action (removing the 2-foot arrow) be represented in a number
              sentence?

         c.   What if Zariah *removed* the 3-foot-long arrow instead, leaving both of the
              other arrows in the diagram above? How does removing this movement
              change the overall length of the sequence? How can this action (removing
              the backwards 3-foot arrow) be represented in her expression? How can it
              be represented by changing the diagram? Discuss this with your team or
              the class until the way the expression is written makes sense.

3-32.   **Additional Challenge:** Add parentheses to make each subtraction equation
         true.

         a. $1-3-5-7=0$ b. $1-3-5-7=-14$

         c. $1-3-5-7=-4$ d. $1-3-5-7=10$

3-33.   With your team, discuss the questions that appear at the beginning of this lesson.
         (They are reprinted below.) Be prepared to explain your ideas to the class.

                     How can we remove negative tiles when
                     the collection has only positive tiles?

                 How can we think about subtraction when there are
                     not enough to "take away"?

                 When does subtracting make the result larger?

METHODS AND MEANINGS

Evaluating Algebraic Expressions

An **algebraic expression** consists of one or more variables, or a combination of numbers and variables connected by mathematical operations. Examples of algebraic expressions include $4x$, $3(x-5)$, and $4x-3y+7$.

To **evaluate** an algebraic expression for particular values of the variables, replace the variables in the expression with their known numerical values and simplify. Replacing variables with their known values is called **substitution**. An example is provided below.

Evaluate $4x-3y+7$ for $x=2$ and $y=1$.

Replace x and y with their known values of 2 and 1, respectively, and simplify.

$$4(2)-3(1)+7$$
$$=8-3+7$$
$$=12$$

3-34.   The number 6 is represented with + and − tiles at right. $+ + + + + + + + +$ $- - -$
For each problem below, start with this diagram and then
show how to remove the appropriate number of tiles to represent the problem given. State the final answer for each part.

   a. $6-7$

   b. $6-(-2)$

   c. $6-3$

3-35.   Use a number line to show the distance between the two given integers. Plot each integer as a point on the number line, and then find the distance between the two points. Write each situation as a subtraction problem using absolute value symbols.

   a.   7 and 4

   b.   5 and −2

   c.   −1 and −3

3-36.   Consider the expression $5+4+2(-3)+7+(-5)$.

   a.   Draw the expression using $+$ and $-$ tiles.

   b.   Simplify the expression to find the number it represents.

   c.   Remove the last number from the expression (-5) and find the sum again.
        Show how this would change your drawing. How much larger or smaller is
        the answer? Explain how your answer makes sense when compared to the
        answer in part (b).

3-37.   Read the Math Notes box in this lesson. Then use the information to answer the
         following questions.

         Jorge was thinking about using variables to represent lengths of a tightrope
         walker's many tricks.

   a.   Jorge wrote the expression $x+x+x+x+3$
        to represent the sequence shown in the
        diagram at right. Does his expression make
        sense? Explain.

   b.   Write an expression to represent the sequence
        shown in the diagram at right.

   c.   In part (a), if $x=5$ feet, how long is the tightrope?

   d.   In part (b), if $j=3$ feet and $k=2$ feet, how long is the tightrope?

3-38.   Simplify the following fraction expressions. Show all of your work.

   a. $\frac{3}{4}+\frac{2}{3}$ b. $\frac{7}{8}-\frac{1}{4}$ c. $\frac{3}{5}\cdot\frac{1}{3}$ d. $\frac{4}{7}\cdot\frac{2}{3}$

3.2.2 What patterns can I find?

Connecting Addition and Subtraction

You have investigated relationships between addition and multiplication as well as subtraction and multiplication. You also know that multiplication and division are closely related. Are these the only relationships between operations? Today you will investigate this question as you look for relationships between the subtraction and addition.

3-39.   Put ten − tiles on your table. With your team, find at least four different sequences of steps (adding or removing any number of + or − tiles in each step) to end up with tiles that represent −4. Represent each of these methods with an expression.

   a.   Are any of your expressions or methods more efficient than others? Is it possible to combine movements or steps so that you can complete the task in only one step?

   b.   How many different expressions can you create that accomplish this task in only one step? Be prepared to share your conclusions with the class.

3-40.   Now start with five + tiles and find ways to end up with only two + tiles. Use your ideas from problem 3-39 above to find the two most efficient ways to do this with only one step. Describe how the two expressions accomplish the same task.

3-41.   Rewrite the expression $7 - (-2)$ as an addition expression that gives the same result. Justify your addition expression using the integer tiles.

3-42.   **HOW CAN WE REWRITE IT?**

Do you think that every subtraction problem can be rewritten as an addition problem that gives the same result?

Your Task: Work with your team to develop a convincing argument to answer this question. You may use examples from the list below or make up your own.

$6+(-2)$	$6-2$	$7.85-(-5)$	$7.85+5$
$-\frac{3}{5}-\frac{3}{10}$	$-\frac{3}{5}+(-\frac{3}{10})$	$-8-(-12)$	$-8+12$
$0-5$	$0+(-5)$	$0-(-0.125)$	$0+0.125$

3-43.   When would rewriting subtraction problems into addition problems be useful? With your team, decide which of the following expressions you may want to rewrite and why. Be prepared to share your reasons with the class.

a. $-100.86-(-3.86)$ b. $21-(-7)$ c. $-24-6$

d. $-\frac{4}{9}-\frac{3}{9}$ e. $0-1.12$ f. $0-(-37\frac{1}{4})$

3-44.   Work with your team to represent the following problem in at least two ways. First, represent it as an expression containing only addition. Second, represent it as an expression containing addition and subtraction. Be prepared to explain to your class the ways that you see it.

While traveling in France, Juno was entertaining himself by riding in an elevator in a very tall building. He started at the ground floor (which in France is considered the 0th floor) and went up 26 floors. Then he rode down 7 floors. Next, he went up another 3 floors and then down again another 16 floors. What floor did Juno end up on?

3-45.   **LEARNING LOG**

In your Learning Log, explain how subtraction and addition are related. Include several examples with diagrams to justify your response. Title this entry "Connecting Addition and Subtraction" and label it with today's date.

METHODS AND MEANINGS

Subtracting Integers

One method of adding integers, mentioned in a previous Math Notes box, was to start with a diagram of the first integer, add the second integer to the diagram, eliminate zeros, and then record what is left. One method of subtracting integers is to do the same, except that instead of adding the second integer, you remove the second integer. Sometimes this removal will require adding extra zeros to the diagram. Look at the examples below:

Example 1: $-3-(-2)$

– – –

Remove
2 negatives

$-\ominus\rightarrow$

$-3-(-2)=-1$

Example 2: $-5-(2)$

– –
–
– –

Cannot remove
2 positives

– – + +
– –
– –

Add zeros until
you can remove
2 positives

– –
– $(+\ +)\rightarrow$
– –

$-5-(2)=-7$

Example 3:
$3-(-3)$

+ +
+

Cannot remove
3 negatives

+ + + + +
+ – – –

Add zeros until
you can remove
3 negatives

+ + + + +
+ $(-\ -\ -)\rightarrow$

$3-(-3)=6$

Review & Preview

3-46.   Find the value of each expression below. Change any subtraction problem to an equivalent addition problem. Draw a diagram with + and – tiles to justify your answer.

a. $5-7$

b. $-5+(-7)$

c. $-5+7$

d. $-5-(-7)$

3-47. Rewrite each of the following expressions using only addition. Then simplify the expression.

   a. $5(-2) - 3$

   b. $7.69 - (-2.5)(-4)$

   c. $-7 + -3 - (-5)$

   d. $(-4)(-25) - 300$

3-48. Each of the diagrams below represents tightrope moves for an acrobat. For each diagram:

   - Describe what the diagram shows about the routine and the length of the tightrope.

   - Figure out the length of the acrobat's trick.

   a.

   b.

3-49. Copy each expression below and simplify it. Be sure to show the steps you use to get the answer.

   a. $\frac{11}{12} - \frac{7}{12}$

   b. $\frac{1}{2} + \frac{1}{8} + \frac{3}{4}$

   c. $\frac{3}{4} - \frac{1}{6}$

3-50. Sketch the rectangle at right on your paper. Calculate the perimeter and area for the given x-values.

   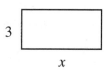

   a. $x = 5$

   b. $x = 9$

   c. $x = 4.6$

3.2.3 How can I multiply integers?

Multiplication as Repeated Subtraction

In this lesson, you will work with your team to continue thinking about what happens when you remove + and − tiles from a collection of tiles representing a number. You will extend your thinking to find ways of making your calculations more efficient when the same number of tiles are removed multiple times. Consider these questions as you work today:

Is there a more efficient way to do this?

How do these ideas compare with what we learned about
adding and multiplying integers in Chapter 2?

3-51. For each expression below, predict what you know about the result without actually calculating it. Can you tell if the result will be positive or negative? Can you tell if it will be larger or smaller than the number you started with? Be ready to explain your ideas.

a. $-1-(-6.5)$

b. $2.2-(-2.2)$

c. $12\frac{1}{2}-22\frac{1}{2}$

d. $-100-(-98)$

e. $-10-(-2)-(-2)-(-2)$

3-52. Now draw (or describe) a diagram for each of the expressions in problem 3-51 and calculate the number that each of them represents.

3-53. Troy and Twana are working with the expression $-10-(-2)-(-2)-(-2)$ from part (e) of problem 3-51.

a. Help them find a shorter way to write this expression.

b. Imagine that their expression does not include the −10. How could they write the new expression? What number would this new expression represent? If you were to describe what this expression represents using + and − tiles, what would you say?

3-54.   How could you evaluate the product $-7(-11)$? Work with your team to make sense of $-7(-11)$. Prepare a brief presentation explaining why your result must be correct.

3-55.   WHAT DOES IT MEAN?

Your Task: Work with your team to create a poster that shows what it means to multiply a negative number by another negative number or to multiply a negative number by a positive number. To demonstrate your ideas, include:

- Examples (from the list below or create your own).
- Pictures or diagrams.
- Any words necessary to explain your thinking.
- Numerical sentences to represent each of your examples.

$4(-3)$	$-4(-3)$	$-4(3)$
$2(-7)$	$-2(-7)$	$-2(7)$

3-56.   Marcy asked Dario, *"Why is $(-1)(-1)=1$?"* Dario helped her by writing the steps at right. Copy, complete, and give a reason for each of Dario's steps to explain to Marcy why $(-1)(-1)=1$.

$$(-1)(0) = 0$$
$$(-1)(-1+1) = 0$$
$$(-1)(-1) + (-1)(1) = 0$$
$$\underline{\hspace{1cm}} + (-1) = 0$$

3-57.   What does $-18 \div 9$ equal? How do you know? Explain why your answer makes sense. Then complete the division problems below.

a. $45 \div (-3)$ b. $-32 \div (-8)$ c. $-54 \div 6$

3-58.   LEARNING LOG

In your Learning Log, describe what you understand about the product of two negative numbers and the product of a negative number and a positive number. Also describe how this is related to division with negatives. Give several examples. Title this entry "Multiplying and Dividing With Negative Numbers" and label it with today's date.

METHODS AND MEANINGS

Connecting Addition and Subtraction of Integers

Another method for subtracting integers is to notice the relationship between addition problems and subtraction problems, as shown below:

$$-3-(-2)=-1 \quad \text{and} \quad -3+2=-1$$

$$-5-(2)=-7 \quad \text{and} \quad -5+(-2)=-7$$

$$3-(-3)=6 \quad \text{and} \quad 3+3=6$$

$$2-(-8)=10 \quad \text{and} \quad 2+8=10$$

These relationships happen because removing a negative amount gives an identical result to adding the same positive amount and vice versa. The result of subtraction of two integers is the same as the result of the addition of the first integer and the *opposite* (more formally, the **additive inverse**) of the second integer.

Example 1: $-2-(7)=-2+(-7)=-9$ Example 2: $2-(-3)=2+(3)=5$

Example 3: $-8-(-5)=-8+(5)=-3$ Example 4: $2-(9)=2+(-9)=-7$

3-59. Copy and simplify each expression below.

   a. $6+(-18)$

   b. $12\frac{1}{2}+(-25)$

   c. $-9+(-9)$

   d. $-12.2+6.1+15.8$

3-60. Find each of the following products or quotients without using a calculator. Draw a diagram or use words to explain how you know your product makes sense.

   a. $6(-3)$

   b. $-6(3)$

   c. $-8(-3)$

   d. $-8(0)$

   e. $-20 \div 5$

   f. $-36 \div (-9)$

3-61. Simplify each of the following expressions without using a calculator. Draw diagrams or use words to show your thinking.

   a. $4(-2\frac{1}{3})+7\frac{1}{6}$

   b. $-8+-2(3)$

   c. $4+-5(-3)+(-7)$

   d. $(-4.25)(2)+(-4.25)(-2)$

3-62. Simplify the following fraction expressions. Show all of your work.

   a. $\frac{5}{6}+\frac{1}{4}$

   b. $\frac{7}{12}-\frac{2}{5}$

   c. $\frac{3}{8}\cdot\frac{2}{3}$

   d. $\frac{4}{5}\cdot\frac{7}{8}$

3-63. Nathan wants you to solve this puzzle: *"I am thinking of a number. If you divide my number by 3 and add –3, you will get 4. What is my number?"* Show all of your work.

Core Connections, Course 2

3.2.4 How does this work with decimals?

Multiplication of Decimals

Just like "*decade*" is another name for *ten* years, a "*deci*mal" number is a number that can be written as a fraction whose denominator is a power of *ten* (10, 100, 1000 etc.). Because our entire number system is based on *ten*, *deci*mals are very important – and they are everywhere! Much of the math you see in science class uses decimals. Of course, you also use them whenever you work with money. Today you will practice working with decimals using what you know about fractions to make sense of the standard algorithm for multiplying decimals. As you work with your team, keep these questions in mind:

How are these decimals like fractions?

What does place value have to do with our answer?

Does our answer make sense?

3-64. Howard went to the mall and saw a banner announcing, "ALL SPORTING GOODS: ONE TENTH OFF!" He saw a pair of roller-blade laces for $0.40 and wanted to find out how much he would save. With your team, follow the steps below to help Howard determine his savings.

Obtain a copy of the Lesson 3.2.4 Resource Page ("Hundredths Grids"). It contains several copies of "hundredths grids," which you will be using throughout this lesson. Hundredths grids are larger versions of unit tiles. Each side measures one unit, divided into ten equal parts.

a. What is the perimeter of each hundredths grid? What is the area?

b. What do each of the small squares in the grid represent? Write your answer in three forms (fraction, decimal, and percent).

c. Why do you think these are called "hundredths grids"?

Problem continues on next page. →

3-64.   *Problem continued from previous page.*

$0.4

d.   Forty cents (the cost of Howard's laces) can also be written as 0.40, or simply 0.4. On your resource page of hundredths grids, lightly shade and label 0.4 or $\frac{4}{10}$ vertically, as shown in the diagram at right.

e.   Next, in the other direction, lightly shade and label $\frac{1}{10}$ of the grid as shown in the diagram at right. What is the fraction of the grid that is darkly shaded? What is the decimal equivalent of the part of the grid that is darkly shaded?

f.   Write two equations that represent this process, one using fractions and one using decimals.

g.   How much money will Howard save with the laces on sale?

3-65.   While in the sporting-goods store, Howard found some new running shoes advertised to weigh only 70% as much as his old running shoes. His old shoes weighed 0.8 kg. Use the problems below to determine how much these new shoes weigh.

a.   Use a hundredths grid to find 70% of 0.8 kg.

b.   Write a fraction equation for this problem. Label the answer with correct units.

c.   Write a decimal equation for this problem. Label the answer with correct units.

d.   Do the new shoes weigh more or less than the old shoes? How much more or less?

3-66.   Another way to think about decimal
         multiplication is with a generic rectangle.

   a.   What multiplication problem is represented
         by the generic rectangle shown at right?
         On your paper, copy this rectangle and
         write the multiplication problem it
         represents.

   b.   Fill in the areas of each of the four sections. What math problem does each
         smaller section represent?

   c.   Write the total area as both a sum and a product. Does your answer make
         sense?

   d.   Use the standard paper-and-pencil method of multiplying
         2.3 by 1.4. Do not use a calculator. Where do you see the
         numbers from this standard algorithm in the generic
         rectangle?

3-67.   Judy is working on part (d) of problem 3-66 and is trying to
         make sense of the standard algorithm for decimal
         multiplication. Her work so far is shown at right.

         "Wait a minute," Judy said, *"I multiplied 2.3 by 0.4 and
         then by 1. How in the world could those products be 92 and
         230? That just doesn't make sense."*

   a.   The decimal points are usually left out of a multiplication problem until the
         last step. You can see that Judy left them out in her work above. If the
         decimal points were to be put in, where would they go in each line of her
         work? That is, is 2.3 times 0.4 equal to 92, 9.2, or 0.92? And then in the
         next line, is 2.3 times 1.0 equal to 230, 23.0, or 2.30?

   b.   Copy Judy's work on your paper and place the decimal points in the correct
         locations. Then complete the work. What is 2.3 times 1.4?

3-68.   When multiplying decimals, how do you know where to place the decimal point? Think about this as you do parts (a) through (d) below.

a.   Write two equations for multiplying 0.3 by 0.16. One equation should express the factors and product using decimals, and one using fractions.

b.   In part (a), you multiplied tenths by hundredths to get thousandths. Do you always get thousandths if you multiply tenths by hundredths? Why or why not? What do you get if you multiply tenths by tenths? Hundredths by hundredths? Use several examples to justify your answers.

c.   When a multiplication problem is written using decimals, there is a relationship between the number of decimal places in the parts (or factors) of the problem and the number of decimal places in the answer (or product). Describe this relationship.

d.   Describe a shortcut for locating the decimal point in the answer to a problem involving decimal multiplication.

3-69.   For each of the following problems, use a hundredths grid if needed. Write both a fraction and a decimal equation with your answer.

a. $(0.3)(0.6)$ b. $(0.5)(-0.4)$ c. $-0.2 \cdot -0.7$

3-70.   Jerry's teacher gave him the problem $(-2.4)(5.3)$. He decided to use a generic rectangle to find the answer. He used the generic rectangle below and found that $(-2.4)(5.3) = -8.48$.

Jerry's teammate Ron knows that $(2.4)(5.3) = 12.72$, so he thinks that the answer to $(-2.4)(5.3)$ is -12.72.

Who is correct, and what was the mistake that was made by the incorrect student?

	−2	+ 0.4
5	−10	2.0
+ 0.3	−0.6	0.12

$-10 + 2.0 - 0.6 + 0.12 = -8.48$

3-71.   Draw generic-rectangle diagrams and write equations to find the following products.

a. $(-6.5)(-4.7)$ b. $(-3.8)(4.4)$

3-72.   Howard, in his new lightweight running shoes, was able to walk at the rate of 0.83 meters per second. His coach timed his walking at this steady pace for 12.2 seconds. How far did he walk during that time? Use paper and a pencil to show your work, and then check your answer with a calculator.

METHODS AND MEANINGS

Multiplication of Integers

Multiplication by a positive integer can be represented by combining groups of the same number:

$$(4)(3) = 3 + 3 + 3 + 3 = 12 \quad \text{and} \quad (4)(-3) = -3 + (-3) + (-3) + (-3) = -12$$

In both examples, the 4 indicates the number of groups of 3 (first example) and −3 (second example) to combine.

Multiplication by a negative integer can be represented by removing groups of the same number:

$$(-4)(3) = -(3) - (3) - (3) - (3) = -12 \quad \text{means "remove four groups of 3."}$$

$$(-4)(-3) = -(-3) - (-3) - (-3) - (-3) = 12 \quad \text{means "remove four groups of −3."}$$

In all cases, if there are an *even* number of negative factors to be multiplied, the product is *positive*; if there are an *odd* number of negative factors to be multiplied, the product is *negative*.

This rule also applies when there are more than two factors. Multiply the first pair of factors, then multiply that result by the next factor, and so on, until all factors have been multiplied.

$$(-2)(3)(-3)(-5) = -90 \quad \text{and} \quad (-1)(-1)(-2)(-6) = 12$$

3-73.   Use what you learned during today's lesson to answer the following questions.

a.   Show (2.3)(5.06) as a fraction multiplication problem and explain why the answer is in thousandths (three decimal places).

b.   Show (0.004)(3.42) as a fraction multiplication problem and explain why the answer is in hundred-thousandths (five decimal places).

3-74.   Mentally calculate the following products. Use the rule for decimal multiplication to write an equation in which the decimal point is written in the correct location.

a.   (−0.04)(−0.1)   b.   (0.03)(−0.02)   c.   (0.7)(0.4)

d.   Stacey said, "*Stephanie, look at my answer to the last problem, 0.7·0.4 = 0.28. Usually when I multiply, I get a bigger answer than the numbers I start with. Twenty-eight hundredths, 0.28, is less than either 0.4 or 0.7. I must have made a mistake.*"

Stephanie responded, "*Well, one half times one half is one fourth, and one fourth is less then one half. I think when you multiply by a fraction or decimal less than one, you get less than you started with.*"

Write a sentence or two about who you think is correct and why.

3-75.   The highest point in the United States is Mount McKinley, also called Denali, in Alaska. Its summit is 20,335 feet above sea level. Badwater, a basin located in Death Valley, is the lowest point in the United States at 282 feet below sea level. How high is the summit of Denali above the Death Valley location? Show your calculation using absolute value symbols.

3-76.   Find the mean, range, and median of these values: 12, 4, −2, 0, 9, −2, 1, 7, 8, 2. Recall that the range is calculated by finding the difference between the largest and smallest data values.

3-77.   Simplify each multiplication problem below.

a. $\frac{5}{8} \cdot \frac{2}{3}$ b. $\frac{3}{4} \cdot \frac{2}{5}$

3.2.5 What can I do with integers?

Addition, Subtraction, Multiplication, and Division of Integers

In this lesson, you will have an opportunity to practice adding, subtracting, multiplying, and dividing integers as you play a game against a partner. As you play, consider these questions:

> Which operation with these integers will move us farthest?

> Which operation with these integers will move us in the direction we want?

> Will any operation with these integers allow us to win?

3-78.   TUG-O-WAR

Obtain a Lesson 3.2.5 Resource Page from your teacher and play Tug-o-War against your partner. Keep track of any strategies that you use or discover as you are playing. Play until your teacher calls time. The rules are printed below.

How to Play

−15 −14 −13 −12 −11 −10 −9 −8 −7 −6 −5 −4 −3 −2 −1 0 1 2 3 4 5 6 7 8 9 10 11 12 13 14 15

Winner   Winner

1. Place your marker at zero.

2. Spin both spinners. You may choose to add, subtract, multiply, or divide the two numbers. The result of your calculation determines how many steps you will take and in which direction. For example, if you spin a −2 and a −1, and you choose to add them to get $-2 + (-1) = -3$, you would move three spaces to the left. Note that you always need to land on an integer space (one of the circles), so that may limit your choices.

3. For each move, record on your paper your starting position, the expression and the result for your chosen move, and your ending position.

4. If your move causes your marker to go off the board on any play, you lose your turn.

5. The game ends when one player lands exactly on a "Winner" space.

3-79.   With your team and then as a class, discuss any strategies that you used or discovered as you played the Tug-o-War game. Use the focus questions at the beginning of this lesson to guide your discussion.

3-80.   Cynthia, Devin, Gavin, and Mark are playing the Tug-o-War game.

   a.   Cynthia begins her turn with her marker at 15. She spins a 1 and a –3. She thinks that she might be able to get to the winner space at 11 with this spin. Is she correct? Explain why or why not.

   b.   Devin takes his turn. His marker is on the 1, and he spins a 4 and a –3. Is it possible for Devin to get to one of the winner spaces (at 11 and –11) with these numbers? Explain your answer.

   c.   Gavin now has his marker at 12, and he spins a –3 and a –2. Gavin is wondering if he can win on this turn. Can he? Explain your answer.

   d.   Mark is currently at –14 and spins a –3 and a –1. He sees a way to win. How can he do this? Is there more than one way? Explain your answer.

3-81.   Roger went home to play the Tug-o-War game with his older brother, Hank. Hank looked at the spinners, thought for a bit, and then told Roger that the game is flawed because you cannot get all of the integers from –10 to +10. Roger wondered if Hank was right.

   Are there any integers from –10 to +10 that you cannot get using any of the operations with the results of a spin on each spinner? Do you think that this would make the game unfair or flawed? Work with your team to build a convincing argument that demonstrates whether or not Hank's claim is true.

MᴇᴛHODS AND Mᴇᴀɴɪɴɢs

Multiplicative Inverses and Reciprocals

Two numbers with a product of 1 are called **multiplicative inverses**.

$$\frac{8}{5} \cdot \frac{5}{8} = \frac{40}{40} = 1 \qquad 3\frac{1}{4} = \frac{13}{4}, \text{ so } 3\frac{1}{4} \cdot \frac{4}{13} = \frac{13}{4} \cdot \frac{4}{13} = \frac{52}{52} = 1 \qquad \frac{1}{7} \cdot 7 = 1$$

In general $a \cdot \frac{1}{a} = 1$ and $\frac{a}{b} \cdot \frac{b}{a} = 1$, where neither a nor b equals zero. You can say that $\frac{1}{a}$ is the **reciprocal** of a and $\frac{b}{a}$ is the reciprocal of $\frac{a}{b}$. Note that 0 has no reciprocal.

Review & Preview

3-82. Simplify each expression without using a calculator. For each expression, draw a diagram or use words to explain how you know your answer makes sense.

a. $-8 \div -4$ b. $18 \div -3$ c. $-24 \div 2$ d. $17 \div -1$

3-83. Follow the Order of Operations (use circling the terms if it is helpful) to simplify the following expressions:

a. $-7 + 4 \div (-2)$ b. $17.5 \div (-7) + -8.1(2)$

c. $(8 + -3)(-5\frac{3}{5})$ d. $(4 - (-3)) + (5 \div (-5))$

3-84. Read the Math Notes box in this lesson. Use the information to find the multiplicative inverse, or reciprocal, of each number below.

a. $\frac{7}{13}$ b. $\frac{1}{5}$ c. 2 d. $2\frac{5}{8}$

e. Check your answers by multiplying the given number with your answer and verifying that the product of the numbers is 1.

3-85. Write at least three expressions that use each of the numbers 2, 3, 6, and 8 only once and any operations and grouping symbols (addition, subtraction, multiplication, division, and parentheses). Each expression should have a different value, with one being equal to 28.

3-86. Copy and complete each problem mentally.

a. $\frac{5}{7} \cdot \frac{7}{5} = \square$ b. $\frac{8}{13} \cdot \frac{\square}{\square} = 1$

c. $\frac{\square}{\square} \cdot \frac{31}{27} = 1$ d. $\frac{5}{\square} \cdot \frac{2}{\square} = 1$

e. What do all of the problems have in common?

3.3.1 How can I divide?

Division with Rational Numbers

A fraction is really just a symbolic representation of the quotient (answer to a division problem) of two quantities. The fraction $\frac{3}{4}$ means $3 \div 4 = 0.75$. In this lesson, you will work with dividing fractions, positive and negative mixed numbers, and decimals.

3-87.   A **rational number** is any number that can be written as a quotient or fraction of integers, that is, in the form $\frac{a}{b}$, with the denominator not equal to zero.

   a.   What mathematical operation does a fraction represent?

   b.   Represent each division problem below as a fraction.

   i. $2 \div 8$ *ii.* $72 \div 5$ *iii.* $51 \div 94$

   c.   Why do you think that the denominator of a fraction cannot equal zero?

   d.   When would it be most useful to use a fraction to find the answer to a division problem instead of using long division?

3-88.   Think about how you rewrote the division problems above as fractions. This can also be done with negative rational numbers (fractions). Is $-\frac{2}{3}$ different from $\frac{-2}{3}$, $\frac{2}{-3}$, and $\frac{-2}{-3}$? Discuss this with your team and decide whether these rational numbers are the same or different. Be prepared to share your answers with the class.

Core Connections, Course 2

3-89.   Huy, Madison, and Ramona were working the following problem and each began her work differently.

$$1\tfrac{3}{8} \div \tfrac{3}{4}$$

Ramona's work:

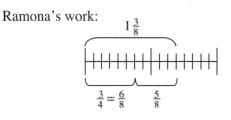

$1\tfrac{3}{8}$

$\tfrac{3}{4} = \tfrac{6}{8}$ $\tfrac{5}{8}$

There is one $\tfrac{3}{4}$ in $1\tfrac{3}{8}$ and $\tfrac{5}{8}$ left over. Then since $\tfrac{3}{4}$ equals $\tfrac{6}{8}$ those $\tfrac{5}{8}$ are really $\tfrac{5}{6}$ of one group. That means the answer is $1\tfrac{5}{6}$, that is, $\tfrac{3}{4}$ divides $1\tfrac{3}{8}$ into $1\tfrac{5}{6}$ pieces of lengths $\tfrac{3}{4}$.

Madison's work:

$1\tfrac{3}{8} = \tfrac{11}{8}$ $\tfrac{3}{4} = \tfrac{6}{8}$

$11 \div 6 = \tfrac{11}{6} = 1\tfrac{5}{6}$

Since $1\tfrac{3}{8}$ is the same as $\tfrac{11}{8}$ and $\tfrac{3}{4}$ is the same as $\tfrac{6}{8}$, this problem is really the same as $\tfrac{11}{8} \div \tfrac{6}{8}$. I can think of this as dividing 11 pieces into groups of 6 or $11 \div 6$.

Huy's work:

$1\tfrac{3}{8} \div \tfrac{3}{4} = \dfrac{1\tfrac{3}{8}}{\tfrac{3}{4}} = \dfrac{\tfrac{11}{8}}{\tfrac{3}{4}}$

$\dfrac{\tfrac{11}{8}}{\tfrac{3}{4}} \cdot \dfrac{\tfrac{4}{3}}{\tfrac{4}{3}} = \dfrac{\tfrac{44}{24}}{1} = \tfrac{44}{24} = 1\tfrac{20}{24} = 1\tfrac{5}{6}$

Since a fraction is division, I can write a super fraction and use a Super Giant One to make an equivalent fraction with a denominator of one. Then I just simplify.

Your Task: Work with your team to make sense of each student's approach to the problem. Then use each of the three approaches to do the following two problems.

$$\tfrac{4}{5} \div \tfrac{1}{2} \qquad\qquad 2\tfrac{1}{2} \div \tfrac{3}{4}$$

3-90.   You have seen three methods for dividing fractions: a diagram, finding a common denominator, and using a Super Giant One. If you need more review of these methods, look at the Math Notes box that follows this lesson. Decide with your team which method you will use for each part (a) and (b) below. Write the problem as a fraction division problem, solve it, and explain what each part of the division problem represents in each story.

a.   Gerard loves to cook. His aunt visited Switzerland and brought him back four pounds of Swiss chocolate. Gerard's favorite cookie recipe takes $\frac{3}{4}$ of a pound of chocolate. How many batches of the chocolate cookie recipe can Gerard make using all the chocolate that he has?

b.   Lauren was bringing food to a party. She bought a 4-foot sub sandwich and cut it into servings that were each $\frac{3}{5}$ of a foot long. How many servings did she get if she used the whole 4-foot sandwich?

3-91.   Use any strategy to solve the following division problems.

a. $-2\frac{1}{8} \div \frac{1}{3}$

b. $\left(-1\frac{3}{4}\right) \div \left(-\frac{2}{5}\right)$

c.   How are the sign rules for simplifying expressions with rational numbers similar to the sign rules for simplifying expressions with integers?

3-92.   Stella wants to find the **quotient** (answer to a division problem) $0.016 \div 0.25$, but she is not sure how to divide decimals. She decided to rewrite the numbers as fractions.

a.   With your team, rewrite $0.016 \div 0.25$ using fractions and use what you know about dividing fractions to find an answer that is *one* fraction.

b.   Stella knew that her teacher would want her to write the answer as a decimal, since the original problem was written with decimals. Convert your answer from part (a) to a decimal.

c.   Find the quotient $2.38 \div 0.04$.

METHODS AND MEANINGS

Fraction Division

Method 1: Using diagrams.

To divide by a fraction using a diagram, create a model of the situation using rectangles, a linear model, or a visual representation of it. Then break that model into the fractional parts named.

For example, to divide $\frac{7}{8} \div \frac{1}{2}$, you can draw the diagram at right to visualize how many $\frac{1}{2}$-sized pieces fit into $\frac{7}{8}$. The diagram shows that one $\frac{1}{2}$ fits, with $\frac{3}{8}$ of a whole left. Since $\frac{3}{8}$ is $\frac{3}{4}$ of $\frac{1}{2}$, you can see that $1\frac{3}{4}$ $\frac{1}{2}$-sized pieces fit into $\frac{7}{8}$, so $\frac{7}{8} \div \frac{1}{2} = 1\frac{3}{4}$.

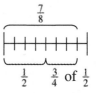

Method 2: Using common denominators.

To divide a number by a fraction using common denominators, express both numbers as fractions with the same denominator. Then divide the first numerator by the second. An example is shown at right.

$$\frac{2}{5} \div \frac{3}{10} = \frac{4}{10} \div \frac{3}{10}$$
$$= \frac{4}{3}$$
$$= 1\frac{1}{3}$$

Method 3: Using a Super Giant One.

To divide by a fraction using a Super Giant One, write the two numbers (dividend and divisor) as a complex fraction with the dividend as the numerator and the divisor as the denominator. Use the reciprocal of the complex fraction's denominator to create a Super Giant One. Then simplify as shown in the following example.

$$\frac{3}{4} \div \frac{2}{5} = \frac{\frac{3}{4}}{\frac{2}{5}} \cdot \frac{\frac{5}{2}}{\frac{5}{2}} = \frac{\frac{3 \cdot 5}{4 \cdot 2}}{1} = \frac{3}{4} \cdot \frac{5}{2} = \frac{15}{8} = 1\frac{7}{8}$$

Division with fractions by the Super Giant One method can be generalized and named the **invert and multiply** method. To invert and multiply, multiply the first fraction (dividend) by the reciprocal (or multiplicative inverse) of the second fraction (divisor). If the first number is an integer, write it as a fraction with a denominator of 1. If it is a mixed number, write it as a fraction greater than one. Here is the same problem in the third example above solved using this method:

$$\frac{3}{4} \div \frac{2}{5} = \frac{3}{4} \cdot \frac{5}{2} = \frac{15}{8} = 1\frac{7}{8}$$

3-93. Complete each of the following division problems by first writing each of them as a fraction.

   a. $-6 \div 8$ b. $6 \div (-8)$ c. $0 \div 8$ d. $6 \div 0$

3-94. Use any method to divide.

   a. $\frac{3}{4} \div \frac{1}{6}$

   b. $\frac{5}{12} \div \left(-\frac{1}{6}\right)$

   c. $-\frac{2}{3} \div \frac{1}{2}$

   d. $-2\frac{2}{3} \div \left(-\frac{1}{2}\right)$

3-95. One third of a rectangular playground is designed for young children. In that part of the playground, a play structure covers $\frac{2}{5}$ of the children's space.

   a. Use a drawing to represent the portion of the playground that is the play structure.

   b. Represent the problem with multiplication.

   c. What fraction of the total playground is the play structure? Show all of your work.

3-96. Represent each operation below by drawing – tiles. Then simplify each expression.

   a. $-6 + (-2)$ b. $-6 - (-2)$

3-97. If the line segment at right is subdivided into equal parts, what is the length of the marked portion of the line?

3.3.2 Why would I use decimals?

Division with Decimals

Today you will review and practice working with decimals. While you might usually use a calculator when dividing decimals, it is important that you understand how decimal division works. This way, when you encounter problems that involve both decimals and variables, you will be able to simplify expressions and manipulate the symbols correctly and efficiently. Today's problems will help you extend what you know about fraction division to make sense of decimal division.

For today's lesson, you may only use your calculator to check answers that you have first calculated by hand or when you are specifically directed to use it.

3-98.   **SPACE FOR SPACERS**

Mr. Garcia needs to cut short pieces out of a 16-foot-long board to use as spacers in the wall of his new house. The pieces he needs for spacers must be 9 inches long. Without using your calculator, how would you determine how many such spacers could be cut from Mr. Garcia's board?

3-99.   Sloan is a fraction wizard and prefers to convert all numbers in any problem to fractions, but her teacher insists that she be able to do Mr. Garcia's problem with decimals as well. Sloan knows that 9 inches is the same as $\frac{3}{4}$ of a foot, so she first wrote Mr. Garcia's problem as $\frac{16}{\frac{3}{4}}$.

> *"I suppose I could use decimals,"* Sloan moaned. *"I know the decimal equivalent for $\frac{3}{4}$ is 0.75."* And then she wrote the division as

$$\frac{16}{0.75} = \frac{16}{\frac{75}{100}}.$$

> *"Oops… I'm just back to fractions. What do I do now?"* Sloan asked her teammates.

a.   Which Giant One would you have to multiply by to change Sloan's fraction to a fraction with integers? Multiply by that fraction and record your answer.

b.   Decide with your team if "1600 divided by 75" is the same problem as "16 divided by 0.75." Why or why not?

c.   Write a note to Sloan explaining your answer to part (a). Include the steps to complete Sloan's work using the long division algorithm to divide $75\overline{)1600}$. Show all your work. Write the answer in decimal form.

3-100. Many people have difficulty locating the decimal point in the answer to a problem like $0.5\overline{)16}$. Use your answer to part (b) of problem 3-99 to rewrite $0.5\overline{)16}$ with whole numbers. Then find the answer using long division. Do not use a calculator.

3-101. Use your calculator to do the following problems quickly. As you do them, write an equation for each problem on your paper.

a. 3 divided by 4

b. 1.5 divided by 0.25

c. 15 divided by 2.5

d. 30 divided by 40

e. 0.003 divided by 0.004

f. 0.15 divided by 0.025

g. $\frac{3}{10}$ divided by $\frac{4}{10}$

h. 0.0015 divided by 0.00025

What do you notice about these problems? How can you explain the similarities and differences?

3-102. Eloise wants to divide $0.07 \div 0.4$ and thinks she sees a shortcut. *"Can I just divide $7 \div 4$?"* she wonders.

a. What do you think? Will her shortcut work? Discuss this with your team and be prepared to explain why or why not.

b. Determine the answer to $0.07 \div 0.4$, and show how you found your answer.

3-103. Set up the division problems below with whole numbers, as shown in the previous problem, to help you solve the problems below. Show all of your work.

a. $\frac{2.5}{0.25}$

b. $\frac{-1.12}{0.7}$

c. $\frac{59.1}{0.3}$

3-104. Tom's kitchen is 12.5 feet wide. He wants to tile the floor with 0.75-foot-wide tiles. How many tiles will be needed for one row of tiles that extend across the length of the floor? Write and solve a division problem and explain what each part of the problem represents in the story.

3-105.　For each problem below, write and solve a story problem. Be sure to explain what each part of the division problem represents in the story. Be ready to share your stories with the class.

　　a.　$11.25 \div 0.4$　　　　　　　　b.　$4.3 \div 0.25$

3-106.　LEARNING LOG

In your Learning Log, explain how to find the answer to a division problem with rational numbers. Title this entry "Division with Rational Numbers" and label it with today's date.

Review & Preview

3-107.　Answer the questions below using your work from this lesson.

　　a.　Find $15.75 \div 0.25$ using the standard algorithm for division.

　　b.　Find $15.75 \div 0.25$ using a Giant One.

　　c.　Which method do you prefer?

3-108. Write an equation and find the answer for each of the following problems. Give answers in decimal form.

    a. What is the product of three tenths and four hundredths?

    b. What is the sum of five and thirteen hundredths plus twelve and six tenths?

    c. What is forty-seven and seven tenths minus twenty-three and nineteen hundredths?

    d. What is the product of twenty hundredths and sixty-five thousandths?

    e. What is the sum of fourteen tenths and fourteen hundredths?

3-109. Each problem below has an error in the answer. Find the error, explain how to correct the mistake, and correct it.

    a.
$$\begin{array}{r} 10 \\ \times\ 0.5 \\ \hline 50 \end{array}$$

    b.
$$\begin{array}{r} 467.92 \\ +\ 1.293 \\ \hline 479.85 \end{array}$$

    c.
$$\begin{array}{r} 100 \\ -\ 62.837 \\ \hline 38.837 \end{array}$$

    d.
$$\begin{array}{r} 1.234 \\ \times\ 0.003 \\ \hline 0.3702 \end{array}$$

    e.
$$\begin{array}{r} 4006.3 \\ -\ \ 34.98 \\ \hline 3971.48 \end{array}$$

    f.
$$\begin{array}{r} 45.6 \\ 32.87 \\ +\ 0.003 \\ \hline 374.6 \end{array}$$

3-110. This problem is a checkpoint for multiplication of fractions and decimals. It will be referred to as Checkpoint 3.

Multiply each pair of fractions or each pair of decimals. Simplify if possible.

    a. $\frac{3}{4} \cdot \frac{3}{5}$

    b. $\frac{9}{20} \cdot \frac{4}{9}$

    c. $3\frac{1}{6} \cdot 1\frac{1}{3}$

    d. $2\frac{1}{4} \cdot 3\frac{1}{5}$

    e. $3.62 \cdot 3.4$

    f. $0.26 \cdot 0.0008$

Check your answers by referring to the Checkpoint 3 materials located at the back of your book.

Ideally, at this point you are comfortable working with these types of problems and can solve them correctly. If you feel that you need more confidence when solving these types of problems, then review the Checkpoint 3 materials and try the practice problems provided. From this point on, you will be expected to do problems like these correctly and with confidence.

3-111. Complete the following division problems using any method.

    a. $\frac{6}{5} \div \left(-\frac{3}{2}\right)$

    b. $\frac{7}{4} \div \frac{3}{5}$

    c. $-\frac{4}{0} \div 5\frac{11}{14}$

    d. $-\frac{2}{3} \div \left(-1\frac{1}{4}\right)$

3.3.3 How can I simplify numerical expressions?

Arithmetic Properties

Remember when operations with numbers were simple? In elementary school, you learned to add, subtract, multiply, and divide whole numbers. As you have seen, there is a lot to consider when operating with different kinds of numbers. In this lesson, you will put together much of your understanding of operations with integers and simplifying numerical expressions to draw conclusions about order and grouping of operations.

3-112. Juno was working on simplifying the expression $24 + 3 + (-4) + 7$. *"I know!"* he exclaimed. *"It must be equal to 30, because 20 plus 10 is 30."*

 a. Is Juno correct? Is the value of the expression 30?

 b. How could Juno have found 20 and 10 in this expression? Discuss this with your team and be prepared to share your ideas with the class.

3-113. In problem 3-112, Juno used his understanding of two different properties: the **Commutative Property of Addition** and the **Associative Property of Addition**. The Commutative Property of Addition allows Juno to rearrange $24 + 3 + (-4) + 7$ into a different order, such as $24 + (-4) + 3 + 7$. The Associative Property of Addition allows him to group numbers in different ways, so instead of adding from left to right, he can add in two groups and then combine them like this: $(24 + (-4)) + (3 + 7) = 20 + 10 = 30$.

 a. Talk with your team about the Commutative Property of Addition. Does it work for other operations? In other words, can multiplication, division, and subtraction be done in any order? Be ready to explain your ideas to the class.

 b. Talk with your team about the Associative Property of Addition. Does it work for other operations? In other words, can multiplication, division, and subtraction be done in any grouping? Be ready to explain your ideas to the class.

3-114. Consider expressions involving addition *and* subtraction, such as $7 - 2 + 4$.

  a. Work with your team to calculate the value of this expression. Be prepared to explain your method to the class.

  b. Does the grouping matter? In other words, is $(7 - 2) + 4$ the same as $7 - (2 + 4)$? Explain.

  c. Does order matter? In other words, is $7 - 2 + 4$ the same as $2 - 7 + 4$? Explain.

  d. In expressions that involve addition and subtraction, in what order should those operations be calculated? Consider the following expressions to help you think about this.

  i. $10 - 2 + 4$ *ii.* $3 - 5 - 2 + 6$ *iii.* $7 - 3 - 2$

3-115. Juno has another idea. *"Wait!"* he says. *"Can't subtraction be rewritten using addition? Since order doesn't matter when we add, can't we just rewrite the subtraction as addition so we can use any order?"*

Discuss Juno's idea with your team and then rewrite each of the following expressions so that each one involves only addition. Then use the fact that the numbers are all being added and the order can be changed to find a way to simplify each expression efficiently.

  a. $17 - 4 - 11 + 15$ b. $2 - 2 \cdot 3 - 4 - 2(-4)$

3-116. Maria and Jorge were trying to simplify the expression $\left(-\frac{4}{3}\right)\cdot 1\frac{2}{5}\cdot\left(-\frac{3}{4}\right)$. Maria started by rewriting $1\frac{2}{5}$ as $\frac{7}{5}$. Her work is below.

$$\left(-\frac{4}{3}\right)\cdot\frac{7}{5}\cdot\left(-\frac{3}{4}\right)$$

$$\left(-\frac{4}{3}\right)\cdot\left(-\frac{21}{20}\right)$$

$$\frac{84}{60}=1\frac{24}{60}=1\frac{2}{5}$$

Jorge had a different idea. He multiplied $\left(-\frac{4}{3}\right)\cdot\left(-\frac{3}{4}\right)$ first.

a. Simplify the expression $1\frac{2}{5}\cdot\left(-\frac{4}{3}\right)\cdot\left(-\frac{3}{4}\right)$ using Jorge's method. Is your answer equal to Maria's?

b. Jorge used the **Commutative Property of Multiplication**. Why might Jorge have decided to multiply $\left(-\frac{4}{3}\right)\cdot\left(-\frac{3}{4}\right)$ first?

c. In a multiplication problem, the factors can be grouped together in different ways. This is called the **Associative Property of Multiplication**. Use this property and show that $\left(\frac{3}{4}\cdot\frac{2}{5}\right)\cdot(-2)$ and $\frac{3}{4}\cdot\left(\frac{2}{5}\cdot(-2)\right)$ are equivalent.

d. Simplify each expression. First decide if you want to group some factors together.

  i. $(-9)\cdot\frac{1}{9}\cdot\frac{3}{8}$ *ii.* $-\frac{5}{12}\cdot\frac{3}{7}\cdot\frac{4}{9}$ *iii.* $-8.1\cdot 5\cdot 2$

3-117. **Additional Challenge:** Use each integer $-6, 2, -3,$ and 1 once with any of the four operations or parentheses to make:

a. The largest possible answer.

b. Zero or the closest number to zero.

c. The smallest possible answer.

3-118.   You have learned several methods for solving problems with decimals and fractions. As you solve these problems, clearly show all of your work. Also show the connection between the parts of the word problem and the parts of your math problem. Be sure to explain what your answer represents in the story.

   a.   Tinaya worked 42.2 hours last week. If she is paid $15.65 an hour, what was her total pay (before taxes) for the week?

   b.   Joe has a medicine bottle with $6\frac{2}{3}$ oz of liquid medicine in it. If each dose is $\frac{1}{4}$ oz, how many doses does Joe have if he will use all the medicine?

   c.   If the temperature changes –2.6 degrees each hour for 8.2 hours, how much does the total temperature change?

   d.   Jack and some friends climbed Long's Peak in Rocky Mountain National Park. Then he and his friends started down the mountain, losing $1515\frac{1}{4}$ feet of elevation each hour. They hiked for $6\frac{1}{5}$ hours to get back down to the parking lot. How many feet of elevation did they lose?

   e.   Mr. Solomon, the art teacher, has 49.6 pounds of clay. If he gives every student 1.6 pounds of clay and has none left, how many students are in his class?

3-119.   Your teacher will assign you one of the situations from problem 3-118 to make a stand-alone poster. A stand-alone poster means explaining all your thoughts in writing because you will not be explaining it orally.

   On your poster, be sure to write the original story problem, write the math problem, and show how to solve the problem two different ways. Using drawings or words, show what each part of the math problem and the answer represents.

METHODS AND MEANINGS

Dividing Decimal Numbers

When you are dividing by a decimal number, one way to proceed is to count how many digits the decimal point must move to the right in the divisor so that it becomes an integer (whole number).

Then move the decimal point in the dividend the same direction and the same number of digits.

Example: $8.3 \div 4.07$

$$\text{divisor} \longrightarrow 4.\underset{\smile\smile}{07})\overline{8.30\overset{\bullet}{\underset{\smile\smile}{\wedge}}} \longleftarrow \text{dividend}$$

Moving the decimal point two places to the right is the same as multiplying both numbers by 100.

The Giant One (Identity Property of Multiplication) illustrates this as shown below.

$$8.3 \div 4.07 = \frac{8.3}{4.07} \cdot \boxed{\frac{100}{100}} = \frac{830}{407}$$

Review & Preview

3-120. Hilda was simplifying some numerical expressions and made each of the following sequences of calculations. Name the mathematical property, operation, or idea that justifies how Hilda went from each step to the next step.

a. $5 \cdot \left(-\frac{4}{3}\right) \cdot \left(\frac{2}{5}\right)$

$= \left(-\frac{4}{3}\right) \cdot 5 \cdot \left(\frac{2}{5}\right)$

$= \left(-\frac{4}{3}\right) \cdot \left(5 \cdot \left(\frac{2}{5}\right)\right)$

$= \left(-\frac{4}{3}\right) \cdot \left(\frac{2}{1}\right) = -\frac{8}{3} = -2\frac{2}{3}$

b. $17 + 29 + 3 + 1$

$= 17 + 3 + 29 + 1$

$= (17 + 3) + (29 + 1)$

$= 20 + 30$

$= 50$

3-121. Simplify each of the following expressions.

a. $3 + 4(10 - 8)$

b. $3 + 4 \cdot 10 - 8$

c. $(3 + 4)(10 - 8)$

3-122.   Refer to the diagram at right to answer the questions below.   + + + +
          - - - - -

    a. Copy the diagram and add two tiles so that the result is a value of –2. You
        can add positive and/or negative tiles. Show the tiles you added to get this
        answer.

    b. Copy the diagram again, but this time remove four tiles (again positives
        and/or negatives) so that the result is a value of 2. Show the tiles you
        removed to get this answer.

3-123.   Copy and complete each of the Diamond Problems below.
          The pattern used in the Diamond Problems is shown at right.

    a.   b.   c.   d.

3-124.   Greta is trying to determine the portion of green candies in various bags of
          green and yellow candies. Using the information below, determine the portion
          of green candies in each bag.

    a. Bag A: Two thirds of the candies are yellow. What portion of the candies
        is green?

    b. Bag B: 29% of the candies are yellow. What portion of the candies is
        green?

    c. Bag C: 4 out of every 9 candies are yellow. What portion of the candies is
        green?

3-125.   Solve the following problems without paper or pencil. Just write the answer but
          be ready to explain your thinking.

    a. $2\frac{1}{2} \div \frac{1}{2}$ b. $2\frac{2}{3} \div \frac{1}{3}$

3-126.   Simplify each of the following expressions.

    a. $3 - 2 \cdot 5$ b. $7(4 + 3 \cdot 2)$ c. $10 - 6 \div 2 \cdot 4 + 2$

3-127.   Four friends worked together to wash all of the cars that the Kish family owns. They received $42.36 for doing the work and agreed to divide the earnings evenly. How much money will each friend earn? Show how you know.

3-128.   Find each product. Express your answer as both a fraction and a decimal.

   a. $1.25 \cdot \left(-\frac{3}{5}\right)$

   b. $\left(-3\frac{2}{7}\right) \cdot 0.14$

   c. $-4.37 \cdot (-5.2)$

3-129.   Cecil the Acrobat walked $3\frac{1}{2}$ feet on his tightrope, backed up 1 foot, then walked $6\frac{1}{2}$ feet to get to the other side.

   a.   Write an expression to represent Cecil's walk.

   b.   How far did Cecil walk?

   c.   Cecil started at the beginning again and walked $6\frac{1}{2}$ feet, backed up 1 foot, then walked $3\frac{1}{2}$ feet. How far did he walk this time? How does this compare to your answer from part (b)? Explain why these answers are the same or different in a sentence or with a drawing.

Chapter 3 Closure   What have I learned?

Reflection and Synthesis

The activities below offer you a chance to reflect
about what you have learned during this chapter.
As you work, look for concepts that you feel very
comfortable with, ideas that you would like to learn
more about, and topics you need more help with.

①   SUMMARIZING MY UNDERSTANDING

This section gives you an opportunity to show what you know about the main
math ideas in this chapter.

Writing a Code

You and your team are involved in a very important, top-secret mission! You
will work together to create a secret code.

Your Task: Get a secret number and a set of four code-writing numbers from
your teacher.

- Work with your team and use your code-writing numbers to write *at
  least* three expressions that have the value of your secret number and
  meet the requirements in the list below.

  o Each expression must use all four code-writing numbers *at least*
    once. You may only use your code-writing numbers, but you may
    use each one as many times as you wish.

  o Each expression must include *at least* three of the four basic
    operations $(+, -, \cdot, \div)$.

  o When you have finished writing all of your expressions, you must
    have used all four basic operations and grouping symbols
    (parentheses).

- Draw diagrams or use words to show how you know each of your
  expressions has the value of your secret number.

- Explain each of your expressions and diagrams to your teacher.

Cracking the Code

Get a set of three expressions from another team. Simplify each of their
expressions to crack their code. Be prepared to explain how you know that you
have correctly found their secret number.

         Core Connections, Course 2

WHAT HAVE I LEARNED?

Doing the problems in this section will help you to evaluate which types of problems you feel comfortable with and which ones you need more help with.

Solve each problem as completely as you can. The table at the end of this closure section provides answers to these problems. It also tells you where you can find additional help and where to find practice problems like them.

CL 3-130.   At right is a representation of the number 6. Copy
this diagram and use it to illustrate each of the
subtraction problems shown below.

$+\ +\ +\ +\ +\ +\ +\ +\ +$
$-\ -\ -$

a. $6-8$

b. $6-(-1)$

CL 3-131.   Simplify each of the following expressions.

a. $(-2)(-5)+7$

b. $4.18+3(-4.6)-2.36$

c. $(3.71+(-5.25))(4+(-9))$

d. $-3(4+(-7))+(-2(5)-17)$

CL 3-132.   Robert found a game spinner that was not
completely labeled. The spinner is shown at
right. Help Robert figure out what fraction of
the spinner is missing.

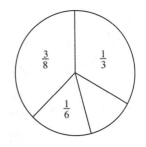

CL 3-133.   What number is represented by each of the letters on the number lines below?

a.

b.

CL 3-134. The diagram at right represents an acrobat's sequence on a tightrope, where m represents the distance in feet that she covers each time she does a leap.

a. How long is each of her leaps? How can you tell?

b. How long is the tightrope?

c. Write expressions to represent each of her two sequences across the tightrope.

CL 3-135. Complete a portions web for each representation of a rational number below.

a. $\frac{70}{100}$

b. 118%

c. 0.085

d.

CL 3-136. Without using a calculator, find the following products.

a. $\frac{11}{4}$ of $\frac{3}{7}$

b. $\frac{5}{12} \cdot 2$

c. $4.16(0.2)$

d. $4\frac{2}{5} \cdot 1\frac{1}{3}$

CL 3-137. Without using a calculator, find the following quotients.

a. $\frac{3}{7} \div \frac{2}{3}$

b. $1.2 \div 0.04$

c. $8\frac{2}{3} \div 4\frac{1}{2}$

d. $5.4 \div \frac{3}{5}$

CL 3-138.   For each of the problems above, do the following:
- Draw a bar or number line that represents 0 to 10.

- Color or shade in a portion of the bar that represents your level of understanding and comfort with completing that problem on your own.

If any of your bars are less than a 5, choose *one* of those problems and do one of the following tasks:
- Write two questions that you would like to ask about that problem.
- Brainstorm two things that you DO know about that type of problem.

If all of your bars are at 5 or above, choose one problem and do one of these tasks:
- Write two questions you might ask or hints you might give to a student who was stuck on the problem.
- Make a new problem that is similar and more challenging than that problem and solve it.

③　　WHAT TOOLS CAN I USE?

You have several tools and references available to help support your learning: your teacher, your study team, your math book, and your Toolkit, to name only a few. At the end of each chapter, you will have an opportunity to review your Toolkit for completeness. You will also revise or update it to reflect your current understanding of big ideas.

The main elements of your Toolkit should be your Learning Logs, Math Notes, and the vocabulary used in this chapter. Math words that are new appear in bold in the text. Refer to the lists provided below and follow your teacher's instructions to revise your Toolkit, which will help make it useful for you as you complete this chapter and as you work in future chapters.

Learning Log Entries

- Lesson 3.1.1 – Grouping Integers

   Lesson 3.1.2 – Simplifying Expressions with Multiplication and Addition
- Lesson 3.2.2 – Connecting Addition and Subtraction
- Lesson 3.2.3 – Multiplying and Dividing with Negative Numbers
- Lesson 3.3.2 – Division with Rational Numbers

Math Notes

- Lesson 3.1.2 – Expressions, Terms, and Order of Operations
- Lesson 3.2.1 – Evaluating Algebraic Expressions
- Lesson 3.2.2 – Subtracting Integers
- Lesson 3.2.3 – Connecting Addition and Subtraction of Integers
- Lesson 3.2.4 – Multiplication of Integers
- Lesson 3.2.5 – Multiplicative Inverses and Reciprocals
- Lesson 3.3.1 – Division with Fractions
- Lesson 3.3.2 – Multiplying Decimal Numbers
- Lesson 3.3.3 – Dividing Decimal Numbers

Mathematical Vocabulary

The following is a list of vocabulary found in this chapter. Some of the words have been seen in the previous chapter. The words in bold are words that are new to this chapter. Make sure that you are familiar with the terms below and know what they mean. For the words you do not know, refer to the glossary or index. You might also add these words to your Toolkit so that you can reference them in the future.

additive inverse	**algebraic expression**	**Associative Property**
Commutative Property	**evaluate**	integers
multiplicative inverse	**numerical term**	**Order of Operations**
quotient	rational numbers	**reciprocal**
simplify	**substitution**	**terms**

Answers and Support for Closure Problems
What Have I Learned?

Note: MN = Math Note, LL = Learning Log

Problem	Solution	Need Help?	More Practice
CL 3-130.	a. $= -2$ b. $= 7$	Lesson 3.2.1 MN: 3.2.2	Problems 3-34, 3-46, 3-96, and 3-122
CL 3-131.	a. 17 b. −11.98 c. 7.7 d. −18	Sections 3.1 and 3.2 MN: 3.1.2, 3.2.2, and 3.2.4 LL: 3.1.1, 3.1.2, 3.2.2, and 3.2.3	Problems 3-7, 3-20, 3-47, 3-61, 3-83, 3-121, and 3-126

Problem	Solution		Need Help?	More Practice
CL 3-132.	$\frac{3}{24}$ or $\frac{1}{8}$		Lessons 1.2.2 and 1.2.8 MN: 1.2.3	Problems CL 1-144, CL 2-134, and 3-124
CL 3-133.	a. A: –3, B: 6, C: 15 b. D: –350, E: 1050, F: 1750		Lessons 2.3.1 and 2.3.2 MN: 1.2.2 and 2.3.2	Problems CL 2-137 and 3-97
CL 3-134.	a. $m = 3$ feet b. 10 feet c. $m + 7$ and $m + m + 4$		MN: 3.2.1	Problems 3-37 and 3-48
CL 3-135.	a. $\frac{7}{10}$, 0.7, 70%, seven tenths b. $\frac{118}{100}$ or $\frac{59}{50}$, 1.18, one and eighteen hundredths c. $\frac{85}{1000}$ or $\frac{17}{200}$, 8.5%, eighty-five thousandths d. $\frac{175}{100}$ or $1\frac{3}{4}$, 1.75, 175%, one and seventy-five hundredths		Lessons 2.1.1 and 2.1.2 MN: 2.1.1 and 2.1.2	Problems 2-27, 2-82, CL 2-130, and 3-23
CL 3-136.	a. $\frac{33}{28}$ c. 0.832	b. $\frac{10}{12}$ or $\frac{5}{6}$ d. $\frac{88}{15}$	Lesson 3.2.4 MN: 3.3.2	Problems 3-77, 3-110, and 3-128
CL 3-137.	a. $\frac{9}{14}$ c. $\frac{52}{27} = 1\frac{25}{27}$	b. 30 d. 9	Lessons 3.3.1 and 3.3.2 MN: 3.2.5, 3.3.1, and 3.3.3 LL: 3.3.2	Problems 3-94, 3-107, and 3-111

Proportions and Expressions

4

CHAPTER 4   Proportions and Expressions

In Section 4.1, you will investigate how to enlarge and reduce figures so that they maintain their same shape. Your work with similar figures and scale drawings, such as maps and blueprints, will lay the foundation for much of the rest of the chapter.

Maps, blueprints, and scale models all have one thing in common: they are proportional to what they represent. This is a concept that you will explore in Section 4.2. You will also study proportional relationships using tables, graphs, and the Giant One.

Section 4.3, you will begin to build expressions using a new tool called "algebra tiles." You will use a variable to help you describe the perimeter and area of shapes built with tiles when one dimension is unknown or represents various possible lengths. You will write expressions and simplify them.

Guiding Questions

Think about these questions throughout this chapter:

What's the relationship?

How can I solve it?

What is being compared?

Which shapes are similar?

Are these representations equivalent?

In this chapter, you will learn how to:

➢ Find solutions to problems involving proportional relationships.

➢ Identify proportional relationships in tables, graphs, and equations.

➢ Calculate unit rates.

➢ Combine like terms and simplify algebraic expressions.

➢ Rewrite expressions by combining like terms and using the Distributive Property.

➢ Simplify and compare two algebraic expressions.

Chapter Outline

Section 4.1 You will examine several similar shapes to determine how those shapes are related. You will use the patterns that you identify to find missing lengths and areas on shapes and to make scale drawings.

Section 4.2 This section introduces the idea of a proportional relationship through tables, graphs, equations, and real-life situations. You will learn strategies for solving proportional situations.

Section 4.3 Here, you will be introduced to algebra tiles. You will use their areas and perimeters to build expressions and combine like terms. You will work with algebraic expressions, simplifying and evaluating them for given values.

4.1.1 Are the figures the same shape?

Similar Figures

Today you will extend your study of ratios by looking at enlargements and reductions of geometric figures. Think of a copy machine and what it does to a picture when the "enlargement" button is selected. The machine makes *every length* of the picture larger or smaller by multiplying it by the same number, called the **multiplier**. That multiplier is also called the **scale factor**.

4-1. Karen is learning how to use the copy machine at her school's main office and decides to scale the figure shown at right by 300%. She wonders what will happen to the figure.

> Note: For all of these problems, the original size dot paper in the enlargement (or reduction) is kept the same so that you may compare the sizes of the figures.

a. Copy the original figure on your dot paper and label the length of each side. Then scale the figure by 300%. That is, make another copy of the figure and multiply each of the side lengths by 3. Label the length of each new side. What do you notice about the two figures? Note the sides and the angles.

b. Refer to the darkened side on the original figure. Then darken the **corresponding** (matching) side on the copy. What is the length of this side on the original figure? What is the length of this side on the copy? Write and simplify the ratio of this pair of sides in the order $\frac{copy}{original}$.

c. Choose another pair of corresponding sides in the figures. Write and simplify the ratio of these sides in the order $\frac{copy}{original}$.

d. Predict the simplified ratio you would get for another pair of corresponding sides of the two figures. Now test your prediction. Write and simplify the ratio for the remaining pairs of corresponding sides. Was your prediction correct?

e. Compare your simplified ratios from parts (b), (c), and (d). What do you notice? How do your answers relate to the scale factor of 300%?

4-2.   Karen wants to try scaling the figure shown at right by
         50%. What do you think will happen to the figure?

    a.   Sketch the figure shown at right and make a copy of
         the figure scaled by 50% on your dot paper. What is
         the same about the copy and the original? What is
         different?

    b.   How is your copy different than the copy you made in problem 4-1?

    c.   Locate at least three pairs of corresponding sides. There are nine in all.
         Then write and simplify the ratio of each pair of corresponding sides in the
         order $\frac{copy}{original}$.

    d.   Compare the ratios from each pair of corresponding sides with the scale
         factor. What do you notice? How do your ratios compare to the scale
         factor?

4-3.   Examine the figure at right.

    a.   Use dot paper to sketch the original figure.

    b.   With your team, choose a scale factor the will make
         the figure larger. Sketch the copy. What was your
         scale factor? What is the ratio of the corresponding
         sides? How do the angles compare?

    c.   With your team, choose a scale factor that will make the figure smaller.
         Sketch the copy. What was your scale factor? What is the ratio of the
         corresponding sides? How do the angles compare?

4-4.   **Similar figures** are figures that have the same shape but are not necessarily the same size. One characteristic of similar shapes is that ratios of the sides of one figure to the corresponding sides of the other figure are all the same. Another characteristic is that the corresponding angles of the two figures are the same.

Patti claims she made a similar copy of each of the original figures shown in parts (a) and (b) below. For each pair of figures, write and simplify the ratios for each pair of corresponding sides in the order $\frac{copy}{original}$. Compare the ratios. Are the figures similar? That is, did Patti really make a copy?

a.   Original   Copy   b.   Original Copy

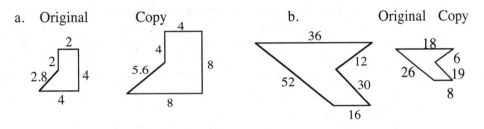

4-5.   **Additional Challenge:** Draw a rectangle on dot or graph paper. Then enlarge the sides of the rectangle using a scale factor of 3.

a.   Compute the perimeter and area of both the new and enlarged rectangles.

b.   Write and reduce each of the following ratios:

   $\frac{new\ perimeter}{original\ perimeter}$ $\frac{new\ area}{original\ area}$

c.   How does each ratio compare with the scale factor?

Ⓜ️ETHODS AND MEANINGS

Mathematical Properties

When two numbers or variables are combined using addition, the order in which they are added does not matter. For example, $7 + 5 = 5 + 7$. This fact is known as the **Commutative Property of Addition**.

Likewise, when two numbers are multiplied together, the order in which they are multiplied does not matter. For example, $5 \cdot 10 = 10 \cdot 5$. This fact is known as the **Commutative Property of Multiplication**.

These results can be generalized using variables:

$$a + b = b + a \text{ and } a \cdot b = b \cdot a$$

Note that subtraction and division do not satisfy the Commutative Property, since $7 - 5 \neq 5 - 7$ and $10 \div 5 \neq 5 \div 10$.

When three numbers are added, you usually add the first two of them and then add the third one to that result. However, you could also add the last two together and then add the first one to that result. The **Associative Property of Addition** tells you that the order in which the numbers are added together does not matter. The answer to the problem $(7 + 5) + 9$, for example, is the same as $7 + (5 + 9)$.

Likewise, when three numbers are multiplied together, which pair of numbers are multiplied together first does not matter. For example, $(5 \cdot (-6)) \cdot 10$ is the same as $5 \cdot (-6 \cdot 10)$. This is the **Associative Property of Multiplication**.

These results can be generalized using variables:

$$(a + b) + c = a + (b + c) \text{ and } (a \cdot b) \cdot c = a \cdot (b \cdot c)$$

Note that subtraction and division are *not* associative, since:

$$(7 - 5) - 1 \neq 7 - (5 - 1) \text{ and } (10 \div 2) \div 5 \neq 10 \div (2 \div 5).$$
$$2 - 1 \neq 7 - 4 \qquad\qquad 5 \div 5 \neq 10 \div 0.4$$

To multiply $8(24)$, written as $8(20 + 4)$, you can use the generic rectangle model at right.

	20	+ 4
8	$8 \cdot 20$	$8 \cdot 4$

The product is found by $8(20) + 8(4)$. So $8(20 + 4) = 8(20) + 8(4)$. This example illustrates the **Distributive Property**.

Symbolically, for any numbers a, b, and c: $a(b + c) = a(b) + a(c)$.

4-6. Simplify the expressions below.

    a. $8-13-(-4)$ b. $4-(-7)+(-2)$ c. $-7+3-20$

4-7. Copy each expression and simplify it. Show all of your steps.

    a. $1.234+0.58+5.316$ b. $6.1-1.536$ c. $4.8(0.6)$

4-8. Tina's rectangular living-room floor measures 15 feet by 18 feet.

    a. How many square feet of carpet will Tina need to cover the entire floor?

    b. The carpet Tina likes is sold by the square yard. How many square yards will she need? (1 yard = 3 feet)

4-9. Find the missing parts of each number line. Assume that the lines have been split into equal parts.

    a.   ?   0   42   b.   ?   0   64   c.   ?   0   24

4-10. Copy and simplify each expression.

    a. $7\cdot(-2)$ b. $-3\cdot10$

    c. $4\cdot(-3)$ d. $-8\cdot(-6)$

4.1.2 How can I use a scale drawing?

Scale Drawings

Maps are examples of **scale drawings**. They are reduced versions of the original regions. A map is **similar** to the original region, because it has the same shape. Because of this, maps conveniently allow users to determine distances between two points.

In a scale drawing, it is important to decide on the unit of measure. Maps made in the United States usually represent distances in miles, but they certainly cannot use actual miles as the unit of measure. Otherwise, a map of Pennsylvania would be over 250 miles long and 450 miles wide! A map includes a **scale**, which shows the units in which the map is drawn. An example is shown at right.

1 inch
5 miles

A

4-11. Suppose Eulalia uses a map of Pennsylvania to determine that Valley Forge is 14 miles from downtown Philadelphia. Did she really measure 14 miles? Explain how she probably determined the distance.

4-12. Guillermo needs a scale drawing of his house placed on its suburban lot. The lot is 56' wide and 100' deep. The garage is 20' back from the street. He has a sketch of his house – *not* drawn to scale – with the measurements shown at right.

a. Use graph paper and a ruler to create a scale drawing of Guillermo's house on its lot. Be sure to state your scale.

b. Guillermo wants to put a rectangular swimming pool in his backyard. What is the largest pool you would advise him to have installed?

Core Connections, Course 2

4-13. The scale drawing at right shows the first floor of a house. The actual dimensions of the garage are 20 feet by 25 feet. All angles are right angles.

a. How many feet does each inch represent? That is, what is the scale?

b. What are the length and width of the living room on the scale drawing (in inches)?

c. What are the actual length and width of the living room (in feet)?

d. If the family wants to lay carpet in the living room and carpeting costs $1.25 per square foot, how much will the carpet cost?

4-14. Use your ruler to complete the following problems.

a. Notice that the scale on the map shown above only gives kilometers and miles. Use your ruler to determine how many inches represent 0.5 miles.

b. What is the distance on the map from Sentinel Fall to Sentinel Dome, in inches?

c. What is the distance from Sentinel Fall to Sentinel Dome, in miles?

4-15. Hank is planning his vegetable garden. He has created the scale drawing below. The actual area for the tomatoes will be 12 feet by 9 feet. All angles are right angles.

a. What scale did Hank use?

b. If the horizontal length of the zucchini plot shown in the diagram is $1\frac{5}{8}$ inches, what is the area of the entire vegetable garden in square feet?

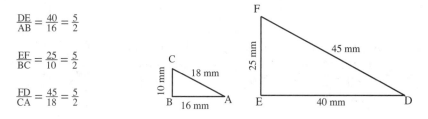

METHODS AND MEANINGS

MATH NOTES

Similarity and Scale Factor

Two figures are **similar** if they have the same shape but not necessarily the same size. In similar figures, the lengths of all corresponding pairs of sides have the same ratio and the measures of corresponding angles are equal.

A **scale factor** compares the sizes of the parts of the scale drawing of an object with the actual sizes of the corresponding parts of the object itself. The scale factor in similar figures is the simplified ratio of any pair of corresponding sides.

Example: $\triangle ABC$ is the original triangle.

$\frac{DE}{AB} = \frac{40}{16} = \frac{5}{2}$

$\frac{EF}{BC} = \frac{25}{10} = \frac{5}{2}$

$\frac{FD}{CA} = \frac{45}{18} = \frac{5}{2}$

The simplified ratio of every pair of corresponding sides is the same. The scale factor is $\frac{5}{2}$.

Review & Preview

4-16.   Draw a diagram that could be represented by each of the following number expressions. Then circle the terms and calculate the value of each expression.

a. $4 + 2(5) + (-3)$

b. $4 + 2(5 + (-3))$

4-17.   While Mrs. Poppington was visiting the historic
         battleground at Gettysburg, she talked with the
         landscapers who were replacing the sod in a park
         near the visitor center. The part of the lawn being
         replaced is shown in the diagram at right.
         Measurements are in yards. The diagram is not
         drawn to scale, but all corners are right angles.

   a.   Use your ruler to make a scale drawing of the lawn that is being replaced.
        Let $\frac{1}{4}$ inch equal 1 yard.

   b.   How many square yards of sod will be needed?

   c.   At $2.43 a square yard, how much will the sod cost?

   d.   The area will be surrounded by a temporary fence that costs $0.25 per
        linear foot to rent. How many feet will be needed, and how much will
        it cost?

   e.   What will be the total cost of materials for the sod and fencing?

4-18.   Troy has a number cube with the numbers 1 through 6 on it. Assuming each
         side is equally likely to appear when he rolls the cube, find the following
         probabilities. Note: When two or more numbers are multiplied, each of the
         numbers is a factor of the product.

   a.   P(rolls a 2)   b.   P(rolls an odd number)

   c.   P(rolls a factor of 6)

4-19.   Copy and complete each of the Diamond Problems below.
         The pattern used in the Diamond Problems is shown at right.

   a.   b.   c.   d.

4-20.   Simplify each expression below.

   a. $(4.76)(12.5)$ b. $45.6 + 23.68$

   c. $48 - 12.62$ d. $10(0.034)$

   e. $368.9 - 234.78$ f. $13.6 + 23.05 + 0.781$

4.2.1 How does it grow?

Recognizing Proportional Relationships

Grocery stores often advertise special prices for fruits and vegetables that are in season. You might see a sign that says, "Special Today! Buy 2 pounds of apples for $1.29!" How would you use that information to predict how much you need to pay if you want to buy six pounds of apples? Or just 1 pound of apples? The way that the cost of apples grows or shrinks allows you to use a variety of different strategies to predict and estimate prices for different amounts of apples. In this section, you will explore different kinds of growth patterns. You will use those patterns to develop strategies for making predictions and deciding if answers are reasonable.

As you work in this section, ask yourself these questions to help you identify different patterns:

How are the entries in the table related?

Can I double the values?

What patterns can I see in a graph?

4-21.   COLLEGE FUND

Five years ago, Gustavo's grandmother put some money in a college savings account for him on his birthday. The account pays simple interest, and now, after five years, the account is worth $500. Gustavo predicts that if he does not deposit or withdraw any money, then the account balance will be $1000 five years from now.

a.   How do you think Gustavo made his prediction?

b.   Do you agree with Gustavo's reasoning? Explain why or why not.

4-22.   Last week, Gustavo got his bank statement in the mail. He was surprised to see a graph that showed that, although his balance was growing at a steady rate, the bank predicted that in five years his account balance would be only $600. *"What is going on?"* he wondered. *"Why isn't my money growing the way I thought it would?"*

With your team, discuss how much Gustavo's account appears to be growing every year. Why might his account be growing in a different way than he expected? Be ready to share your ideas.

4-23.   Gustavo decided to look more carefully at his balances for the last few years to
         see if the bank's prediction might be a mistake. He put together the table
         below.

Time Since Original Deposit (years)	2	3	4	5
Bank Balance (dollars)	440	460	480	500

   a.   How has Gustavo's bank balance been growing?

   b.   Does Gustavo's money seem to be doubling as the number of years
        doubles? Explain your reasoning.

   c.   Is the bank's prediction a mistake? Explain your answer.

4-24.   Once Gustavo saw the balances written in a
         table, he decided to take a closer look at the
         graph from the bank to see if he could figure
         out where he made the mistake in his
         prediction. Find the graph at right on the
         Lesson 4.2.1 Resource Page.

   a.   There is additional information about
        Gustavo's account that you can tell from
        the graph. For example, what was his
        starting balance? How much does it
        grow in 5 years?

   b.   Gustavo had assumed his money would double after 10 years. What would
        the graph look like if that were true? Using a different color, add a line to
        the graph that represents what Gustavo was thinking.

   c.   Is it possible that Gustavo's account could have had $0 in it in Year 0?
        Why or why not?

4-25.   FOR THE BIRDS

When filling her bird feeder, Sonja noticed that she
paid $27 for four pounds of bulk birdseed. *"Next time,
I'm going to buy 8 pounds instead so I can make it
through the spring. That should cost $54."*

a.   Does Sonja's assumption that doubling the amount
     of birdseed would double the price make sense?
     Why or why not? How much would you predict
     that 2 pounds of birdseed would cost?

b.   To check her assumption, she found a receipt for 1 pound of birdseed. She
     decided to make a table, which is started below. Copy and complete her
     table.

Pounds	0	1	2	3	4	5	6	8
Cost		$6.75			$27			

c.   How do the amounts in the table grow?

d.   Does the table confirm Sonja's doubling relationship? Give two examples
     from the table that show how doubling the pounds will double the cost.

4-26.   What makes Sonja's birdseed situation (problem 4-25) different from Gustavo's college fund situation (problem 4-21)? Why does doubling work for one situation but not in the other? Consider this as you examine the graphs below.

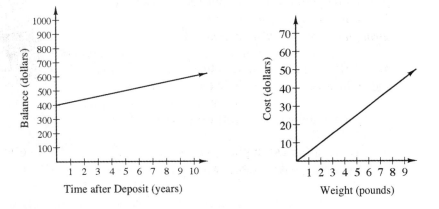

a.   With your team:

•   Describe how each graph is the same.

•   Describe what makes each graph different.

b.   How do the differences explain why doubling works in one situation and not in the other? Generalize why doubling works in one situation and not in another.

c.   The pattern of growth in Sonja's example of buying birdseed is an example of a **proportional relationship**. In a proportional relationship, if one quantity is multiplied by a scale factor, the other is scaled by the same amount. Gustavo's bank account is *not* proportional, because it grows differently; when the number of years doubled, his balance did not.

Work with your team to list other characteristics of proportional relationships, based on Sonja's and Gustavo's examples. Be as specific as possible.

4-27.   IS IT PROPORTIONAL?

When you are making a prediction, it is important to be able to recognize whether a relationship is proportional or not.

Your Task: Work with your team to read each new situation below. Decide whether you think the relationship described is **proportional** or **non-proportional** and justify your reasoning. Be prepared to share your decisions and justifications with the class.

a.   Carlos wants to buy some new video games. Each game he buys costs him $36. Is the relationship between the number of games Carlos buys and the total price proportional?

b.   A single ticket to a concert costs $56, while buying five tickets costs $250. Is the relationship between the number of tickets bought and the total price proportional?

c.   Vu is four years older than his sister. Is the relationship between Vu and his sister's age proportional?

d.   Janna runs at a steady pace of 7 minutes per mile. Is the relationship between the number of miles she ran and the distance she covered proportional?

e.   Carl just bought a music player and plans to load 50 songs each week. Is the relationship between the number of weeks after Carl bought the music player and the number of songs on his player proportional?

f.   Anna has a new video game. It takes her five hours of playing the game to master level one. After so much time, Anna understands the game better and it only takes her three hours of playing the game to master level two. Is the number of hours played and the game level proportional?

4-28.   LEARNING LOG

In your Learning Log, explain how you can tell if a relationship is proportional. Give several examples of a proportional relationship and at least one that is not proportional. Label this entry "Recognizing Proportional Relationships" and include today's date.

# of Lemonades	Price ($)
1	
2	3.60
3	
4	
5	
6	
7	
8	

4-29. The lemonade stand at the county fair sells the lemonade at a price of two cups for $3.60. Complete the table at right to find what Paula's family will pay to buy lemonade for all eight members of the family.

4-30. Carmen is downloading music for her πPod. Each song costs $1.75. Is this relationship proportional? Explain your reasoning. What is the cost for five songs?

4-31. Simplify each expression.

a. −3 + 7

b. 7 + (−8)

c. −6 − 9

d. −3 + 4(−2)

e. 4 − 2(−5)

f. (−7 + 3)(4 − 5·2)

4-32. Copy and complete each of the Diamond Problems below. The pattern used in the Diamond Problems is shown at right.

a.   b.   c.   d.

4-33. Lucy keeps track of how long it takes her to do the newspaper's crossword puzzle each day. Her recent times, in minutes, were:

8   22   19   12   18   19   10   35   12   19   16   21

a. What is the median of her data?   b. What is the mean?

4.2.2 How can I see a proportion?

Proportional Relationships with Tables and Graphs

In Lesson 4.2.1, you learned that you could identify proportional relationships by looking for a constant multiplier. In fact, you have already seen a relationship with a constant multiplier in this course. Today you will revisit the earlier situation that contains a proportional relationship.

4-34.   GRAPHING THE PENNY-TOWER DATA

In Chapter 1, you found a multiplicative (or proportional) relationship between the height of a stack of pennies and the number of pennies in the stack. That is, you could always find one piece of information by multiplying the other by a constant number.

Height of Tower (cm)	# of Pennies
1	
15	
4	28
	63
3	
12	

a.   Copy the table at right and work with your team to fill in the missing values. What strategies did you use to determine the missing numbers?

b.   How many pennies are in a tower with a height of 0 cm? Add a row to your table with this value.

c.   Graph this data. Be sure to scale the axes so that all of the points in your table are visible on your graph.

d.   What do you notice about the graph of height and the number of pennies? How does this graph compare to Sonja's graph of birdseed weight and cost that you made in Lesson 4.2.1? What do the graphs have in common? How are they different?

4-35.   Kaci loves cheese and buys it whenever she can. Recently, she bought 5 pounds of mozzarella cheese for $15.00 and 3 pounds of havarti for $7.50.

a.   Obtain a copy of the Lesson 4.2.2 Resource Page for each member of your team. Then work together to record, plot, and label Kaci's two cheese purchases.

b.   With your team, find another point that you could plot on the graph for *each* kind of cheese. Record these points in the tables. That is, find another combination of pounds of cheese and the associated cost for the mozzarella and then another combination of pounds and cost for the havarti.

c.   Work with your team to discuss and answer the following questions. Then decide how best to complete the two tables and graphs that you started in parts (a) and (b).

  • Can you find any other points that should be in the mozzarella table and graph? Add them.

  • Can you find any other points that should be in the havarti table and graph? Add them.

  • Should the points on each graph be connected? If so, why does that make sense? If not, why not?

d.   How do the graphs for each type of cheese compare? What is the same and what is different?

e.   Which cheese is more expensive (costs more per pound)? How can you tell by looking at the graph? How can you tell by looking at the table?

f.   What is significant about the point $(1, y)$ for each line on the graph or in your table?

4-36.   Look back at the tables and graphs you created for proportional relationships in the previous problems.

a.   How can you use a table to decide if a relationship is proportional?

b.   How can you use a graph to decide if a relationship is proportional?

4-37.   Which of the tables below shows a proportional relationship between x and y?
How can you tell?

a.

x	y
1	2
2	4
3	6
4	8

b.

x	y
1	2
2	3
3	4
4	5

4-38.   The following graphs show examples of relationships that are *not* proportional.
For each graph, explain what makes the relationship different from the
proportional relationships you have studied.

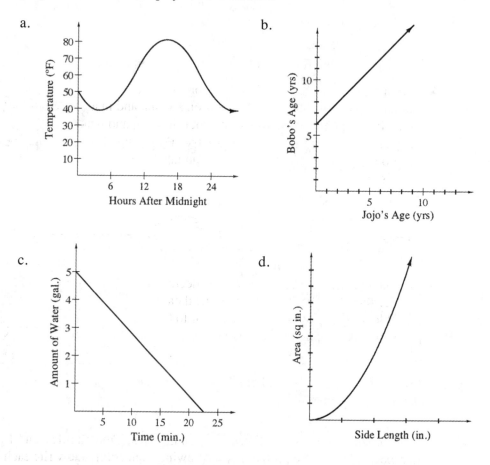

a.

b.

c.

d.

4-39. Use your understanding of proportions to help Kaci find each of the missing quantities below, using the information given in problem 4-35. Be prepared to explain your strategies.

   a. How much do 7.5 pounds of mozzarella cheese cost?

   b. How much do 1.5 pounds of havarti cheese cost?

   c. How much mozzarella cheese can Kaci buy for $12?

   d. How much havarti cheese can Kaci buy for $10?

   e. **Challenge:** Write an equation relating the amount of cheese to the cost of the cheese. Verify that you get the same answers for parts (a) through (d) above when using your equation.

4-40. LEARNING LOG

In your Learning Log, explain what a proportional relationship is and how you can see it on a graph and in a table. Include diagrams to illustrate your thinking and make an example of your own. Title this entry "Proportional Relationships in Graphs and Tables" and label it with today's date.

4-41. On your own graph paper, draw axes, decide on a scale, and plot points to represent the data in the table at right. Does this data appear to be proportional? Explain why or why not.

Quantity x	Quantity y
2	6.3
6	18.9
9	28.35
5	15.75
1	3.15

4-42. A bag contains 4 brown marbles, 3 green marbles, 2 red marbles, and 1 purple marble. Calculate the probability of drawing each color, and write each answer as a fraction, as a percent, and as a decimal.

4-43.   Each of the diagrams below represents a sequence for a tightrope walker. For each one, explain the sequence and find the length of the unknown trick.

a.

b.

4-44.   Identify the mathematical property, operation, or idea that justifies each sequence of expressions below. Then find the value of the expression.

a. $7 \cdot 2 + 4 - 2(7 + 3)$
     $7 \cdot 2 + 4 - 2(7) - 2(3)$
     $7 \cdot 2 - 7(2) + 4 - 2(3)$

b. $6 \cdot 3 + 3 \cdot 4 - 8$
     $18 + 12 - 8$
     $18 - 8 + 12$

c. $3^2 + 5(1 - 3) + 4 \cdot 5 + 1$
     $3^2 + 4 \cdot 5 + 1 + 5(-2)$
     $9 + 20 + 1 - 10$

d. $\left(8 + (-12)\right) + 10 + 2$
     $8 + (-12 + 10 + 2)$

4-45.   Write three different sentences that could describe the relationship between the quantities below.

$$\$27, \$81$$

4.2.3 How can a graph help?

Unit Rate and Proportional Equations

Proportional relationships can be identified in both tables and graphs. Today you will have an opportunity to take a closer look at how graphs and tables for proportional relationships can help you organize your work to find any missing value quickly and easily.

4-46. Robert's new hybrid car has a gas tank that holds 12 gallons of gas. When the tank is full, he can drive 420 miles. Assume that his car uses gas at a steady rate.

a. Is the relationship between the number of gallons of gas used and the number of miles that can be driven proportional? For example, does it change like Sonja's birdseed prediction, or is it more like Gustavo's college savings? Explain how you know.

b. Show how much gas Robert's car will use at various distances by copying and completing the table below.

Gas used (gallons)	0	3	6	12
Distance driven (miles)				420

c. Robert decided to graph the situation, as shown at right. The distance Robert can travel using one gallon of gas is called the **unit rate**. Use Robert's graph to predict how far he can drive using one gallon of gas. That is, find his unit rate.

d. While a graph is a useful tool for estimating, it is often difficult to find an exact answer on a graph. What is significant about the point labeled $(1, y)$? How can you calculate y?

e. Use the table in part (b) and your result in part (d) to find Robert's unit rate.

f. Work with your team to write the equation to find the exact number of miles Robert can drive with any number of gallons of gas. Be prepared to share your strategy.

g. Use your equation to find out how many gallons of gas Robert will need to drive 287 miles.

4-47.   THE YOGURT SHOP

Jell E. Bean owns the local frozen yogurt
shop. At her store, customers serve
themselves a bowl of frozen yogurt and
top it with chocolate chips, frozen
raspberries, and any of the different
treats available. Customers must then
weigh their creations and are charged by
the weight of their bowls.

Jell E. Bean charges $32 for five pounds of dessert, but not many people buy
that much frozen yogurt. She needs you to help her figure out how much to
charge her customers. She has customers that are young children who buy only
a small amount of yogurt as well as large groups that come in and pay for
everyone's yogurt together.

a.   Is it reasonable to assume that the weight of the yogurt is proportional to its
     cost? How can you tell?

b.   Assuming it is proportional, make a table that lists the price for at least ten
     different weights of yogurt. Be sure to include at least three weights that
     are not whole numbers.

c.   What is the unit rate of the yogurt? (Stores often call this the unit price.)
     Use the unit rate to write an equation that Jell E. Bean can use to calculate
     the amount any customer will pay.

d.   If Jell E. Bean decided to start charging $0.50 for each cup before her
     customers started filling it with yogurt and toppings, could you use the
     same equation to find the new prices? Why or why not?

4-48.   Lexie claims that she can send 14 text messages in 22 minutes. Her teammates Kenny and Esther are trying to predict how many text messages Lexie can send in a 55-minute lunch period if she keeps going at the same rate.

   a.   Is the relationship between the number of text messages and time in minutes proportional? Why or why not?

   b.   Kenny represented the situation using the table shown below. Explain Kenny's strategy for using the table.

Kenny's work

Messages	Minutes
14	22
7	11
	55

   c.   Esther wants to solve the problem using an equation. Help her write an equation to determine how many text messages Lexie could send in any number of minutes.

   d.   Find the missing value in Kenny's table.

   e.   Solve Esther's equation. Will she get the same answer as Kenny?

   f.   What is Lexie's unit rate? That is, how many text messages can she send in 1 minute?

4-49.   **Additional Challenge:** Use your reasoning skills to compute each unit rate (the price per pound).

   a. $4.20 for $\frac{1}{2}$ pound of cheese

   b. $1.50 for $\frac{2}{3}$ pound of bananas

   c. $6.00 for $\frac{3}{4}$ pound of deli roast beef

   d. $7.50 for $\frac{5}{6}$ pound of sliced turkey

METHODS AND MEANINGS

Proportional Relationships

A relationship is **proportional** if one quantity is a multiple of the other. This relationship can be identified in tables, graphs, and equations.

Table: Equivalent ratios of $\frac{y}{x}$ (or $\frac{x}{y}$) can be seen in a table.

Graph: A straight line through the origin.

Equation: An equation of the form $y = kx$ where k is the **constant of proportionality**.

Example: Three pounds of chicken cost $7.00. What is the cost for x pounds?

Equation: $y = \frac{7}{3}x$

Pounds (x)	0	3	6	9	12
Cost (y)	0	7	14	21	28

The relationship between pounds and cost is proportional. The table has equivalent ratios ($\frac{7}{3} = \frac{14}{6} = \frac{21}{9}$), the graph is a straight line through the origin, and the equation is of the form $y = kx$.

Example: The county fair costs $5.00 to enter and $1.00 per ride.

Equation: $y = 1x + 5$

Rides (x)	0	1	2	3	4
Cost (y)	5	6	7	8	9

The relationship between rides and cost is not proportional, because the table does not contain equivalent ratios ($\frac{6}{1} \neq \frac{7}{2} \neq \frac{8}{3}$), the graph does not pass through the origin, and the equation contains addition.

4-50.   Complete the proportion table below and graph the results.

Pounds of Nails	2	3		6		10		x
Cost ($)			2.15	2.58	3.44		8.60	

   a.   What is the unit rate (price) of the graph?

   b.   What does the unit rate (price) tell you about the cost of the nails?

4-51.   The choir is planning a trip to the water park. The cost to use a school bus is $350. Complete the table at right then graph your result. Is this a proportional relationship?

Number of Students on the Trip	Bus Cost per Student ($)
10	
15	
20	
35	

4-52.   Paige traveled to Australia and is making her favorite bread recipe. She usually bakes the bread in a 350°F oven. She is surprised to learn that the oven temperatures in Australia are measured in degrees Celsius. In the formula at right, F stands for Fahrenheit and C stands for Celsius. Use the formula and the Order of Operations to help Paige determine how she should set the oven in degrees Celsius.

$$C = \frac{5(F-32)}{9}$$

4-53.   Simplify each of the following expressions.

   a. $\frac{2}{5} - \frac{1}{6}$

   b. $\frac{3}{7} - \frac{7}{14}$

   c. $\frac{5}{8} - \frac{2}{3}$

4-54.   The probability of getting a white marble from a bag is $\frac{1}{5}$. If there are 37 white marbles in the bag, what is the total number of marbles in the bag?

4.2.4 What are the connections?

Connecting Representations of Proportional Relationships

In the previous lessons, you studied different ways to represent proportional relationships. You organized information into tables and graphs. You also wrote equations modeling the proportional relationships. Proportional relationship equations are of the form $y = kx$, where k is the **constant of proportionality**. Today you will find connections between different representations of the same proportional relationship, explore each representation more deeply, and learn shorter ways to go from one representation to another. As you work today, keep these questions in mind:

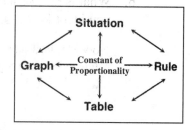

How can you see growth in the rule?

How do you know your rule is correct?

What does the representation tell you?

What are the connections between the representations?

4-55. Graeme earns $4.23 for each half-hour that he works. How much money does he earn during a given amount of time?

    a. Represent this situation using a table.

    b. What is the constant of proportionality (or the unit rate)? How can you find it from a table?

    c. How can you use a table to determine if a relationship is proportional?

4-56. Jamie ran 9.3 miles in 1.5 hours. How far can she run in a given amount of time, if she runs at a constant rate?

    a. Represent this situation with a graph.

    b. What is the constant of proportionality? How can you find it on a graph?

    c. How can you use a graph to determine if a relationship is proportional?

4-57.   A recipe calls for $2\frac{2}{3}$ cups of flour to make two regular batches of cookies. Shiloh needs to make multiple batches of cookies.

   a.   Represent this situation with an equation.

   b.   What is the constant of proportionality? How can you identify it in an equation?

   c.   How can you use an equation to determine if a relationship is proportional?

4-58.   CONNECTIONS WEB FOR PROPORTIONAL RELATIONSHIPS

   Your teacher will assign your team a situation from the previous problems. Your team's task is to create a poster showing every way you can represent the proportional relationship and the connections between each representation. Use the web at right to help you get started.

4-59.   LEARNING LOG

   In your Learning Log, create a generic connections web for proportional relationships. For each representation, explain how you know the relationship is proportional. Title this entry "Connections Web for Proportional Relationships" and label it with today's date.

METHODS AND MEANINGS

Unit Rate

A **rate** is a ratio that compares, by division, the amount one quantity changes as another quantity changes.

$$\text{rate} = \frac{\text{change in one quantity}}{\text{change in another quantity}}$$

A **unit rate** is a rate that compares the change in one quantity to a one unit change in another quantity. For example, *miles per hour* is a unit rate, because it compares the change in miles to a change of one hour. If an airplane flies 3000 miles in 5 hours and uses 6000 gallons of fuel, you can compute several unit rates.

It uses $\frac{6000 \text{ gallons}}{5 \text{ hours}} = \frac{1200 \text{ gallons}}{1 \text{ hour}}$ or $\frac{6000 \text{ gallons}}{3000 \text{ miles}} = \frac{2 \text{ gallons}}{1 \text{ mile}}$.

It travels at $\frac{3000 \text{ miles}}{5 \text{ hours}} = \frac{600 \text{ miles}}{1 \text{ hour}}$.

Review & Preview

4-60.   Is the relationship shown in the table at right proportional? If so, use it to complete a Proportions Web. If not, explain why it is not.

Hours Worked	Amount of Dirt Excavated (cubic yards)
3	6.6
4	8.8
8	17.6
9	19.8

4-61.   In a recent snail race, the winning snail traveled 5.85 cm in $\frac{3}{4}$ of a minute. How fast was the snail traveling in centimeters per second?

4-62.   Find the area and perimeter of the shape at right.

Core Connections, Course 2

4-63.   Circle terms and simplify each of the following expressions.

   a. $3+1\cdot4+(-7)$

   b. $50+3(-10)+2(-20)$

   c. $4+(-50)\cdot2$

   d. $(4+(-170))(5+(-4))$

4-64.   CECIL'S LATEST TRICK

   To amaze the audience, Cecil set up four tightropes
   in a rectangle, each connected at a pole as shown in
   the diagram at right. A ladder down from the ropes
   is located at point A.

12 feet

15 feet

   a.   If Cecil starts at point A and must travel completely
        around the rectangle, how far must Cecil travel?

   b.   How can Cecil's distance be represented by an expression?

4-65.   State whether each equation below represents a proportional relationship. How
         can you tell?

   a. $y=x+2.3$ b. $y=\frac{6}{13}x$ c. $7-y=2x$

4-66.   A stack of six bricks is two feet high. Use that information to answer the
         questions below.

   a.   How many bricks are in a stack 20 feet high?

   b.   How high is a stack of 20 bricks?

4-67.   Alexa is looking at the shape at right. She needs to
         make several different figures that are similar to it.

   a.   If she uses the scale factor $\frac{8}{5}$, will the new shape
        that she creates be larger or smaller than the
        original? Justify your answer.

   b.   List two different scale factors Alexa could use to make a smaller shape.

   c.   List two different scale factors Alexa could use to make a larger shape.

4-68.   Kirk is helping his grandparents set up their new portable music players. His grandmother, Maude, has 1 jazz album, 2 country-western albums, and 5 heavy-metal albums. Kirk's grandfather, Claude, has 3 classical albums, 2 rap albums, and 7 heavy-metal albums.

If Kirk's grandparents' portable music players are on random shuffle mode, who has the greater chance of listening to a heavy-metal album? Explain how you know.

4-69.   At your first job, you may be amazed to learn that one fourth of your paycheck will go to pay taxes.

Suppose the amounts listed in parts (a) through (c) below are the earnings for three employees. Determine how much of each paycheck will go to pay taxes.

a. $84   b. $128   c. $210

$4.3.1$ How can I simplify?

Combining Like Terms

Mathematics can be used to describe patterns in the world. Scientists use math to describe various aspects of life, including how cells multiply, how objects move through space, and how chemicals react. Often, when scientists try to describe these patterns, they need to describe something that changes or varies. Scientists call the quantities that change **variables**, and they represent them using letters and symbols.

In this course, you will spend time learning about variables, what they can represent, and how they serve different purposes. To start, you will use variables to describe the dimensions and areas of different shapes. You will begin to organize the descriptions into **algebraic expressions**.

As you work with your teammates, use these questions to help focus your team's discussion:

How can you organize groups of things?

What is the area?

Which lengths can vary?

Core Connections, Course 2

4-70.   AREA OF ALGEBRA TILES

Your teacher will provide your team with a set of algebra tiles. Remove one of each shape from the bag and put it on your desk. Trace around each shape on your paper. Look at the different sides of the shapes.

a.   With your team, discuss which shapes have the same side lengths and which ones have different side lengths. Be prepared to share your ideas with the class. On your traced drawings, color-code lengths that are the same.

b.   Each type of tile is named for its area. In this course, the smallest square will have a side length of 1 unit, so its area is 1 square unit. This tile will be called "one" or the "unit tile." Can you use the unit tile to find the side lengths of the other rectangles? Why or why not?

c.   If the side lengths of a tile can be measured exactly, then the area of the tile can be calculated by multiplying these two lengths together. The area is measured in square units. For example, the tile at right measures 1 unit by 5 units, so it has an area of 5 square units.

The next tile at right has one side length that is exactly one unit long. If the other side length cannot have a numerical value, what can it be called?

d.   If the unknown length is called "x," label the side lengths of each of the four algebra tiles you traced. Find each area and use it to name each tile. Be sure to include the name of the type of units it represents.

4-71.   When a collection of algebra tiles is described with mathematical symbols, it is called an **algebraic expression**. Take out the tiles shown in the picture below. Then work with your team to do the following tasks.

- Use mathematical symbols (numbers, variables, and operations) to record the area of this collection of tiles.

- Write at least three different algebraic expressions that represent the area of this tile collection.

4-72.   Put the tiles pictured in each collection below on your table. Then work with your team to find the area as you did in problem 4-71.

a.

b.

c.

4-73.   The perimeter of each algebra tile can be also written as an expression using variables and numbers.

a. Write at least two different expressions for the perimeter of each tile shown at right.

b. Which way of writing the perimeter seems clearest to you? What information can you get from each expression?

c. Lianna wrote the perimeter of the collection of tiles at right as $2x+1+1+1+2x+1$ units, but her teammate Jonah wrote it as $4x+4$. How are their expressions different?

d. Which expression represents the perimeter?

4-74. The expressions that you have written to represent area and perimeter are made up of **terms** that are separated by addition and subtraction.

a. Write an expression for the perimeter of the figure at right.

b. How many x lengths are represented in the expression in part (a)? How many unit lengths?

c. **Combining like terms** (like terms contain the same variable raised to the same power) is a way of simplifying an expression. Rewriting the perimeter of the shape above as $P = 4x + 6$ **combines** the separate x-terms as $4x$ and combines the units in the term 6.

If you have not already done so, combine like terms for the perimeter expressions that you wrote in problem 4-73.

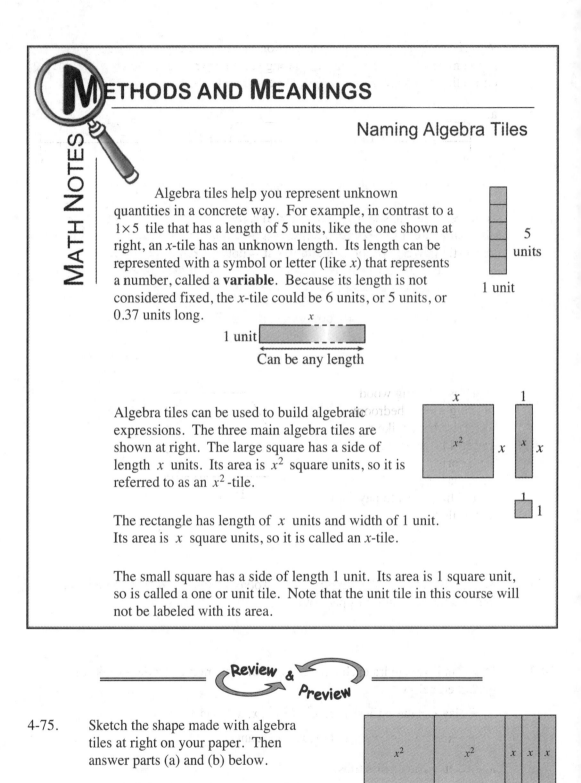

Ⓜ️ETHODS AND MEANINGS

Naming Algebra Tiles

MATH NOTES

Algebra tiles help you represent unknown quantities in a concrete way. For example, in contrast to a 1×5 tile that has a length of 5 units, like the one shown at right, an x-tile has an unknown length. Its length can be represented with a symbol or letter (like x) that represents a number, called a **variable**. Because its length is not considered fixed, the x-tile could be 6 units, or 5 units, or 0.37 units long.

5 units

1 unit

x

1 unit

Can be any length

Algebra tiles can be used to build algebraic expressions. The three main algebra tiles are shown at right. The large square has a side of length x units. Its area is x^2 square units, so it is referred to as an x^2-tile.

x 1

x^2 x | x | x

1

The rectangle has length of x units and width of 1 unit. Its area is x square units, so it is called an x-tile.

The small square has a side of length 1 unit. Its area is 1 square unit, so is called a one or unit tile. Note that the unit tile in this course will not be labeled with its area.

Review & Preview

4-75.   Sketch the shape made with algebra tiles at right on your paper. Then answer parts (a) and (b) below.

x^2 x^2 x | x | x

a.   Find the area and perimeter of the shape.

b.   If the algebra tiles were rearranged into a different shape, how would the area change?

4-76.   What is the length of the marked portion of each line segment? Copy the
         segment onto your paper before finding the missing length. Assume that the
         entire line segment is subdivided into equal sections.

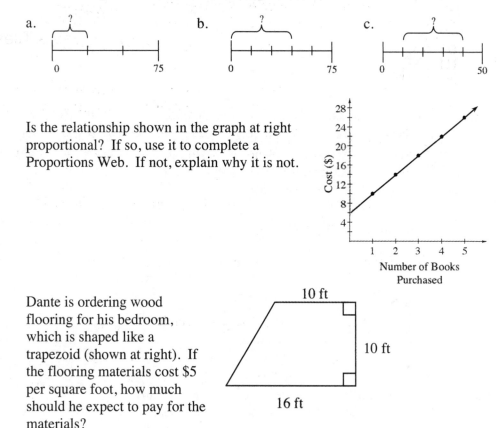

a.   b.   c.

0   75   0   75   0   50

4-77.   Is the relationship shown in the graph at right
         proportional? If so, use it to complete a
         Proportions Web. If not, explain why it is not.

4-78.   Dante is ordering wood
         flooring for his bedroom,
         which is shaped like a
         trapezoid (shown at right). If
         the flooring materials cost $5
         per square foot, how much
         should he expect to pay for the
         materials?

4-79.   Sammy is training for a running race. Today he ran $3\frac{3}{5}$ miles in 33 minutes.
         What is his pace in miles per hour?

4-80.   Daisy and Alexandra each have a group of algebra tiles on their desks as
         described below.

         Daisy has these tiles: $x, x, x^2, 1, x^2, x, x^2$, and x.

         Alexandra has $x^2, x, 1, 1, 1, x, x^2, x$, and 1.

         a.   Sketch each girl's tiles.

         b.   If the girls put their tiles together, how many of each type of tile will they
              have? Write an expression that represents this sum.

4-81.   Copy and complete the portions web at right.

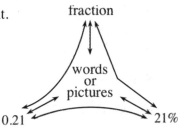

4-82.   For each shape drawn below, choose one of the names on the list above them
that best describes that shape. Be as specific as you can. If you do not
remember what one of the shape names means, you may look in the glossary of
this book for more information.

right triangle	scalene triangle	obtuse triangle
equilateral triangle	parallelogram	rectangle
rhombus	trapezoid	acute triangle

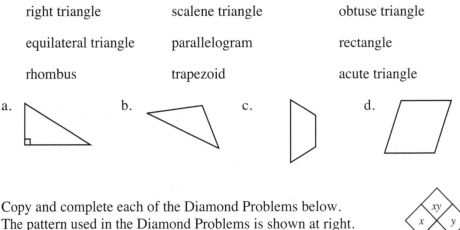

4-83.   Copy and complete each of the Diamond Problems below.
The pattern used in the Diamond Problems is shown at right.

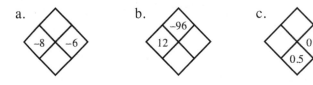

4-84.   Daniel needed to paint his patio, so he made a
scale drawing of it. He knows the width of the
patio is 10 feet, but the scale drawing is in inches.

a.   Find the length of the patio in feet.

b.   Find the area of the patio so Daniel knows
how much paint to buy.

c.   One can of paint covers 125 square feet. How many cans of paint will
Daniel need to buy?

Core Connections, Course 2

4.3.2   How can I group them?

Distributive Property

In Lesson 4.3.1, you used variables to name lengths that could not be precisely measured. Using variables allows you to work with lengths that you do not know exactly. Today you will work with your team to write expressions for the perimeters of different shapes using variables. As you work with your teammates, use these questions to help focus your team's discussion:

Which lengths can vary?

How can you see the perimeter?

How can you organize groups of things?

4-85.   Using algebra tiles on your desk, make the shapes shown below. Trace each shape and label the length of each side on your drawing. With your team, find and record the total perimeter and area for each shape. If possible, write the perimeter in more than one way.

a.

b.

c.

4-86.   In problem 4-85, x is a variable that represents a number of units of length. The value of x determines the size of the perimeter and area of the shape.

Using the shapes from problem 4-85, sketch and label each shape with the new lengths given below. Then **evaluate** each expression for the given value of the variable. That is, rewrite the expressions, replacing the variable with the number given, and then simplify them to determine the perimeter and area of each shape.

a. $x = 6$ for all three shapes

b. $x = \frac{1}{2}$ for all three shapes

c.   Compare your method for finding perimeter and area with the method your teammates used. Is your method the same as your teammates' methods? If so, is there a different way to find the perimeter and area? Explain the different methods.

4-87.   Build each of the shapes below using algebra tiles. Look carefully at the lengths of the right sides.

i.

ii.

a.   Discuss with your team how to label the length of the right side of each figure. Label each length on your paper. Explain your reasoning.

b.   Find the perimeter of each figure. Write the perimeter in simplest form by combining the like terms.

4-88.   Build the shape at right using algebra tiles. Then, on graph paper, draw the shape when x is equal to each of the lengths below.

a. $x = 5$ units   b. $x = 3$ units   c. $x = 2$ units   d. $x = 1$ unit

4-89. Parentheses in an algebraic expression allow you to show that tiles are grouped together.

    a. Build these steps with algebra tiles. Use an x tile to represent "any number."

               1. Think of any number.

               2. Triple it.

               3. Add 1.

               4. Multiply by 2.

    b. Look at the algebra tiles you used to build the final step of part (a). Write two different algebraic expressions to represent those tiles.

4-90. Build the following expressions with algebra tiles. Then rewrite the expression a different way. Remember that parentheses in an algebraic expression allow you to show that tiles are grouped together.

    a. $4(2x+3)$ b. $12x+18$

    c. $10+15x$ (Hint: Divide into as many equally-sized groups as possible)

4-91. You have been writing expressions in different ways to mean the same thing. These expressions depend on whether you see tiles grouped (like four sets of $2x+3$ in part (a) of problem 4-90) or whether you see separate tiles (eight x-tiles and 12 unit tiles). These two expressions are equivalent based on a mathematical property called the **Distributive Property**.

Use the Distributive Property to write an equivalent expression for $21x+7$. See if you can do it by visualizing tiles.

4-92. **LEARNING LOG**

In your Learning Log, explain what you know now about the Distributive Property and how to use it to write equivalent expressions. Include an example of different ways to write an expression with numbers and with variables, such as $3(x+4)$, by drawing pictures and writing equivalent expressions. Title this entry "Distributive Property" and include today's date.

METHODS AND MEANINGS

Combining Like Terms

This course uses tiles to represent variables and single numbers (called **constant terms**). Combining tiles that have the same area to write a simpler expression is called **combining like terms**. See the example shown at right.

$$x^2 + 2x + 2$$

More formally, **like terms** are two or more terms that have the same variable(s), with the corresponding variable(s) raised to the same power.

Examples of like terms: $2x^2$ and $-5x^2$, $4ab$ and $3ab$.

Examples that are *not* like terms: 5 and $3x$, $5x$ and $7x^2$, a^2b and ab.

When you are not working with the actual tiles, it helps to visualize them in your mind. You can use these images to combine those terms that are the same. Here are two examples:

Example 1: $2x^2 + x + 3 + x^2 + 5x + 2$ is equivalent to $3x^2 + 6x + 5$.

Example 2: $3x^2 + 2x + 7 - 2x^2 - x + 7$ is equivalent to $x^2 + x + 14$.

When several tiles are pushed together and form a more complicated figure, the area of the new figure is the sum of the areas of the individual pieces, and the perimeter is the sum of the lengths around the outside. Area and perimeter expressions can be **simplified**, or rewritten, by combining like terms.

For the figure at right, the perimeter is:
$x + 1 + x + 1 + 1 + 1 + 1 + 1 + x + x = 4x + 6$ units.

4-93.   Copy the diagrams of algebra tiles below on your paper. Then find the perimeter of each shape.

a.   b.

4-94.   Figures A and B at right are similar. Assuming that figure A is the original figure, find the scale factor and find the lengths of the missing sides of figure B.

4-95.   What fraction of one hour (60 minutes) is represented by the following numbers of minutes? Simplify each fraction whenever possible. A sketch of a clock might help you.

a.   10 minutes   b.   15 minutes   c.   30 minutes   d.   20 minutes

4-96.   Rainer bought 1.43 pounds of lunch meat at the store for $10.98. What was the unit rate (price) of the lunch meat?

4-97.   Use absolute value to write an expression describing the size of each amount.

a.   An elevation of 250 feet.

b.   A credit card balance of $23.75.

c.   A football player rushed for –5 yards.

d.   A bank balance of $198.32.

e.   An elevation of Death Valley of –86 m.

4-98.   Sketch the algebra tile shape shown at right on your
         paper. Then:

    • Write an expression for the area of the shape.

    • Write and simplify an expression for the
      perimeter of the shape.

    • Calculate the area and perimeter of the shape for each value of x.

    a. $x = 7$ b. $x = 2.5$ c. $x = 15$

4-99.   Find the perimeter of the figure at right.

4-100.   Multiply $\frac{4}{5} \cdot \frac{1}{3}$. You may want to show your
         thinking with a diagram.

4-101.   Copy and simplify each expression.

    a. $-2 + 5$ b. $(-4) \cdot (6)$ c. $4 - (-3)$

    d. $10 + (-2) - 7$ e. $-5 - 3(2 - 6)$ f. $(3 - 3)(10^2 - 11)$

4-102.   Copy and complete the portions web at right by
         including a picture, a decimal, and a percent
         representation of $\frac{9}{20}$.

         $\frac{9}{20}$

         words
         or
         pictures

         decimal   percent

4.3.3   How can I simplify with negatives?

Simplifying With Zero

In the previous lessons, you simplified and rewrote algebraic expressions. In this lesson, you will continue to explore various ways to make expressions simpler by finding parts of them that make zero.

Zero is a relative newcomer to the number system. Its first appearance was as a placeholder around 400 B.C. in Babylon. The Ancient Greeks philosophized about whether zero was even a number: *"How can nothing be something?"* East Indian mathematicians are generally recognized as the first people to represent the quantity zero as a numeral and number in its own right about 600 A.D.

Zero now holds an important place in mathematics both as a numeral representing the absence of quantity and as a placeholder. Did you know there is no year 0 in the Gregorian calendar system (our current calendar system of 365 days in a year)? Until the creation of zero, number systems began at one.

Consider the questions below as you work today.

How can I create a zero?

How can I rewrite this expression in the most efficient way?

4-103.   CONCEPTS OF ZERO

Zero is a special and unusual number. As you read above, it has an interesting history. What do you know about zero mathematically? The questions below will test your knowledge of zero.

a.   If two quantities are added and the sum is zero, what do you know about the quantities?

b.   If you add zero to a number, how does the number change?

c.   If you multiply a number by zero, what do you know about the product?

d.   What is the opposite of zero?

e.   If three numbers have a product of zero, what do you know about at least one of the numbers?

f.   Is zero even or odd?

4-104. When you use algebra tiles, +1 is represented with algebra tiles as a shaded small square and is always a positive unit. The opposite of 1, written –1, is an open small square and is always negative. Let's explore the variable x-tiles.

a. The variable x-tile is shaded, but is the number represented by a variable such as x always positive? Why or why not?

b. The opposite of the variable x, written $-x$, looks like it might be negative, but since the value of a variable can be any number (the opposite of –2 is 2), what can you say about the opposite of the variable x?

c. Is it possible to determine which is greater, x or $-x$? Explain.

d. What is true about $6+(-6)$? What is true about $x+(-x)$ (the sum of a variable and its opposite)?

4-105. Get a Lesson 4.3.3 Resource Page from your teacher, which is called "Expression Mat." The mat will help you so you can tell the difference between the expression you are working on and everything else on your desk.

Expression Mat

From your work in problem 4-104, you can say that situations like $6+(-6)$ and $x+(-x)$ "create zeros." That is, when you add an equal number of tiles and their opposites, the result is zero. The pairs of unit tiles and x-tiles shown in that problem are examples of "zero pairs" of tiles.

Build each collection of tiles represented below on the mat. Name the collection using a simpler algebraic expression (one that has fewer terms). You can do this by finding and removing zero pairs and combining like terms. Note: A zero pair is two of the same kind of tile (for example, unit tiles), one of them positive and the other negative.

a. $2+2x+x+(-3)+(-3x)$

b. $-2+2x+1-x+(-5)+2x$

4-106.   An **equivalent expression** refers to the same amount with a different name.

Build the expression mats shown in the pictures below. Write the expression shown on the expression mat, then write its simplified equivalent expression by making zeros (zero pairs) and combining like terms.

a.

b.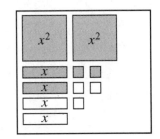

4-107.   On your Expression Mat, build what is described below. Then write two different equivalent expressions to describe what is represented. One of the two representations should include parentheses.

a.   The area of a rectangle with a width of 3 units and a length of $x+5$.

b.   Two equal groups of $3x-2$.

c.   Four rows of $2x+1$.

d.   A number increased by one, then tripled.

4-108.   Copy and rewrite the following expressions by combining like terms and making zeros. Using or visualizing algebra tiles may be helpful.

a. $(-1)+(-4x)+2+2x+x$

b. $2.5x+4+(-3.25)+3x$

c. $3x^2+(-2x^2)+5x+(-4x)$

d. $x-6+4\frac{1}{2}x+5\frac{1}{3}$

4-109.   Earlier, you used properties of addition and multiplication to create equivalent expressions with numbers. You can do the same with expressions that have variables. For each pair of expressions below, identify the property used from the list below.

a. $3x + 18 + (-2x) + 2$

$= 3x + (-2x) + 18 + 2$

$= x + 20$

b. $3x + 2(4x - 8)$

$= 3x + (8x - 16)$

$= 11x - 16$

c. $3x \cdot 4$

$= 4 \cdot 3x$

$= 12x$

d. $(3x + 4) - 6$

$= 3x + (4 - 6)$

$= 3x - 2$

A. Associative Property of Addition

B. Commutative Property of Addition

C. Commutative Property of Multiplication

D. Distributive Property

4-110.   **Additional Challenge:** Division by zero is an interesting concept. Some students believe that when you divide by zero, the result is zero. Consider how the numerical equation $30 \div 6 = 5$ can be reversed to make the multiplication equation $5 \cdot 6 = 30$.

a.   Reverse the division equation $24 \div 4 = 6$ into a multiplication equation.

b.   Now take the equation $24 \div 0 = x$ and reverse it into a multiplication equation. What value of x can make this equation true? Explain.

c.   Why do you think the solution to a number divided by zero is called "undefined?"

d.   Is $0 \div 24$ also "undefined"? Why or why not?

4-111.   LEARNING LOG

In your Learning Log, explain in your own words how to simplify expressions. Include an example of different ways to write the expression $3x + 5 - 2(x + 4) + 3$ by drawing pictures and writing equivalent expressions. Title this entry "Simplifying Expressions" and include today's date.

232

METHODS AND MEANINGS

Distributive Property

The **Distributive Property** states that multiplication can be "distributed" as a multiplier of each term in a sum or difference. It is a method to separate or group quantities in multiplication problems. For example, $3(2+4) = 3 \cdot 2 + 3 \cdot 4$. Symbolically, it is written:

$$a(b+c) = ab + ac \quad \text{and} \quad a(b-c) = ab - ac$$

For example, the collection of tiles at right can be represented as 4 sets of $x+3$, written as $4(x+3)$. It can also be represented by 4 x-tiles and 12 unit tiles, written as $4x+12$.

4 sets of $x+3$

$4(x+3) = 4x + 12$

Review & Preview

4-112. Find the perimeter and area of each figure made of algebra tiles below.

a.

b.

c.

4-113. Sketch each collection of tiles below. Name the collection using a simpler algebraic expression, if possible. If it is not possible to simplify the expression, explain why not.

a. $(-2x) + 5 + 3x - 4x + (-1) + (-x)$

b. Six plus four times a number, plus four minus four times the number.

c. Three groups of a number plus two.

d. $5 + 7x^2 + 4x$

e. $4x^2 - 2x^2 + (-6) + 3$

4-114. Complete the portions webs below.

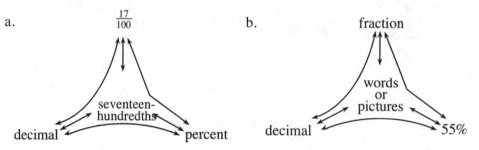

a. $\frac{17}{100}$ b. fraction

4-115. Copy each expression and simplify it. Be sure to show the steps you use to get the answer.

a. $\frac{19}{20} - \frac{1}{4}$ b. $\frac{22}{25} - \frac{7}{10}$ c. $\frac{9}{32} + \frac{7}{8}$

4-116. Rewrite each percent as a fraction and each fraction as a percent.

a. 20%   b. $\frac{2}{5}$ c. 75%   d. $\frac{2}{3}$

4-117. Write the expression as shown on the Expression Mats, then simplify by making zeros and combining like terms.

▇ = +1
☐ = −1

a.

x	☐
x	▇
x	☐
▇	☐

b.

x	x^2
x	▇
x	☐

4-118. Joan's Candy Emporium is having a sale. Three pounds of gummy bunnies are selling for $4.00.

a. How much will two pounds cost?

b. What is the unit rate for gummy bunnies?

4-119. Evaluate each expression below for the given value. That is, find the value of the expression when the variable is equal to the value given.

a. $2a - 7$ when $a = 3$ b. $10 + 4m$ when $m = -2$

c. $9 + (-2n)$ when $n = 4$ d. $\frac{x}{2} + 5$ when $x = 6$

4-120.   Identify the length of the missing section of each line. Assume that the lines are divided into equal parts.

a.

b.

c.
```
   ?
 ⌢⌢⌢⌢
├─┼─┼─┼─┼─┼─┼─┤
0                16
```

4-121.   Kris said, *"The Rawlings Rockets basketball team does not have any really tall players."* These are the player's heights in inches: 70, 77, 75, 68, 88, 70, and 72.

a.   Which number does not seem to fit this set of data?

b.   Do you agree or disagree with Kris? Explain.

Chapter 4 Closure   What have I learned?

Reflection and Synthesis

The activities below offer you a chance to reflect
about what you have learned during this chapter.
As you work, look for concepts that you feel very
comfortable with, ideas that you would like to learn
more about, and topics you need more help with.

①   SUMMARIZING MY UNDERSTANDING

This section gives you an opportunity to show what you know the main math
ideas in this chapter.

SHAPE CHALLENGE – PART ONE

You and your team will choose four algebra tiles and
use them to build a shape to challenge your
classmates. You may choose whatever tiles you
would like to use as long as you use exactly four tiles.

As a team, decide on the shape you want to make. Experiment
with different shapes until you find one you think will have a
challenging perimeter and area for your classmates to find.
Then, to share your challenge with the class:

- Build the shape with algebra tiles in the middle of your team so everyone
  can see it.

- Get an index card from your teacher. On one side, neatly draw the shape
  and label each side.

- Write a simplified expression for the perimeter and for the area on the
  same side of the card. This will be the answer key. Show all of your
  steps clearly.

- Turn the card face down so the answer is hidden, put the names of your
  team members on the top of the card, and then put it beside the shape
  you built with your algebra tiles.

Remember that your work needs to be clear enough for your classmates to
understand.

Follow your teacher's directions to complete challenges created by other teams.
As you look at their shapes, sketch them on your paper. Work with your team
to label the sides and find the perimeter and area of each shape. Be sure to
combine like terms to make the expressions as simple as possible.

①   **SHAPE CHALLENGE – PART TWO**

Choose two of the shapes from "Shape Challenge – Part One." Sketch each shape and label it with its perimeter and area. Do not forget the correct units. It is not necessary to draw the figures to scale. Rewrite each expression with the values given below and then evaluate it.

a. $x = 1.5$ units

b. $x = 3\frac{3}{4}$ units

②   **WHAT HAVE I LEARNED?**

Doing the problems in this section will help you to evaluate which types of problems you feel comfortable with and which ones you need more help with.

Solve each problem as completely as you can. The table at the end of this closure section provides answers to these problems. It also tells you where you can find additional help and where to find practice problems like them.

CL 4-122.   Hilda was simplifying some numerical expressions and made each of the following sequences of calculations. Name the mathematical property, operation, or idea that justifies how Hilda went from each step to the next step.

a. $5 \cdot 412$
$= 5(400 + 10 + 2)$
$= 5 \cdot 400 + 5 \cdot 10 + 5 \cdot 2$
$= 2000 + 50 + 10$
$= 2060$

b. $15 + 32 + 5 - 2$
$= 15 + 5 + 32 - 2$
$= (15 + 5) + (32 - 2)$
$= 20 + 30$
$= 50$

CL 4-123.   Copy and complete each of the Diamond Problems below. The pattern used in the Diamond Problems is shown at right.

a.   b.   c.   d.

Diamond Problem a: top is empty, left $\frac{1}{5}$, right $\frac{2}{3}$, bottom empty.

Diamond Problem b: top empty, left -3, right 6, bottom empty.

Diamond Problem c: left empty, right $\frac{4}{5}$, bottom $\frac{21}{20}$, top empty.

Diamond Problem d: left empty, right -1, bottom 11, top empty.

The pattern diamond at right shows $x \cdot y$ at top, x at left, y at right, $x + y$ at bottom.

CL 4-124. Copy the following expressions on your paper and simplify them by combining like terms. Using algebra tiles may be helpful.

   a. $4x+2+2x+x^2+x$ b. $10x+4-3+8x+2$

   c. $4+x^2+3x+2x^2+4$ d. $x+4+(x-1)+3+2x$

CL 4-125. The shapes at right are similar.

   a. What is the scale factor?

   b. Find the sides labeled x and y.

CL 4-126. Simplify each expression.

   a. $\frac{3+(-7)}{-2}$ b. $\frac{4-16}{-2(-2)}$

   c. $5(2+(-9))+(-25)$ d. $-3(4)+5(4)-2(7)$

CL 4-127. A speed skater covered 1500 meters in 106.43 seconds. Find his unit rate of speed in meters per second.

CL 4-128. Which table or tables below show a proportional relationship? Justify your answers.

  a.

x	5	7	9	−8	0	11	15
y	9	13	17	−17	−19	21	29

  b.

x	7	14	91	9	−12	−36	81
y	$3\frac{1}{2}$	7	$45\frac{1}{2}$	$4\frac{1}{2}$	−6	−18	$40\frac{1}{2}$

  c.

x	−3	−10	0	10	5	4	$\frac{1}{2}$	−3
y	−27	−1000	0	1000	125	48	$\frac{1}{8}$	−27

CL 4-129.   A box contains 15 yellow, 15 orange, and 15 green tennis balls. If Izzy draws a tennis ball at random out of the box, what is the probability that she drew either a green or an orange tennis ball? Show your work and express your answer as a percent.

CL 4-130.   For each of the problems above, do the following:
   • Draw a bar or number line that represents 0 to 10.

   • Color or shade in a portion of the bar that represents your level of understanding and comfort with completing that problem on your own.

If any of your bars are less than a 5, choose *one* of those problems and do one of the following tasks:
   • Write two questions that you would like to ask about that problem.
   • Brainstorm two things that you DO know about that type of problem.

If all of your bars are a 5 or above, choose one of those problems and do one of these tasks:
   • Write two questions you might ask or hints you might give to a student who was stuck on the problem.
   • Make a new problem that is similar and more challenging than that problem and solve it.

WHAT TOOLS CAN I USE?

You have several tools and references available to help support your learning: your teacher, your study team, your math book, and your Toolkit, to name only a few. At the end of each chapter, you will have an opportunity to review your Toolkit for completeness. You will also revise or update it to reflect your current understanding of big ideas.

The main elements of your Toolkit should be your Learning Logs, Math Notes, and the vocabulary used in this chapter. Math words that are new appear in bold in the text. Refer to the lists provided below and follow your teacher's instructions to revise your Toolkit, which will help make it useful for you as you complete this chapter and as you work in future chapters.

Learning Log Entries
- Lesson 4.2.1 – Recognizing Proportional Relationships
- Lesson 4.2.2 – Proportional Relationships in Graphs and Tables
- Lesson 4.2.4 – Connections Web for Proportional Relationships
- Lesson 4.3.3 – Simplifying Expressions

Math Notes
- Lesson 4.1.1 – Mathematical Properties
- Lesson 4.1.2 – Similarity and Scale Factor
- Lesson 4.2.3 – Proportional Relationships
- Lesson 4.2.4 – Unit Rate
- Lesson 4.3.1 – Naming Algebra Tiles
- Lesson 4.3.2 – Combining Like Terms
- Lesson 4.3.3 – Distributive Property

Mathematical Vocabulary

The following is a list of vocabulary found in this chapter. Some of the words have been seen in the previous chapter. The words in bold are words that are new to this chapter. Make sure that you are familiar with the terms below and know what they mean. For the words you do not know, refer to the glossary or index. You might also add these words to your Toolkit so that you can reference them in the future.

algebraic expression	Associative Property	**combining like terms**
Commutative Property	**constant term**	**constant of proportionality**
corresponding parts	Distributive Property	**equivalent expressions**
evaluate	proportional relationship	**scale drawing**
scale factor	**similar figures**	simplify
terms	**unit rate**	**variable**

Answers and Support for Closure Problems
What Have I Learned?

Note: MN = Math Note, LL = Learning Log

Problem	Solution		Need Help?	More Practice
CL 4-122.	a. Decomposed 412, Distributive Property, multiplied each term, added terms together.		Lesson 3.3.3 MN: 4.1.1	Problems 4-44 and 4-109
	b. Commutative Property of Addition, Associative Property of Addition, added as indicated by grouping symbols, added each term.			
CL 4-123.	a. $\frac{2}{15}, \frac{13}{15}$ c. $\frac{4}{20}$ or $\frac{1}{5}, \frac{1}{4}$	b. $-18, 3$ d. $12, -12$	Problem 2-16	Problems 2-81, 2-116, 3-123, 4-19, 4-32, and 4-83

Problem	Solution		Need Help?	More Practice
CL 4-124.	a. $x^2 + 7x + 2$ b. $18x + 3$ c. $3x^2 + 3x + 8$ d. $4x + 6$		Lessons 4.3.1 and 4.3.3 MN: 4.3.2 LL: 4.3.3	Problems 4-80, 4-108, and 4-113
CL 4-125.	a. $\frac{1}{3}$ b. $x = \frac{8}{3}$ or $2\frac{2}{3}$ $y = \frac{5}{3}$ or $1\frac{2}{3}$		Lesson 4.1.1 MN: 4.1.2	Problems 4-1, 4-2, 4-3, and 4-94
CL 4-126.	a. 2 c. −60	b. −3 d. −6	Sections 3.1 and 3.2 MN: 3.1.2, 3.2.2, and 3.2.4 LL: 3.1.1, 3.1.2, 3.2.2, and 3.2.3	Problems CL 3-131, 4-16, and 4-63
CL 4-127.	$\approx \frac{14.09 \text{ meters}}{1 \text{ second}}$		Lesson 4.2.3 MN: 4.2.4	Problems 4-50, 4-61, 4-79, 4-96, and 4-118
CL 4-128.	Table (b) is proportional because it is the only one that could contain $(0,0)$ and grows using a Giant One.		Section 4.1 MN: 4.2.3 LL: 4.2.1, 4.2.2 and 4.2.4	Problems 4-29, 4-30, 4-41, 4-50, 4-51, 4-60, and 4-77
CL 4-129.	$66\frac{2}{3}\%$		Lessons 1.2.1, 1.2.2, and 1.2.3 MN: 1.2.3 LL: 1.2.1	Problems CL 1-148, CL 2-136, 4-42, 4-54, and 4-68

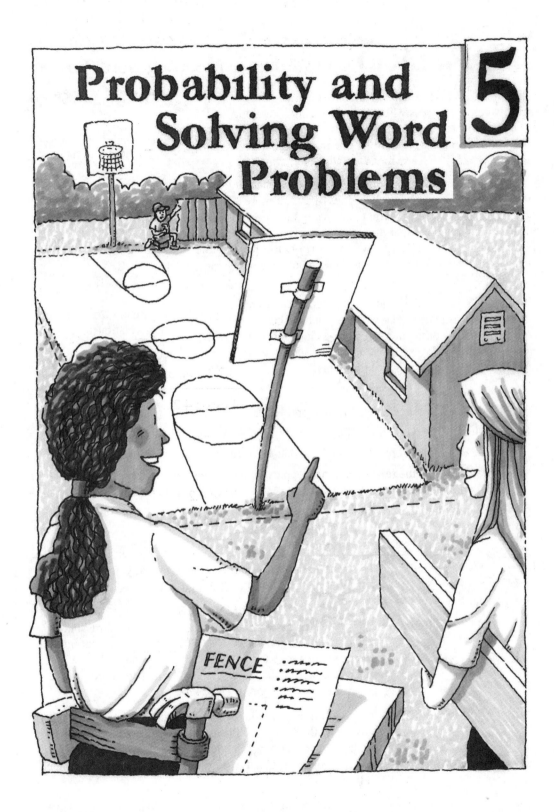

Probability and Solving Word Problems

5

CHAPTER 5 Probability and Solving Word Problems

How often do you need to compare one thing to another? You probably compare prices when you are buying something, and you may compare heights of basketball players as you watch a game. In mathematics, comparing one thing to another is an important strategy to learn about how they are related.

In Section 5.2, you will continue your study of probability. You will learn how to calculate probabilities of two or more events and how to decide when different games are fair. You will also calculate the probability that more than one event will take place. As you do this, you will learn new ways to organize the possible outcomes and will explore situations where one outcome is more likely than another.

In Section 5.3, you will use variables to represent a single unknown number in different contexts, such as the length of the side of a figure or the number of frogs in a pond. You will learn about the 5-D Process, a strategy to organize your thinking that can help you solve problems.

In this chapter, you will learn how to:

➢ Find and use percentages to solve problems.

➢ Calculate the probability of compound (multiple) events.

➢ Use experimental results to make and test conjectures about unknown sample spaces.

➢ Describe how the relationship between experimental and theoretical probabilities for an experiment changes as the experiment is conducted many times.

➢ Solve situational problems using the 5-D Process.

Guiding Questions

Think about these questions throughout this chapter:

What is the part?

What is the whole?

Which is more likely?

Is it fair?

How can I represent the relationship?

How can I organize my thinking?

Chapter Outline

	Section 5.1	This section introduces a linear diagram that you will use to represent relationships between parts and the whole to solve problems.
	Section 5.2	You will investigate probability using a deck of cards and a random number generator. You will learn to represent multiple events using a probability tree, a list, and a table. You will also revisit the idea of the fairness of events and compare experimental and theoretical probabilities.
	Section 5.3	This section will introduce the 5-D Process as a problem-solving method. You will learn how to understand a problem by drawing, describing, and defining its elements. You will learn strategies that lead to writing and solving equations later in the course.
	Mid-Course Reflection	Finally, you will reflect about the content and work you have done in Chapters 1 through 5.

5.1.1 How can I find a percentage?

Part-Whole Relationships

Food labels tell you about what is in the food you eat. The nutrition-facts label lists the percentages of macronutrients (protein, carbohydrates, and fat) as well as vitamins and minerals in each serving. However, it often does not tell you exactly how much of each thing is in the food or how much you should have each day to be healthy.

If you know how much Vitamin C is in a serving, can you figure out how much is needed in a day? To help you answer a question like that, in this section you will develop strategies for finding information about parts and wholes.

5-1.   **WHAT ARE YOU EATING?**

The government has created guidelines for how much of various nutrients, vitamins, and minerals a person should eat or drink each day to be healthy. These guidelines are then used to create labels like the one shown above to inform the public about the nutritional content of food.

According to the sample label above, one serving of Cheesy Mac macaroni and cheese contains 15% of the recommended daily amount of saturated fat that a person should eat. Nutritionists recommend that a person should have no more than a certain amount of saturated fat each day. One serving of Cheesy Mac has 3 grams (3g) of saturated fat. How many grams of saturated fat should a person eat in one day?

Your Task: With your team, determine how many grams of saturated fat a person should eat each day. Look for more than one way to solve the problem and be ready to explain your reasoning.

Discussion Points

What information do you have about the part?

What do you know about the whole?

How could you represent this situation with a number line?

Further Guidance

5-2.   To help you represent the situation in problem 5-1, copy the number line below on your paper.

Recommended Daily Intake of Saturated Fat

0%   100%

a.   With your team, decide how to **partition** the line (divide it into equal parts) so that 15% is shown. Why did you choose to make that number of parts? Is there another way that you could have divided the line?

b.   The amount of saturated fat in one serving of Cheesy Mac is 3 grams. Where should 3g be labeled on the number line? Add this number to your diagram and justify your decision.

c.   Use your diagram to help you decide how much saturated fat is in the recommended daily serving. Record your thinking.

————   *Further Guidance
section ends here.*   ————

5-3.   One way to write a percentage is as a **ratio** (comparison) of parts out of 100. For example, the ratio $\frac{15}{100}$ represents 15 parts out of 100 total parts.

a.   Jill represented the amount of saturated fat in the recommended daily amount with the ratio $\frac{3}{20}$. What does the 3 represent? What does the 20 represent?

b.   The ratios $\frac{15}{100}$ and $\frac{3}{20}$ are two different ways to compare the saturated fat in one serving to the recommended daily amount. How can you show that the ratios are equivalent (the same)?

Core Connections, Course 2

5-4.   One granola bar contains 4g of dietary fiber. The label says that 4g is 16% of the daily recommended amount. Louis decided to draw a diagram like the one below to understand this situation.

Recommended Daily Intake of Fiber

a.   Copy the diagram on your paper and add the label for 16%.

b.   How many grams of fiber are recommended each day? How can you show this with equal ratios?

c.   What percent of fiber should Louis get from other foods? Why is this percent equivalent to the ratio $\frac{21\ g}{25\ g}$?

d.   What other amounts are missing on the diagram? Add labels for all parts, percents, and the whole.

e.   Chris is eating cookies that contain 12g of dietary fiber, which he says is 48% of the recommended daily amount. How can you use ratios and part (b) above to check that 12g is equivalent to 48%?

5-5.   One large carrot contains approximately 6 mg of Vitamin C. The recommended daily intake of Vitamin C is 60 mg. Resa wanted to find out what percentage of her daily Vitamin C she gets from one carrot. She started with a line divided into 10 parts.

Recommended Daily Intake of Vitamin C

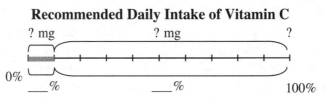

a.   Why do you think she divided the line segment into 10 parts?

b.   Copy the diagram on your paper and fill in the missing labels.

c.   The ratio $\frac{6\ mg}{60\ mg}$ represents the portion of Vitamin C in one large carrot. Work with your team to find this ratio in the diagram. Where do you see each amount? What other ratio could you write that would be equal to this?

d.   Use the diagram to help you find and write at least two other ratios on the number line that are equal to each other.

5-6.   Resa was mixing blue and red paint to create purple paint. She created the
        drawing below to show the portions of blue paint to red that she used.

a.   What does the picture tell you about the paint mixture? What statements
     can you make?

b.   If you have not stated it yet, what percent of the paint is blue? What
     percent of the paint is red? Justify your answer.

5-7.   **Additional Challenge:** Turner Middle School has 110 boys. Fifty-six percent
        of the students in the school are girls. How many students go to this school?

a.   Create a model like Resa's from problem 5-5. Label the percentage of
     girls, the percentage of boys, and the number of boys on your drawing, as
     well as 0% and 100%.

b.   How many students go to the school? How do you know?

c.   How many girls go to the school? Explain your reasoning.

5-8.   **Additional Challenge:** Maria is making paper flowers as decorations for the
        fall dance. She has made 40 flowers so far, and she is 16% finished. If she
        plans to finish making 70% of the total flowers needed by tonight, how many
        more will she need to make by then? Show your work.

METHODS AND MEANINGS

Equivalent Ratios

A **ratio** is a comparison of two quantities by division. A ratio can be written in words, as a fraction, or with colon notation. Most often in this course, ratios will be written as fractions or stated in words.

For example, if there are 28 students in a math class and 15 of them are girls, you can write the ratio of the number of girls to the number of students in the class as:

15 girls to 28 students $\quad \frac{15 \text{ girls}}{28 \text{ students}} \quad$ 15 girls : 28 students

You used a Giant One to write equivalent fractions in Chapter 1. To rewrite any ratio as an **equivalent ratio**, write it as a fraction and multiply it by a fraction equal to one. For example, you can show that the ratio of raisins to peanuts is the same for a larger mixture using a Giant One like this:

$$\frac{4 \text{ raisins}}{7 \text{ peanuts}} \cdot \boxed{\frac{20}{20}} = \frac{80 \text{ raisins}}{140 \text{ peanuts}}$$

Equivalent fractions (or ratios) can be thought of as families of fractions. There are an infinite number of fractions that are equivalent to a given fraction. You may want to review the basis for using a Giant One — the Multiplicative Identity — in the Math Notes box in Lesson 1.2.5.

5-9. Find the missing values on the diagram below. Assume that each line is evenly divided.

5-10. A fish tank that holds 80 gallons of water is 55% full.

a. Create a drawing like Louis's in problem 5-4 to represent this situation.

b. How many gallons are in the tank now? How many more gallons are needed to fill the tank?

5-11. Fill in the missing numbers in each number sentence.

a. $\frac{5}{8} \cdot \boxed{\frac{3}{3}} = \frac{?}{?}$ b. $\frac{9}{15} \cdot \boxed{\frac{?}{?}} = \frac{?}{60}$ c. $\frac{7}{20} \cdot \boxed{\frac{?}{?}} = \frac{?}{110}$ d. $\frac{44}{100} \cdot \boxed{\frac{?}{?}} = \frac{?}{60}$

e. What strategies did you use to find the numbers in the Giant One in parts (b), (c), and (d)?

5-12. Complete a Proportions Web for the following situation.

Clifford works 40 hours per week while working as a laboratory technician. He earns $453.60 for each week of work.

5-13. Simplify the following expressions.

a. $\frac{2}{3} + \frac{4}{5}$ b. $\left(\frac{4}{5}\right)\left(\frac{2}{3}\right)$ c. $\frac{4}{5} - \left(-\frac{2}{3}\right)$

5.1.2 What is the percentage of the whole?

Finding and Using Percentages

How are sales advertised in different stores? In a clothing store, items are often marked with signs saying, "20% off" or "40% discount." In a grocery store, sale items are usually listed by price. For example, pasta is marked, "Sale price 50¢," or boxes of cereal are marked "$2.33 each." In the clothing store, you are able to see how much the discount is, but the price you will pay is often not stated. On the other hand, sometimes in the grocery store it is not possible to tell the size of the discount. It might only be a small fraction of the original price.

The actual dollar amount of the discount and the percentage comparing it to the whole are important pieces of information that help you decide if you are getting a good deal. Today you will create complete information about a sale situation from the information given in a problem.

By the end of this lesson, you will be expected to answer these target questions:

How can I find a percentage of a whole?

How can I find a percent if I have two parts that make a whole?

How can I find the whole amount if I know the parts?

5-14.   Marisa is always looking for a great deal while shopping. She found a sale rack where all of the jeans are marked 40% off. Her favorite jeans regularly cost $65.

a.   To figure out if she has enough money to buy a pair of jeans, Marisa decides to estimate. She thinks that the jeans will cost approximately $30. Is her estimate reasonable? Explain your thinking.

b.   To find the exact answer, Marisa created the diagram below. How could she add marks to partition the line evenly? Partition the line and calculate the missing values.

c.   How much money will Marisa save? What is the price she will have to pay?

d.   Marisa wants to check her answer from part (c). How could she use ratios with the amount she saved and the original price to verify that she received a 40% discount?

5-15.   At the same sale, Kirstin sees a shirt on sale for just $37.50. It originally cost $50.

   a.   Estimate the percentage of the discount on the shirt.

   b.   Draw a diagram to represent this situation. Label all parts.

   c.   What percent is the discount on Kirstin's shirt?

   d.   What is the relationship between the discount, the sale price, and the original price? Write a statement that shows the relationship between the sale price, discount, and original price.

5-16.   So far in this section, you have used a linear model to represent percent problems in various contexts.

   a.   Obtain a Lesson 5.1.2 Resource Page and use the linear models to find parts and wholes when different types of information are provided on the diagrams.

   b.   For each diagram, write at least three statements describing how parts and percentages are related. Some statements are started for you.

5-17.   When Kirstin was about to pay for her clothes, she realized that she had forgotten to include an 8% sales tax.

   a.   The belt Kirstin wants to buy costs $15. She does not have paper to draw a linear model. To estimate tax, she figured that calculating 10% would be close enough. Explain how Kirstin might find 10% of $15 without a linear model.

   b.   Calculate exactly how much the 8% sales tax will cost Kirstin. What will be the total amount she will have to pay to the store?

METHODS AND MEANINGS

Part-to-Whole Relationships

Percentages, fractions, and decimals are all different ways to represent a portion of a whole or a number. Portion-whole relationships can also be described in words.

You can represent a part-to-whole relationship with a linear model like the one below. To solve a percentage problem described in words, you must first identify three important quantities: the percent, the whole, and the part of the whole. One of the quantities will be unknown. A diagram can help you organize the information. For example:

Once the parts have been identified, you can use reasoning to extend the part to the whole. For example, if 220 students are 40% of eighth graders, then 10% must be $220 \div 4 = 55$. Then 100% must be $55 \cdot 10 = 550$ students. Another way to solve the problem is to find the ratio of 220 boys to the whole (all students) and compare that ratio to 40% and 100%. This could be written:

You can see above that the total number of 8th graders is 550.

To remember how to rewrite decimals or fractions as percents, and to rewrite percents as fractions or decimals, refer to the Math Notes box at the end of Lesson 1.3.1.

5-18.   A shade of orange paint is made with 5 parts red paint and 15 parts yellow paint.

   a.   What percent of the paint is red?

   b.   What is the simplified ratio of yellow to red paint?

5-19.   Janelle earned 90% on a test and got 63 points. How many total points were possible on the test? Draw a diagram to organize your information before solving the problem.

5-20.   The diagram at right is the floor plan of Randy's apartment. All measurements are in feet. Use the diagram to answer the following questions.

	bathroom	kitchen
7		
10	bedroom	living room
	9	15

   a.   What are the dimensions (length and width) of Randy's living room?

   b.   Randy's friends are coming to visit him soon. He plans to keep them out of his bedroom. Find the area of each of the other three rooms he will have to clean.

   c.   What is the total area of the rooms he will have to clean?

5-21.   Simplify each expression.

   a. $-\frac{4}{5}+\frac{3}{10}$ b. $2\frac{5}{8}-1\frac{1}{3}$

5-22.   The trapezoids at right are similar shapes.

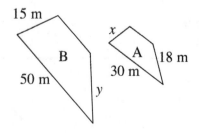

   a.   What is the scale factor from shape A to shape B?

   b.   Find the lengths of the missing sides.

5.2.1   Is it a fair game?

Probability Games

Have you ever played a game where everyone should have an equal chance of winning, but one person seems to have all the luck? Did it make you wonder if the game was fair? Sometimes random events just happen to work out in one player's favor, such as flipping a coin that happens to come up heads four times in a row. But it is also possible that games can be set up to give an advantage to one player over another. If there is an equal chance for each player to win a game, then it is considered to be a **fair game**. If it is not equally likely for each player to win, a game is considered to be **unfair**.

In this lesson you will continue to investigate probability. As you work, ask these questions in your study team:

How many outcomes are possible?

How many outcomes are desirable?

5-23.   PICK A CARD, ANY CARD

What is the probability of picking the following cards from the deck? Write your response as a fraction, as a decimal, and as a percent.

a.   P(black)?

b.   P(club)?

c.   If you drew a card from the deck and then replaced it, and if you repeated this 100 times, about how many times would you expect to draw a face card (king, queen, or jack)? Explain your reasoning.

5-24.   Sometimes it is easier to figure out the probability that something will *not* happen than the probability that it will happen. When finding the probability that something will not happen, you are finding the probability of the **complement**. Everything in the sample space that is not in the event is in the complement.

a.   What is the probability you *do not* get a club, written P(not club)?

b.   What is P(not face card)?

c.   What would happen to the probability of getting an ace on a second draw if you draw an ace on the first draw and do not return it to the deck? Justify your answer.

5-25.   Rob decided to play a card game with his friend, Travis. He told Travis that if he picked a black card with a value of nine or greater, Travis would win. (Jacks, queens, and kings are considered to be greater than nine.) If Rob picked a red card with a value of less than nine, Rob would win. (Aces are considered to have the value of one in this case.)

   a.   What is the probability that Travis will win?

   b.   What is the probability that Rob will win?

   c.   According to the definition in the introduction to this lesson, is this a fair game? Why or why not?

5-26.   The city has created a new contest to raise funds for a big Fourth of July fireworks celebration. People buy tickets and scratch off a special section on the ticket to reveal whether they have won a prize. One out of every five people who play get a free entry in a raffle. Two out of every fifteen people who play win a small cash prize.

   a.   If you buy a scratch-off ticket, is it more likely that you will win a free raffle ticket or a cash prize? Explain your answer.

   b.   What is the probability that you will win something (either a free raffle entry or a cash prize)?

   c.   What is the probability that you will win nothing at all? To justify your thinking, write an expression to find the complement of winning something.

5-27.   Alicia's favorite candies are Fruiti Tutti Chews, which come in three flavors: Killer Kiwi, Crazy Coconut, and Ridiculous Raspberry. This year will be the 50th year that the candy has been made. To celebrate, the company that makes Fruiti Tutti Chews is running new advertisements and introducing a fourth flavor: Perfect Peach.

   a.   One of the new advertisements states that if you reach into any bag of Fruiti Tutti Chews, you have a $\frac{2}{3}$ probability of pulling out a Killer Kiwi candy. Another advertisment says that $\frac{3}{5}$ of each bag is Ridiculous Raspberry. Are the advertisements telling the truth?

   b.   Alicia learns that when she opens a new bag of candy, she has a $\frac{2}{5}$ chance of pulling out a piece of Ridiculous Raspberry and a $\frac{1}{3}$ chance of pulling out a piece of Killer Kiwi. Could she have a $\frac{4}{15}$ chance of pulling out a piece of Perfect Peach? Explain your reasoning.

   c.   When the company introduces the new flavor, it plans to make Perfect Peach $\frac{3}{10}$ of the candy in each bag. If there is an equal amount of the remaining three flavors, what is the probability that the first piece you pull out of the bag will be Crazy Coconut? Justify your answer.

5-28.   LEARNING LOG

So far you have calculated probabilities of different
events and analyzed a game to see if it was fair. Along
the way, you also found the probability of *either* one *or*
another event taking place (such as winning *either* a
raffle entry *or* a cash prize in part (b) of problem 5-26).

Make an entry in your Learning Log and title it "Probability for 'Either/Or'
Events." Create an example and explain how you would calculate the
probability when two different outcomes are favorable (such as the example of
the raffle ticket and cash). Then, record any questions you have about
probability. Your questions might relate to things that you have already worked
on or may be about situations you have not yet studied.

5-29.   Find the probability of each event. Write your answer as a fraction and as a
percent.

a. Drawing a diamond from a standard deck of cards.

b. Rolling a number less than five on a standard number cube.

c. Drawing a blue marble from a bag of 18 marbles, three of which are blue.

5-30.   Imagine a standard deck of cards with all of
the aces and twos removed. Find each
probability below.

a. P(heart)   b. P(black)   c. P(face card)

d. How is the P(face card) different with this deck from the probability if the
deck was not missing any cards? Which probability is greater? Why?

e. P(not heart)

5-31.   The Kennedy High School cross-country running team
ran the following distances in recent practices:

3.5 miles, 2.5 miles, 4 miles, 3.25 miles, 3 miles,
4 miles, and 6 miles.

Find the mean and median of the team's distances.

5-32.   Find the area of each figure below.

a.

b.

5-33.   Evaluate the following expressions using the Order of Operations.

a. $3(8-4)+4^2-(2+3)$

b. $7 \cdot 4 - 3 \cdot 8 + 2^2 - 6$

c. $7-(-3)+(-4+3)$

d. $-6-4(3 \cdot 2)+5^2$

5.2.2 What if it is more complicated?

Computer Simulations of Probability

If you toss a coin ten times, what is the probability of getting three or more "heads" in a row? If an airline overbooks a certain flight, what is the chance more passengers show up than the airplane has seats for? When 67 people get cancer in 250 homes in a small town, could that be due to chance alone, or is polluted well water (or some other cancer-causing source) a more likely explanation of the cluster of cancer cases?

When the mathematics becomes too complicated to figure out the theoretical probability of certain events, statisticians often use computer **simulations** instead.

Many simulations require the use of random numbers. Random numbers have no pattern; they cannot be predicted in any way. Knowing a random number in no way allows you to predict the next random number. An example of a random number generator is a standard number cube, which randomly generates a number from 1 to 6 when you roll it.

Complex simulations like modeling the weather, traffic patterns, cancer radiation therapy, or stock-market swings require tens of billions of random numbers. For those simulations, a large computer running for hours or even days is needed. However, many simple simulations can be done with classroom technology.

5-34.   RANDOM NUMBER GENERATOR

Imagine a random number generator that produces numbers from 1 to 20. In each game below, if the stated outcome happens, Player X wins. If it does not, then Player Y wins.

Game 1:   A prime number = Player X wins

Game 2:   An even number = Player X wins

Game 3:   A number not divisible by three = Player X wins

a.   In each case, what is the theoretical probability that Player X wins? That Player Y wins? Decide whether each game above is fair.

b.   In which of the three games is Player X most likely to win? Why?

c.   In Game 1, the prime number game, if you play 40 times, how many times would you expect Player X to win? What if you played 50 times?

Problem continues on next page. →

5-34.   *Problem continued from previous page.*

    d. Obtain a random number generator from your teacher and set it up to generate integers from 1 to 20. Play the prime number game (Game 1) ten times with a partner. Start by deciding who will be Player X and who will be Player Y. Record who wins each time you play.

    e. How did the experimental and theoretical probabilities of Player X's winning from part (a) and part (d) compare?

5-35.   Janelle is going to babysit her nephew all day five times this summer. She had the idea that one way to entertain him is to walk to McBurger's for a Kids Meal for lunch each time. The Kids Meal comes packed randomly with one of three possible action figures. Janelle would like to know the probability that they get all three figures in five trips.

    a. Call the action figures #1, #2, and #3. Use the random number generator to simulate five trips to McBurger's. Did you get all three action figures?

    b. Simulate another five trips to McBurger's. Did you get all three action figures this time? Do the simulation at least 20 times (that is, 20 sets of 5 random numbers), keeping track of how many times you got all three action figures in five tries, and how many times you did not.

    c. Use your results to estimate the probability of getting all three action figures in 5 trips. Should Janelle be worried?

    d. How could Janelle get an even more accurate estimation of the probability?

5-36.   Janelle's aunt and uncle have three children, two of whom are girls. Assuming that girl children and boy children are equally likely, Janelle thought that the chance of having two or more girls out of 3 children must be 50%. Janelle's brother thought the chance of having so many girls had to be less than 50%.

    a. What do you think? Make a conjecture about the probability of having two or three girls in a family of three siblings.

    b. Do a computer simulation with the random number generator to estimate the probability of having two or three girls in a family of three siblings. Use a 1 to represent a girl and a 0 to represent a boy and simulate a family of three children. Do enough trials to get a good estimate.

Core Connections, Course 2

5-37.   Sophia and her brother are trying to create a fair game in which you roll two number cubes. They cannot agree on the probability that the numbers on both number cubes will be even, so they decide to design a simulation.

   a.   Make a conjecture. What is the probability both dice are even?

   b.   Design a simulation with a random number generator. How many random numbers do you need? In what interval should the numbers be? How many times will you do the simulation?

   c.   Set up and run the simulation that you designed with the random number generator and estimate the probability. How does it compare with your conjecture from part (a)?

5-38.   A BETTER CHANCE OF WINNING

   Each of the problems below describes two different games you can play with a random number generator. In each case, you will win if the random number generator gives you the indicated kind of number. Find the theoretical probability that you win each game below. Decide and justify whether Game I or Game II in each part, (a) through (c), gives you a better chance of winning.

	Game I	**Game II**
a.	Picking a prime number from the integers between 1 and 20	Picking a prime number from the integers between 21 and 40
b.	Picking a multiple of 5 from the integers between 1 and 20	Picking a multiple of 5 from the integers between 1 and 40
c.	Picking a multiple of 7 from the integers between 1 and 40	Picking a multiple of 6 from the integers between 1 and 25

5-39.   If you used a random number generator for the numbers from 1 through 20 to play a game, what is the theoretical probability of getting each of these outcomes?

   a.   A multiple of 3 *or* a multiple of 7, P(multiple of 3 or multiple of 7)

   b.   P(even or odd)

   c.   P(prime or 1)

   d.   How did you find the probabilities of these events? Be ready to share your ideas with the class.

5-40.   The average annual rainfall in Tucson, Arizona is 12 inches. Between January and April, 2.4 inches of rain fell. What percentage of the annual rainfall fell after April (May through December)? You may want to draw a diagram to organize information.

5-41.   Evaluate the expression $2x^2 + x + 6$ for the given values of x below.

   a. $x = 3$ b. $x = -2$ c. $x = 0$ d. $x = 5$

5-42.   Use graph paper to solve the following problem.

   a.   Draw a four quadrant graph and label each axis. Plot the following ordered pairs: $(-3,2)$, $(-8,2)$, $(-10,8)$, and $(-5,8)$. Connect the points in the given order as you plot them. Then connect the fourth point to the first one.

   b.   Describe the shape on your graph. What is its area?

5.2.3   What if there is more than one event?

Compound Independent Events

When you studied probability in earlier lessons, you focused on probabilities of single events (for example, one draw of a card, or picking one cube from a bag). You also examined probabilities of *either* one *or* another of two events occurring (for example, winning either a raffle ticket or cash; drawing either a king or queen). In this lesson, you will begin to investigate when one *and* another event *both* occur, such as flipping two coins or spinning a spinner multiple times. Throughout this lesson, use these questions to help focus your team's discussion:

> Does the result of one event affect the other?

> How many possibilities are there?

5-43.   In Chapter 1, you met Chris and her older sister, Rachel, who made a system for determining which one of them washes the dishes each night. Chris has been washing the dishes much more than she feels is her fair share, so she has come up with a new system. She has proposed to Rachel that they get two coins, and each day she and Rachel will take a coin and flip their coins at the same time. If the coins match, Chris washes the dishes; if they do not match, Rachel washes the dishes.

Rachel thinks that this is a good idea and that her little sister is very silly! She thinks to herself, *"Since there are two ways to match the coins, Heads-**and**-Heads or Tails-**and**-Tails, and only one non-match, Heads-**and**-Tails, then Chris will STILL wash the dishes more often. Ha!"*

a.   Do you agree with Rachel? Why or why not?

b.   Does it matter if they flip the coins at the same time? That is, does the result of one coin flip depend on the other coin flip?

c.   What are all of the possible outcomes when the girls flip their coins? Organize the possibilities. Use the word "and" when you are talking about *both* one thing *and* another occurring.

Problem continues on next page. →

5-43.   *Problem continued from previous page.*

   d.   Look at your list from part (c). Imagine that the coins are a penny and a nickel instead of two of the same coin. Does your list include both the possibilities of getting a heads on the penny and tails on the nickel and vice versa? If not, be sure to add them to your list.

   e.   Is Rachel right? Does this method give her an advantage, or is this a fair game? What is the theoretical probability for each girl's washing the dishes?

5-44.   ROCK-PAPER-SCISSORS

Read the rules for the rock-paper-scissors game below. Is this a fair game? Discuss this question with your team.

How to Play

- At the same time as your partner, shake your fist three times and then display either a closed fist for "rock," a flat hand for "paper," or a partly closed fist with two extended fingers for "scissors."

- Rock beats scissors (because rock blunts scissors), scissors beats paper (because scissors cut paper), and paper beats rock (because paper can wrap up a rock). If you both show the same symbol, repeat the round.

---

   a.   While both players are making their choice at the same time, this game has *two events* in every turn. What are the two events?

   b.   If you and a partner are playing this game and you both "go" at the same time, does your choice affect your partner's choice? Explain.

   c.   Are the two events in this game **dependent** (where the outcome of one event affects the outcome of the other event) or **independent** (where the outcome of one event does *not* affect the outcome of the other event)? Explain your reasoning.

   d.   Work with your team to determine all of the possible outcomes of a game of rock-paper-scissors, played by two people (call them Person A and Person B). Be sure to include the word "and." For each outcome, indicate which player wins or if there is a tie. Be prepared to share your strategies for finding the outcomes with the class.

5-45.   Is rock-paper-scissors a fair game? How can you tell?

5-46. Imagine that two people, Player A and Player B, were to play rock-paper-scissors 12 times.

a. How many times would you expect Player A to win? Player B to win?

b. Now play rock-paper-scissors 12 times with a partner. Record how many times each player wins and how many times the game results in a tie.

c. How does the experimental probability for the 12 games that you played compare to the theoretical probability that each of you will win? Do you expect them to be the same or different? Why?

5-47. Identify the situations below as either dependent or independent events.

a. Flipping a "heads" on a quarter *and* then flipping another "heads."

b. Choosing a jack from a standard deck of cards, not putting it back in the deck, *and* then choosing a king.

c. Picking a blue marble from a bag of marbles, putting it back, *and* then picking a blue marble again.

d. Rolling a 6 on a number cube three times in a row.

5-48. LEARNING LOG

In your Learning Log, make an entry that summarizes your understanding of independent and dependent events. Explain how to decide if two events are independent or dependent when looking at their likelihood. Give a few examples to support your thinking. Title your notes "Independent and Dependent Events" and include today's date.

Independent and Dependent Events

Two events are **independent** if the outcome of one event does not affect the outcome of the other event. For example, if you draw a card from a standard deck of playing cards but replace it before you draw again, the outcomes of the two draws are independent.

Two events are **dependent** if the outcome of one event affects the outcome of the other event. For example, if you draw a card from a standard deck of playing cards and do not replace it for the next draw, the outcomes of the two draws are dependent.

5-49.   For each of the following probabilities, write "dependent" if the outcome of the second event depends on the outcome of the first event and "independent" if it does not.

a.   P(spinning a 3 on a spinner after having just spun a 2)

b.   P(drawing a red 6 from a deck of cards after the 3 of spades was just drawn and not returned to the deck)

c.   P(drawing a face card from a deck of cards after a jack was just drawn and replaced and the deck shuffled again)

d.   P(selecting a lemon-lime soda if the person before you reaches into a cooler full of lemon-lime sodas, removes one, and drinks it)

5-50.   Skye's Ice Cream Shoppe is Mario's favorite place to get ice cream.
Unfortunately, because he was late arriving there, his friends had already
ordered. He did not know what they ordered for him. They told him that it was
either a waffle cone or a sundae and that the ice cream flavor was apricot,
chocolate, or blackberry.

   a.   Make a list of all of the possible ice cream orders.

   b.   What is the probability that Mario will get something with apricot ice
cream?

   c.   What is the probability that he will get a sundae?

   d.   What is the probability that he will get either something with chocolate or a
waffle cone with blackberry?

   e.   What is the probability that he will get orange sherbet?

5-51.   On your paper, sketch the algebra tile shape shown at
right. Write expressions for the area and perimeter of
the shape. Then calculate the area and perimeter of the
shape for each x-value.

   a. $x = 9 \, \text{cm}$

   b. $x = 0.5 \, \text{cm}$

   c. $x = 15 \, \text{cm}$

5-52.   Elin has made twenty-nine note cards for her friends. She plans to send out a
total of forty cards. What percentage of the cards has she finished? Represent
your work clearly on your paper.

5-53.   Copy and simplify the following expressions by combining like terms. Using
algebra tiles may be helpful.

   a. $3 + 4x + 2 + 2x + 2x$ b. $8x + 4 - 3 - x$

   c. $7x^2 + 3x + 4 + 7x^2 + 3x + 4$ d. $5x + 4 + x + x^2 + 1$

5.2.4 How can I find all of the outcomes?

Probability Tables

As you may have noticed in Lesson 5.2.3, considering probabilities with more than one event *and* more than two possibilities for each event (such as with the rock-paper-scissors game) can make keeping track of all of outcomes a challenge. In this lesson, you will learn about **probability tables**, a new strategy for organizing all of the possibilities in a complicated game.

5-54.   TEN O's

In this game, you will create a strategy to play a board game based on your predictions of likely outcomes. You will place ten O's on a number line. Then your teacher will roll two number cubes and add the resulting numbers. As your teacher rolls the number cubes and calls out each sum, you will cross out an O over the number called. The goal of the game is to be the first person to cross out all ten of your O's.

Talk with your team about the possible outcomes of this game. Then draw a number line like the one below on your own paper. Place a total of ten O's on your number line. Each O should be placed above a number. You should distribute them based on what results you think your teacher will get. More than one O can be placed above a number.

Follow your teacher's instructions to play the game.

5-55. Gerald's strategy for the Ten O's game was to place an O on each number from 1 to 10. He was frustrated that his strategy of placing his ten O's was not working, so he decided to analyze the game.

Gerald began by trying to create a table to list all of the possible combinations of rolls. He made the table at right.

Did he list them all? If so, how can you be sure that they are all there? If not, give examples of a few that he has missed.

Cube 1	Cube 2
1	1
2	2
3	3
4	4
5	5
6	6
1	2
2	3
3	4
4	5
5	6
1	3
2	4
3	5
4	6
1	4
2	5
3	6
1	5
2	6
1	6

5-56. Gerald decided that this method was taking too long, that it was too confusing, and that he made too many mistakes. Even if he listed all of the combinations correctly, he still had to find the sums and then find the theoretical probabilities for each one. Inspired by multiplication tables, he decided to try to make sense of the problem by organizing the possibilities in a **probability table** like the one shown at right.

+	1	2	3	4	5	6
1	2	3				
2	3	4				
3	4					
4						
5						
6						

a. How does Gerald's table represent the two events in this situation? What should go in each of the empty cells? Discuss this with your team and then complete Gerald's table on your own paper.

b. How many total possible number combinations are there for rolling the two cubes? Is each combination listed equally likely? That is, is the probability of getting two 1's the same as that of getting two 2's or a 3 and a 1?

c. How many ways are there to get each sum? Are there any numbers on the game board that are not possible to achieve?

d. What is the theoretical probability for getting each sum listed on the Ten O's game board?

e. Now work with your team to determine a better strategy for Gerald to place his ten O's on the game board that you think will help him to win this game. Explain your strategy and your reasoning.

5-57.   Gloria and Jenny each have only one O left on their game board. Gloria's O is at 6, and Jenny's is at 8. Which student is more likely to win on the next roll? Explain.

5-58.   Now go back and analyze the game of rock-paper-scissors using a probability table to determine the possible outcomes.

   a.   Make a probability table and use it to find the probability of Player A's winning and the probability of Player B's winning. Did you get the same answers as before?

   b.   Do the probabilities for Player A's winning and Player B's winning add up to 1 (or 100%)? If not, why not?

5-59.   Imagine that you have a bag with a red block, a blue block, a green block, and a yellow block inside. You plan to make two draws from the bag, replacing the block after each draw.

   a.   Are these two events (the two draws of a block) independent or dependent? Does it matter if you replace the block each time? Why or why not?

   b.   Find the probability of getting a red block and a blue block. (Either color can come first.) Be ready to share your method of organizing the possible outcomes.

METHODS AND MEANINGS

Probability of Compound Events

Sometimes when you are finding a probability, you are interested in either of two outcomes taking place, but not both. For example, you may be interested in drawing a king or a queen from a deck of cards. At other times, you might be interested in one event followed by another event. For example, you might want to roll a one on a number cube and then roll a six. The probabilities of combinations of simple events are called **compound events**.

To find the probability of *either* one event *or* another event that has nothing in common with the first, you can find the probability of each event separately and then add their probabilities. Using the example above of drawing a king or a queen from a deck of cards:

$$P(\text{king}) = \tfrac{4}{52} \quad \text{and} \quad P(\text{queen}) = \tfrac{4}{52} \quad \text{so} \quad P(\text{king or queen}) = \tfrac{4}{52} + \tfrac{4}{52} = \tfrac{8}{52} = \tfrac{2}{13}$$

For two independent events, to find the probability of *both* one *and* the other event occurring, you can find the probability of each event separately and then multiply their probabilities. Using the example of rolling a one followed by a six on a number cube:

$$P(1) = \tfrac{1}{6} \quad \text{and} \quad P(6) = \tfrac{1}{6} \quad \text{so} \quad P(1 \text{ then } 6) = \tfrac{1}{6} \cdot \tfrac{1}{6} = \tfrac{1}{36}$$

Note that you would carry out the same computation if you wanted to know the probability of rolling a one on a green cube and a six on a red cube if you rolled both of them at the same time.

Review & Preview

5-60.   Maggie was at the state fair and decided to buy a sundae from an ice cream stand. The ice cream stand had four flavors of ice cream (chocolate, vanilla, mint chip, and coconut) and two toppings (hot fudge and caramel). How many different sundaes could Maggie create using one scoop of ice cream and one topping? Make a probability table to support your answer.

5-61.   The Aloha Stadium in Honolulu, Hawaii, has seats for 50,000 people. At an upcoming football game, a company is planning to give away free hats to people based on where they are sitting.

   a.   The seats are divided into 40 different sections. If hats are given in only 5 sections, what is the probability of a guest's sitting in a section that gets a hat?

   b.   The company is going to choose three rows in each section to win the hats. There are 46 rows in a section. If you are sitting in a winning section, what is the probability that you are not sitting in a winning row?

   c.   The company plans to give away 750 hats. If you buy a ticket to the game, what is the probability that you will receive a hat?

5-62.   A lemonade recipe calls for using a ratio of 2 cups of lemon juice for every 4 cups of water.

   a.   Draw and label a diagram like the one at right to show the percent of lemonade that is water and the percent that is lemon juice.

Old-Fashioned Lemonade

____ cups
lemon juice

6 cups
lemonade

0%   100%

   b.   What is the ratio of lemon juice to total liquid?

   c.   Angel made 10 cups of lemonade. She used 3 cups of lemon juice in her mixture. Did she follow the same recipe? In other words, did she use the same ratio of lemon juice to total liquid?

5-63.   Robert found an old game in a closet and wanted to play it. However, a portion of the spinner shown at right could not be read. Find the missing portion of the spinner for Robert.

5-64.   Copy and complete each of the Diamond Problems below. The pattern used in the Diamond Problems is shown at right.

   a.   0.32 / 1.2   b.   11 / 25   c.   −9   −7   d.   234 / 31

5.2.5 What if there are more than two events?

Probability Trees

In this lesson you will work with different models for organizing outcomes of multiple events when *both* one event *and* another event occur. Throughout this lesson, use these questions to help focus your team's discussion.

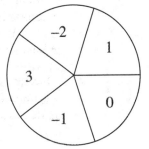

Is there more than one event?

Do *both* one event *and* other events occur?

Are the events independent?

5-65.   THE DOUBLE SPIN

A giant wheel is divided into 5 equal sections labeled $-2, -1, 0, 1,$ and 3. At the Double Spin, players spin the wheel shown at right two times. The sum of their spins determines whether they win.

Work with your team to determine probabilities of different outcomes by answering the questions below.

a.   Make a list of the possible sums you could get.

b.   Which sum do you think will be the most probable?

c.   Create a probability table that shows all possible outcomes for the two spins.

d.   If Tabitha could choose the winning sum for the Double Spin game, what sum would you advise her to choose? What is the probability of her getting that sum with two spins?

5-66. Scott's job at Crazy Creations Ice Cream Shop is to design new ice cream flavors. The company has just received some new ingredients and Scott wants to be sure to try all of the possible combinations. He needs to choose one item from each category to create the new flavor.

Base Flavor	Chunky Mix-In	Fruit Swirl
Vanilla Chocolate	Hazelnuts Sprinkles Toffee bits	Apricot Plum Berry Grape

a. Without talking with your teammates, list three different combinations Scott could try. Make sure you use the word "and." Then share your combinations with your study team. How many different combinations did you find? Do you think you found all of the possibilities?

b. Creating a list of all of the possibilities would take time and require a lot of writing the same words over and over. Because there are more than two options, a probability table is also challenging. An alternative is creating a **probability tree** to show the different combinations. A probability tree, like the one started at right and on the Lesson 5.2.5 Resource Page, shows the different possibilities branching off each other. In this case, the two segments on the left show the base flavors. Each different mix-in choice branches off of the base flavor, and each fruit swirl branches off each mix-in choice. The first letter of each choice is used to label this diagram.

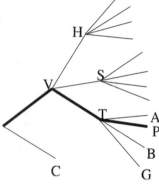

The bold line in the diagram shows the combination vanilla, toffee bits and plum swirl. Complete the probability tree to show all of the possible combinations.

c. How many different flavor combinations are possible? Where do you look on the diagram to count the number of complete combinations?

d. Use your probability tree to help you find the probability that Scott's final combination will include plum swirl.

e. What is the probability that his final combination will include hazelnuts?

5-67.   Scott's sister loves hazelnuts and Scott's little brother loves grape.

   a.   Recall that events are favorable outcomes. List all of the outcomes in
        Scott's sister's event. List all the outcomes in Scott's little brother's event.

   b.   Two events are **mutually exclusive** if they have no outcomes in common.
        Do Scott's sister and little brother have mutually exclusive events?

   c.   What would two mutually exclusive events in the Crazy Creations Ice-
        Cream Shop be?

5-68.   In a power outage, Rona has to reach into her closet in
        the dark to get dressed. She is going to find one shirt and
        one pair of pants. She has three different pairs of pants
        hanging there: one black, one brown, and one plaid. She
        also has two different shirts: one white and one polka dot.

   a.   Draw a probability tree to organize the different
        outfit combinations Rona might choose.

   b.   What is the probability that she will wear *both* a
        polka dot shirt *and* plaid pants?

   c.   What is the probability that she will not wear the black pants?

   d.   For what kinds of problems can you also make a probability table? If it is
        possible, make a probability table for Rona's outfits. Which way of
        representing the outcomes do you like better?

   e.   Are the events polka dot and plaid mutually exclusive? Explain.

   f.   Are the events polka dot and white mutually exclusive? Explain.

5-69.   Represent all of the possible outcomes using a list, probability table, or
        probability tree. Then find the indicated probability in each situation below.

   a.   You flip a coin three times in a row and
        get heads exactly twice.

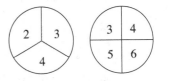

   b.   You spin the two spinners at right and
        exactly one spinner lands on 4.

   c.   At the car rental agency, you will be given either a truck or a sedan. Each
        model comes in four colors: green, black, white, or tan. If there is one
        vehicle of each color for each model available, what is the probability you
        will get a green truck?

5-70.   LEARNING LOG

In your Learning Log, describe the methods for organizing
outcomes in a probability situation that you have learned in
the past few lessons, such as systematic lists, probability
tables and probability trees. Describe situations for which
each tool is appropriate and any advantages and
disadvantages with using it. You may want to include an
example from your recent work to help you explain. Title
this entry "Methods to Organize Probability Outcomes"
and label it with today's date.

METHODS AND MEANINGS

Probability Models for Multiple Events

MATH NOTES

To determine all possible outcomes for multiple events when *both* one event *and* the other occur, there are several different models you can use to help organize the information.

Consider spinning each spinner at right once.

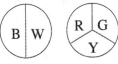

If you use a plan or a pattern to find all of the outcomes in an event, you are making a **systematic list**. For example, assume that you first spin B on spinner 1. Then, list all of the possible outcomes on spinner 2. Next, assume that your first spin is W on spinner 1, and complete the list.

Systematic List

BR	WR
BG	WG
BY	WY

A **probability table** can also organize information if there are exactly two events. The possibilities for each event are listed on the sides of the table as shown, and the combinations of outcomes are listed inside the table. In the example at right, the possible outcomes for spinner 1 are listed on the left side, and the possible outcomes for spinner 2 are listed across the top. The possible outcomes of the two events are shown inside the rectangle. In this table, the top and side are divided evenly because the outcomes are equally likely. Inside the table you can see the possible combinations of outcomes.

Probability Table

	R	G	Y
B	BR	BG	BY
W	WR	WG	WY

A **probability tree** is another method for organizing information. The different outcomes are organized at the end of branches of a tree. The first section has B and W at the ends of two branches because there are two possible outcomes of spinner 1, namely B and W. Then the ends of three more branches represent the possible outcomes of the second spinner, R, G, and Y. These overall possible outcomes of the two events are shown as the six branch ends.

Probability Tree

```
         R   (BR)
    B  < G   (BG)
         Y   (BY)

         R   (WR)
    W  < G   (WG)
         Y   (WY)
```

5-71.   WALKING THE DOG

Marcus and his brother always argue about who will
walk the dog. Their father wants to find a random way
of deciding who will do the job. He invented a game to
help them decide. Each boy will have a bag with three
colored blocks in it: one yellow, one green, and one
white. Each night before dinner, each boy draws a block
out of his bag. If the colors match, Marcus walks the
dog. If the two colors do not match, his brother walks
the dog. Marcus's father wants to be sure that the game
is fair. Help him decide.

a.   Make a probability tree of all of the possible combinations of draws that
     Marcus and his brother could make. How many possibilities are there?

b.   What is the probability that the boys will draw matching blocks? Is the
     game fair? Justify your answer.

5-72.   For Shelley's birthday on Saturday, she received:

   • Two new shirts (one plaid and one striped);

   • Three pairs of shorts (tan, yellow, and green); and,

   • Two pairs of shoes (sandals and tennis shoes).

On Monday she wants to wear a completely new outfit. How many possible
outfit choices does she have from these new clothes? Draw a diagram to
explain your reasoning.

5-73.   In 2009, the federal government budget was $3.1 trillion ($3,100,000,000,000).
         The government was looking to cut costs.

a.   If it decided to cut 1%, how much money did it cut?

b.   If the government reduced the budget by 7%, how much money did it cut?

c.   If the government eliminated $93 billion ($93,000,000,000) from the
     budget, what percentage did it cut?

5-74.   Evaluate each expression.

a. $7+(-3)$ b. $(10)(-5)$ c. $-5+6$ d. $(-2)÷(-2)$

5-75.   Write expressions for the perimeter and the area of this algebra tile shape. Then simplify each expression by combining like terms.

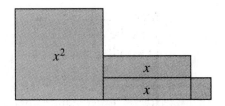

5.2.6 What if the events are not equally likely?

Compound Events

In Lesson 5.2.5, you used systematic lists, probability tables, and probability trees to organize the outcomes of different probability situations. Today you will use a probability table to help organize events when one outcome is more likely than another.

5-76. Nina is buying a new pet fish. At the pet store, the fish tank has an equal number of two kinds of fish: tetras and guppies. Each kind of fish comes in four different colors: yellow, orange, blue, and silver. There are an equal number of each color of fish in the tank.

a. If Nina scoops out a fish at random, what is the probability that she will scoop out a silver tetra? Show how you decided.

b. Nina set up the table below, to organize the different possible outcomes. She represented the kind of fish on one side of her table and the color possibilities on the other. What do the fractions inside her table represent?

	Yellow	Orange	Blue	Silver
Tetra	$YT = \frac{1}{8}$	$OT = \frac{1}{8}$	$BT = \frac{1}{8}$	$ST = \frac{1}{8}$
Guppy	$YG = \frac{1}{8}$	$OG = \frac{1}{8}$	$BG = \frac{1}{8}$	$SG = \frac{1}{8}$

c. As Nina looked at her work, she noticed that her table looked a lot like a rectangle with the area divided into parts. *"Could that help me calculate the probabilities?"* she wondered. She used the length and width of the silver tetra section to set up this equation: $\frac{1}{4} \cdot \frac{1}{2} = \frac{1}{8}$.

How does this equation relate to the length, width, and area of this section of the rectangle? Does this match the probability you found in part (a)?

d. What is the area of the complete large rectangle?

5-77.   TESTING THE AREA MODEL

Nina decided to see if thinking about finding area would help find other probabilities. She put three cubes in a bag: two blue cubes and one yellow cube. She pulled one cube out, put it back in the bag, and then drew another.

a.   Use a systematic list or a probability tree to organize the possible color combinations she could draw. How many are there? What is P(blue and blue)?

b.   This time, Nina made the table at right. Based on the table, what is the probability of drawing two blue blocks? Is this the same probability you found in part (a)?

	B	B	Y
B	BB	BB	BY
B	BB	BB	BY
Y	YB	YB	YY

c.   Looking at her work, Edwin said, *"I think I can simplify this diagram."* His rectangle, also known as an area model, is shown at right. What is the area of the section representing blue and blue? Does this match the probability that Nina found?

	B ($\frac{2}{3}$)	Y ($\frac{1}{3}$)
B ($\frac{2}{3}$)	BB	BY
Y ($\frac{1}{3}$)	YB	YY

5-78.   The pet store sells a lot of pet food. On a slow day at the pet store, three people buy cat food, two people buy dog food, and one person buys food for a pet snake. If half of the customers pay with cash and half pay with credit card, what is the probability that a customer buying pet food will buy dog food with cash? Set up an area model like Edwin's in part (c) of problem 5-77 to help you find the probability.

5-79.   SPINNING ODDS AND EVENS — PART 1

Your team is going to play against your teacher in a game with two hidden spinners. Spinner A has the numbers 2, 3, and 4 on it. Spinner B has the numbers 6, 7, and 8 on it. The rules are:

1. Spin each spinner.

2. Add the results.

3. If the sum is even, one team gets a point. If the sum is odd, the other team gets a point.

4. The first team to earn 10 points wins.

a. Should you choose the odd or even numbers in order to win? Discuss the choices with your team and decide which side to take. Be prepared to justify your choice with mathematics.

b. Play the game at least three times with your teacher. Your teacher will spin the spinners and announce the results. Record the results of each spin and their sum. Is the result odd or even most often? Does this match with your prediction?

c. Make a probability table and determine the theoretical probability for this game.

5-80.   SPINNING ODDS AND EVENS — PART 2

Now that you have played the game several times, obtain a Lesson 5.2.6 Resource Page from your teacher and take a close look at the hidden spinners.

a. Are the spinners different from what you expected? How? Be as specific as you can. Do you still think you made the correct choice of odd or even numbers?

b. What assumption about the spinners did you make in part (c) of problem 5-79?

c. What is the probability of spinning each outcome on Spinner A? On Spinner B?

5-81.   Raul had imagined that the spinners were divided into equal parts before he saw them. He created the probability table at right to organize the outcomes. *"I thought there would be a $\frac{1}{3}$ chance of spinning a 3 on Spinner A. But now that I see the spinners, I know that is not true. I need to make a new rectangle in order to find the probability."*

	6	7	8
2	8	9	10
3	9	10	11
4	10	11	12

a.   Create a new rectangle. Label the top row and left column with the numbers on each spinner and their probabilities.

b.   Write a multiplication problem to show the probability of spinning a 3 and a 7. Calculate P(3 and 7).

c.   Complete the table to show each possible sum and its probability.

d.   What is the probability of spinning an odd sum? What is the probability of spinning an even sum?

e.   Did you make the right choice of an odd or even number in problem 5-80? Explain your reasoning.

5-82.   **Additional Challenge:** Elliot loves music, especially listening to his music player on shuffle. He has songs stored in four categories: country, blues, rock, and classical. Two fifths of his songs are country songs, one sixth of his songs are classical, one third are blues, and the rest are rock.

a.   What is the likelihood that the first two songs will be a country song *and* then a classical?

b.   What is the likelihood that *either* a country song *or* a classical song will come up first?

5-83. Darnell designed the spinner at right for a game. It still has one incomplete section.

a. Help him figure out the probability of selecting a card on any turn. Show how you got your answer.

b. What is the probability that on any turn you will not get to spin again?

c. Which is more likely: to lose a turn or to select a card? Show how you know.

5-84. Manuel used pattern blocks to build the shapes below. The block marked A is a square, B is a trapezoid, C is a rhombus (a parallelogram with equal sides), and D is a triangle. Find the area of each of Manuel's shapes.

a.

b.

5-85. Rachel is collecting donations for the local animal shelter. So far she has collected $245, which is 70% of what she hopes to collect. How much money does Rachel plan to collect for the shelter? Show your work.

5-86. Darnell is designing a new game. He will have 110 different-colored blocks in a bag. While a person is blindfolded, he or she will reach in and pull out a block. The color of the block determines the prize according to Darnell's sign at right.

> blue → small toy
> purple → hat
> green → large stuffed animal

a. If he wants players to have a 60% probability of winning a small toy, how many blue blocks should he have?

b. If he wants players to have a 10% probability of winning a large stuffed animal, how many green blocks should he have?

5-87.   Simplify each expression below.

   a. $1\frac{1}{2}+2\frac{1}{8}$ b. $\frac{4}{5}-\frac{2}{3}+\frac{1}{6}$ c. $5\frac{3}{5}-1\frac{4}{5}$

5-88.   Lucas is having yogurt and an apple for a snack.
         There are five containers of yogurt in the refrigerator:
         three are raspberry, one is vanilla, and one is peach.
         There are also two green apples and three red apples.

   a.   If he reaches into the refrigerator to get a yogurt
        without looking, what is the probability that Lucas
        will choose a raspberry yogurt?

   b.   What is the probability that he will choose a red apple if it is the first item
        he selects?

   c.   What is the probability that Lucas will eat a raspberry yogurt and a red
        apple?

5-89.   A bag contains 3 red, 5 yellow, and 7 purple marbles. Find the probability of
         drawing a purple marble followed by a red marble. The first marble is put back
         in the bag between draws.

5-90.   Use graph paper to complete parts (a) through (c) below.

   a.   Draw an xy-coordinate graph and label each axis. Plot the following
        ordered pairs: $(2,3),(-2,3),(-2,-3),(2,-3)$. Connect the points in the given
        order as you plot them. Then connect the fourth point to the first one.

   b.   Describe the shape on your graph. What is its area? What is its perimeter?

   c.   Change only two points so that the shape has an area of 32 square units.
        List your points. Is there more than one answer?

5-91.   Jerry bought some pears at the store. He paid $4.59 for 5.4 pounds of pears.
         What is the unit price of the pears?

5-92.   Evaluate the following expressions using the Order of Operations.

   a. $7\cdot 8-4(6-2)+18$ b. $6^2-(8\cdot 3)+2^2(7\cdot 3)$

   c. $\frac{14}{2}-3(8-6)+7^2$ d. $-9-3(7-2)+\frac{24}{3}$

5.3.1 How can I draw it?

Describing Relationships Between Quantities

You may not know it, but you use mathematical thinking every day. You think mathematically when you figure out whether you can afford items you want to buy, or when you read a graph on a website. You also think mathematically when you double a recipe or when you estimate how much longer it will take to get somewhere based on how far you still have to go. Math can describe many of the relationships in the world around you.

Building your interpretation skills and developing ways to represent situations will help you solve problems. In this section, you will learn new ways to show your thinking when using math to solve problems. As you work today, think about the following questions:

How can I represent this with a diagram?

Who has more? Who has less?

5-93. Sometimes using the same words in a slightly different way can change their meaning. Read and compare the two situations below.

Situation 1	Situation 2
Myra has 15 marbles. This is ten less than Dahlia.	Myra has 15 marbles. Dahlia has ten less than Myra.

a. For each situation, draw a picture to represent the marbles each girl has. What is the difference between the problems?

b. In which problem does Myra have more marbles than Dahlia?

c. How many marbles does Dahlia have in Situation 1 above? How many does she have in Situation 2?

5-94. Ellie is building a dollhouse. She has boards that are two different lengths. One long board is 7 inches longer than the total length of three of the short boards.

a. Draw a picture showing how the short and long boards are related.

b. What are some possible lengths of her boards?

c. If one of the long boards is 50 inches long, how long is a short board? Be ready to share your thinking with the class.

5-95. Now read and compare Problems A and B below.

Problem A	Problem B
Dianna has $16. Jairo has twice as much money as Dianna. Who has more money?	Dianna has $16. She has twice as much money as Jairo. Who has more money?

a. Represent each problem with a diagram.

b. Compare the amount of money Jairo has in part (a) to the amount he has in part (b). Explain how you know in which situation he has more money.

5-96. Now you are going to reverse your thinking. Examine the pictures below. Then use words to describe the relationship you see in the pictures. Assume the lengths that appear to be equal are equal.

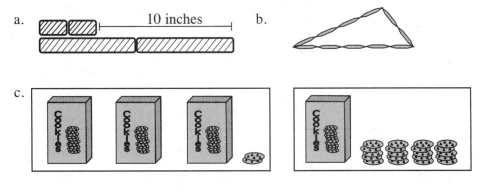

a. ⬜ 10 inches ⬜   b. △

c.

Same number of cookies

5-97.   Rich, Arielle, and Kristen just measured
         how tall they are in feet. Their heights
         are shown in the bar graph at right.

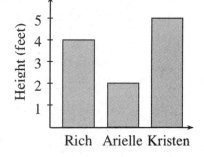

         Decide which statements below are true
         and which statements are false.
         Rewrite the false statements to make
         them true.

         a. Rich is one foot shorter than Kristen.

         b. Arielle is twice as tall as Rich.

         c. Kristen is one foot taller than twice Arielle's height.

         d. The sum of the three children's height is 10 feet.

5-98.   **Additional Challenge:** Represent the description below with a picture.

         Ellen is gluing tiles on the four vertical sides of a rectangular planter box. The
         longer side of the box is covered by six more than two times as many tiles as
         the shorter side.

Review & Preview

5-99.   Mr. Nowling's garden has a length that is 7 feet more than twice the width.
         Draw a diagram to represent this situation. Label each side of the garden, and
         then write an expression for the perimeter.

5-100.   The following number lines are missing some numbers. Use the information
         provided to complete the number lines.

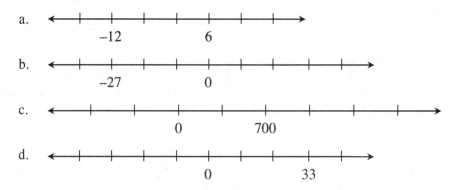

5-101.   Lynn was shopping and found a purse that was marked with a discount of "$\frac{1}{3}$ off." If the original cost of the purse was $80, how much will Lynn pay?

5-102.   Evaluate each expression using the Order of Operations.

a. $-4(-4+3)+2^2$ b. $-3-3-3-(-3)$

c. $-17+2(-2)(-2)$ d. $(2+(-3)(5))(3+2(-6))$

5-103.   Complete a Proportions Web for the following situation.

A candy-wrapping robot can wrap 434 pieces of candy in 5 minutes. How many pieces of candy can it wrap in any number of minutes?

5.3.2 How can I organize it?

Solving a Word Problem

You have seen that being able to draw diagrams and describe relationships is helpful for solving problems. In this lesson, you will learn another way to organize your thinking as you solve word problems.

5-104.   FENCING THE BASKETBALL COURT

The Parent Club at Post Falls Middle
School needs 183 feet of fencing to go
around the rectangular outdoor
basketball court behind the school
gym. The club volunteers will only
need to place a fence on three sides of
the court, because the wall of the gym
will form the fourth side. The length
of the court is 32 feet more than the
width. One of the shorter sides will be
5 feet shorter than the other one to
leave room for a gate.

Your Task: Determine how much fencing will be used on each side of the court. Be prepared to justify your answer and show all of your work. Be sure that someone who is not on your team can read and understand your work.

Discussion Points

What information do you know in the problem?

What do you need to figure out?

What diagram can you draw to represent this situation?

How did you organize your work?

How can a wrong answer help you revise your thinking?

5-105.   If another team came to look at your paper for problem 5-104, could that team understand your work? Why or why not? What else could you do to make it so that someone else could make sense of your work just by looking at it?

5-106.   Daniel, Ronald, and Zeba decided to organize their thinking in a table using a method they call the 5-D Process. Get a Lesson 5.3.2A Resource Page from your teacher that shows their work. Then answer some of the following questions during the whole-class discussion.

- *"What are the students Describing and Drawing?"*

- *"What is in the Define columns?"*

- *"What is the Do column used for?"*

- *"What are they trying to Decide?"*

- *"What might the Declare section be for?"*

5-107.   While one team was working on problem 5-104, the team members decided to see if a width of 30 feet would use all of the 183 feet of fencing. They figured out that, with a 30-foot width, the length would be 62 feet and the side with the gate would be 25 feet. Only 117 feet of fencing would be used.

What is a logical number that they should try next for the width so that all of the fencing is used? Explain your reasoning.

5-108.   Finish problem 5-104 using the 5-D Process. Continue the table you looked at in problem 5-106 to find the answer.

5-109.   Use the steps of the 5-D Process to organize and solve each of the questions below. The Lesson 5.3.2C Resource Page may help you set up your table. Be sure to show each of the "D" steps clearly in your solution process.

a. Laura takes very good care of her vehicles. She owns a blue van and a red truck. Although she bought them both new, she has owned the truck for 17 years longer than she has owned the van. If the sum of the ages of the vehicles is 41 years, how old is the van and how old is the truck?

b. Ryan is thinking of a number. When he multiplies this number by 6 and then subtracts 15 from the answer, he ends up with his original number. What number is Ryan thinking of?

5-110.   The spinner at right is spun twice. Make a table and calculate the probability of each of the following outcomes.

a.   Getting black twice.

b.   Getting green twice.

5-111.   The local theater is raising ticket prices by 20%.

a.   Assuming the current youth ticket price is $7.50, use the diagram at right to find out how much more youth tickets will cost.

b.   What will be the new youth ticket price?

5-112.   Copy each expression below and simplify it using the Order of Operations.

a. $6 + 4(2 + 3)^2$

b. $(6 + 4)(2 + 3)$

c. $6 + 4 \cdot 2^3 + 3$

5-113.   Write the expression as shown on the Expression Mats. Then simplify by making zeros and combining like terms.

a.

b.

5-114.   Look at the algebra tile shape at right.

a.   Write an algebraic expression for the perimeter of the shape in two ways: first, by finding the length of each of the sides and adding them all together; second, by writing an equivalent, simplified expression.

b.   Write an algebraic expression for the area of the shape.

5.3.3 How do I use the 5-D Process?

Strategies for Using the 5-D Process

Math is used to solve challenging problems that apply to daily life. For example, how much fresh water is on the planet? How many area codes for telephone numbers are needed in a city? Where should a city build transportation lines such as city bus systems and subways to reduce traffic on the freeways? Mathematics can provide helpful insights for the answers to these questions.

When you are trying to solve a new and challenging problem, it is useful to have a strategy. The 5-D Process that you learned about in Lesson 5.3.2 will often work when you are trying to solve a problem you have not seen before.

In this lesson, you will practice using this process to solve more word problems. You will also compare the different ways that your classmates use the 5-D Process to help them. Be sure to write your work neatly and be prepared to justify your reasoning.

As you work using the 5-D Process, consider the questions below.

How can you describe the problem?

How can you decide how to label the columns?

How can you organize the columns?

How can you decide which quantity to start with?
Does it matter which one you choose?

How can you decide which number to try first?

At the end of this lesson, your team may be asked to present your responses to one or more of the target questions above.

5-115.   A **scalene triangle** has three unequal side lengths. The medium-length side is 7 cm longer than the shortest side. The longest side is twice as long as the shortest side. The total perimeter is 39 cm. What are the lengths of the sides of the triangle?

5-116.   Travis and Angela were playing a "Guess My Numbers" game. Angela told Travis, "I'm thinking of two positive numbers. The difference of my numbers is 4, and the product of my numbers is 96. What are my numbers?" Help Travis find Angela's numbers.

5-117.　The Potter Valley basketball team did not record how many baskets each player made during the last game. Jenny remembers that she made three times as many baskets as Grace. Alexis knows that she made six more baskets than Grace. Joan thinks that she made 4 fewer baskets than Grace. Tammy is sure that she made the same number of baskets as Joan. Altogether the five players made 40 baskets. How many baskets did each player make?

5-118.　Ms. Pacheco, Mr. Edwards, and Mr. Richards are three math teachers at Turner Middle School. Ms. Pacheco is three years older than Mr. Richards. Mr. Edwards is twice as old as Mr. Richards. The sum of Mr. Richards' age and Mr. Edwards' age is 81. How old is each person?

5-119.　Ramon was studying pond life in Doyle Park. In two hours, he counted four more frogs than turtles. The number of crayfish he counted was three more than twice the number of turtles. In total, he counted 54 turtles and crayfish. How many frogs were there?

5-120.　Dawn is trying to find the dimensions of a parallelogram. She knows that the base is one unit less than twice the height of the shape. The area is 91 square units. How long are the base and height?

5-121.　**Additional Challenge:** If one side of a square is increased by 12 feet and the side connected to it is decreased by three feet, a rectangle is formed. The perimeter of the rectangle is 62 feet. How long was the side of the original square?

5-122.　With your team, re-read the focus questions for this lesson, reprinted below:

How can you describe the problem?

How can you decide how to label the columns?

How can you organize the columns?

How can you decide which quantity to start with?
Does it matter which one you choose?

How can you decide which number to test first?

Discuss the strategies you use with the 5-D Process as a team. Be prepared to share your ideas with the class.

　　　　　　　　　　　　　　　　　　　　　　　Core Connections, Course 2

MᴇᴛHODS AND Mᴇᴀɴɪɴɢs

MATH NOTES

Solving Problems with the 5-D Process

The **5-D Process** is an organized method to solve problems. The D's stand for Describe/Draw, Define, Do, Decide, and Declare. An example of this work is shown below.

Problem: The base of a rectangle is 13 centimeters longer than the height. If the perimeter is 58 centimeters, find the base and the height of the rectangle.

Describe/Draw: The shape is a rectangle and we are looking at the perimeter.

height

base

Define		Do	Decide
Height (trial)	Base (height + 13)	Perimeter 2(base) + 2(height)	58?
Trial 1: 10	10 + 13 = 23		66 is too high

Use a trial value. Use the relationships stated in the problem to determine the values of the other quantities (such as base and perimeter).   Decide if the answer is correct. Revise and make another trial until you find the correct answer.

Trial 2: 7	7 + 13 = 20	2(20) + 2(7) = 54	too low
Trial 3: 8	8 + 13 = 21	2(21) + 2(8) = 58	correct

Declare: The base is 21 centimeters and the height is 8 centimeters.

5-123. If the total area of the rectangle below is 168 square units, how long is each side? To find out how long the x side must be, copy the diagram and table and answer the questions that follow.

Describe/Draw:

$x + 2$

x

Declare:

	Define		Do	Decide
	Side #1	Side #2	(Side one)·(Side two)	Area = 168?
Trial 1:	10	12		
Trial 2:				

a. Describe how the lengths of the two sides are related to each other.

b. Which side of the rectangle does Side #2 represent?

c. Use the 5-D Process to complete the table. Find the lengths of the two sides of the rectangle.

5-124. Evaluate each expression.

a. $\frac{1}{2}(5+13)-4\cdot5$ b. $(5+11)-(24-15)\cdot(3)$ c. $6^2+3\cdot7-9\div3$

5-125. Simplify the following variable expressions.

a. $2x+5+x-6+3x$ b. $x-8+x-5+x+1$

5-126.   A radio station is giving away free t-shirts to students in local schools. It plans to give away 40 shirts at Big Sky Middle School and 75 shirts at High Peaks High School. Big Sky Middle School has 350 students, and 800 students attend High Peaks High School.

   a.   What is the probability of getting a t-shirt if you are a student at the middle school?

   b.   What is the probability of getting a t-shirt if you are a student at the high school?

   c.   Are you more likely to get a t-shirt if you are a student at the high school, or at the middle school?

5-127.   One student rewrote the expression $17 \cdot 102$ as $17(100 + 2)$. Then she simplified to get the expression $1700 + 34$.

   a.   Are the three expressions equivalent? Justify your answer.

   b.   What property of numbers does this demonstrate?

5.3.4 How can I represent it?

Using Variables to Represent Quantities in Word Problems

Today you will continue to use the 5-D Process as you solve word problems. In this lesson, you will use a variable to represent the unknown value in the problem.

Think of these questions as you work on the problems today:

> What is the problem asking?
>
> What is the relationship between the quantities involved?
>
> How can I choose which part of the problem to represent with a variable?

5-128.   Mai has one mini-box of Choco-Blasters candy, and Warren gave her three more pieces. Samara has two mini-boxes of Choco-Blasters and gave six pieces to Will. Now Mai and Samara have the same number of Choco-Blasters.

How many Choco-Blasters are in a mini-box? Assuming all mini-boxes of Choco-Blasters have the same number of pieces in them, use the 5-D Process to solve this problem.

5-129.   Allen's team was working on a problem but did not have time to finish it. They also did not follow the teacher's directions for showing work in the Define section. Discuss with your team what information you can get from Allen's table below.

	DEFINE		**DO**	**DECIDE**
	LENGTH	WIDTH	DOUBLE EACH SIDE AND ADD TOGETHER	TARGET PERIMETER = 36?
TRIAL 1:	3	9	$2(3) + 2(9) = 24$	TOO SMALL
TRIAL 2:	4	?		

a.   Is there enough information in Allen's table to finish the problem? Why or why not?

b.   What would you need to know in order to complete Trial 2? Explain your thinking.

5-130.   Allen's teammate, Scott, was also working on problem 5-129, but he organized his table differently. As Scott explained his table to Allen, he used the pattern in the first two trials to represent the quantities in the third row with a variable, x.

Look at the table below.

a.   How is it different from Allen's table?

b.   What does the x in the table represent?

c.   In words, describe the relationship between the length and the width.

d.   Where did the expression $x+x+(2x+3)+(2x+3)$ come from? Explain your thinking.

DEFINE		DO	DECIDE
LENGTH	WIDTH	ADD ALL 4 SIDES TOGETHER	TARGET PERIMETER = 36?
TRIAL 1: 3	$2(3)+3$	$3+3+9+9=24$	TOO SMALL
TRIAL 2: 6	$2(6)+3$	$6+6+15+15=42$	TOO LARGE
x	$2(x)+3$	$x+x+(2x+3)+(2x+3)$	

5-131.   Izzy's team used a 5-D table to solve a problem that involved **consecutive integers**. Consecutive integers are integers that follow each other on a number line. The numbers $1, 2, 3, \ldots, 14, 15, 16, \ldots,$ or $-5, -4, -3, \ldots$ are all examples of consecutive integers. The table below shows part of their work on the problem.

Copy the table and finish the problem. After you find a solution, apply Scott's idea from problem 5-130 to add a row that uses a variable to summarize the problem's process.

DEFINE			DO	DECIDE
1ST NUMBER	2ND NUMBER	3RD NUMBER	ADD ALL NUMBERS TOGETHER	TARGET SUM = 57
TRIAL 1: 15	$15+1$	$15+2$	$15+16+17=48$	TOO SMALL
TRIAL 2: 20	$20+1$	$20+2$	$20+21+22=63$	TOO LARGE

5-132.   Meiko saw someone's expressions in the 5-D Process table below and wanted to reverse the process. The problem involved a bag of green, red, and blue marbles.

	DEFINE			**DO**	**DECIDE**
	GREEN	RED	BLUE	TOTAL MARBLES	TOTAL = 71?
TRIAL 1:	15				
	x	$x-2$	$2x+5$	$x+(x-2)+(2x+5)$	

a.   One of the variable expressions describes how the number of red marbles compares with the number of green marbles. How can you describe this relationship in words?

b.   Based on the variable expressions, use words to describe how the number of blue marbles compares with the number of green marbles.

c.   How many total marbles are in the bag?

d.   If there are 15 green marbles in the bag, how many red and blue marbles are in the bag? Show your work.

e.   Use the information in the table to find the number of green, red, and blue marbles.

5-133.   Camille knew that a triangle had one side with a length of 16 inches and another side with a length of 20 inches. She did not know the length of the third side, but she did know that the perimeter was five times the length of the unknown side. How long is the unknown side? Copy the table below and complete the table. You may add as many rows as you need to solve the problem. Remember to summarize the relationships with a row that uses a variable and to complete the Declare sentence.

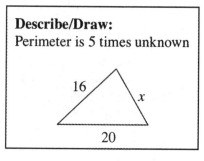

Describe/Draw:
Perimeter is 5 times unknown

	DEFINE		**DO**	**DECIDE**
	UNKNOWN SIDE	PERIMETER	COMPARE SUM TO PERIMETER	SAME?
TRIAL 1:	5	5(5)	$5+16+20 \overset{?}{=} 25$ $41 \neq 25$	No

Declare:

5-134.   Margaret was working on the problem below.

Declan earned four times as much money last
summer as his sister Gwen. Together they earned
$475. How much did each person earn?

The table below shows the first two trials Margaret made. Based on the results,
work with your study team to suggest a number she should try next. (You do
not actually need to solve the problem.)

- Is it reasonable for different members of your team to suggest different
  numbers?

- Are there some numbers that would not be helpful? Explain.

	DEFINE		DO	DECIDE
	GWEN'S EARNINGS	DECLAN'S EARNINGS	ADD BOTH OF THEIR EARNINGS TOGETHER	TARGET SUM = $475
TRIAL 1:	$50	$4($50)$	$50 + $200 = $250	TOO SMALL
TRIAL 2:	$100	$4($100)$	$100 + $400 = $500	TOO LARGE

5-135.   Dawn and Myrna's father has asked them to build a rectangular pen for their
dog. They have 74 feet of fencing. They want the length to be one more than
twice the width. Use the 5-D Process to help Dawn and Myrna find the
dimensions (both length and width) of the pen.

5-136.   **Additional Challenge:** Use the 5-D Process to find three consecutive integers
that have a product of 3360.

5-137.   LEARNING LOG

In your Learning Log, describe how you decide which
number to use as your first trial in the 5-D Process. Then
explain how you use the results of your first trial to choose
your next trial number. You may want to include an example
from your recent work to help you explain. Title this entry
"Defining and Deciding" and label it with today's date.

METHODS AND MEANINGS

Consecutive Integers

Consecutive integers are integers that come "one after another" in order (that is, without skipping any of them). For example: 11, 12, and 13 are three consecutive integers. The numbers 10, 12, 14, and 16 are four **consecutive even integers** because in counting up from 10, no even numbers are skipped. Likewise, 15, 17, and 19 are **consecutive odd integers**.

In algebra, it is sometimes necessary to represent a list of consecutive integers. To represent any list in general, you must use variables. It is common to let x represent the first integer. See the examples below of how to write a list of consecutive integers.

Three consecutive integers: $x, x+1, x+2$

Three consecutive odd integers: $x, x+2, x+4$

Three consecutive even integers: $x, x+2, x+4$

Note that consecutive even integers and odd integers look alike because both even integers and odd integers are two apart.

Review & Preview

5-138. Think about the mathematical process you use as you solve the following problems. Show your work and your solutions.

  a. If there are 100 students in a room and 40 of them are boys, how many are girls?

  b. If there are 17 blue and white stripes on a flag and 9 of them are blue, how many are white?

  c. If there are 250 pennies and dimes in a box and 130 of them are pennies, how many are dimes?

  d. Now it is time to generalize. Imagine you know how many items you have in a collection of two types of things. If you know how many of one of the items you have, how could you find how many of the other item you have?

5-139.   If you can travel 156 miles on 4 gallons of gasoline, how far can you travel on 12 gallons? How many miles on 6 gallons? A diagram may help you with your reasoning. Show your work and explain your thinking.

5-140.   Use the Distributive Property to simplify the following expressions.

   a. $4(x+2)$ b. $-5(9+x)$ c. $7(x-3)$

5-141.   Evaluate the following expressions.

   a. $-5+2(8-12)$ b. $(-5+2)(8-12)$ c. $-5+2\cdot8-12$

   d. $\frac{1}{2}(-6)(4+10)$ e. $-\frac{2}{3}\cdot6+15\div(-3)$ f. $(7-2)^2-5\div5$

5-142.   Find the lengths of the missing sides on the similar shapes at right. What is the scale factor?

original

copy

5.3.5 How can I solve it?

More Word Problem Solving

So far in Section 5.3, you have been using a 5-D Process as a way to organize and solve problems. Today you will continue using this process to solve problems in a variety of situations.

As you work, use the following questions to focus your team's discussion.

What is the problem asking?

What is the relationship between the quantities involved?

How can you decide which part of the problem to represent as x?

What if a different quantity were represented by x?

5-143.   According to many sources, insects are the most diverse group of animals on the planet. The number of species is estimated at between six and ten million. Insects are said to represent more than half of all known living organisms and potentially over 90% of the differing life forms on Earth.

The following problems are about insects and other creepy-crawly creatures. You will use your math skills to find out some fascinating facts about them. Your teacher will assign your team one of the following problems to solve. Be prepared to present your solution, including all steps of your 5-D solving process, to the class.

a.   Many insects migrate (travel) between their summer and winter homes. The desert locust migrates about 800 miles farther than the Monarch butterfly every spring, and the pink-spotted hawk moth migrates about 200 miles less than four times the distance of the Monarch butterfly every spring. Laid end to end, the distances traveled by a Monarch butterfly, a desert locust, and a pink-spotted hawk moth is about 12,600 miles every spring. How far does each species travel?

Problem continues on next page. →

5-143.   *Problem continued from previous page.*

b. Bees, wasps, and ants all live in colonies that have a queen. The queen of the colony is really the mother of all the insects in the colony. During the spring and summer, many eggs are laid in bee, wasp, and ant colonies all over the world.

Queen bees lay about double the number of eggs in a day that queen ants lay. Queen wasps lay about 600 fewer eggs a day than queen ants do. An average queen bee, ant, and wasp together lay about 2600 eggs a day. How many eggs would each type of queen lay in one day?

c. Flies cannot see much farther than 24 to 36 inches away from their eyes, but that is not due to a lack of lenses – dragonflies have thousands of lenses! In one eye, dragonflies have two thousand more lenses than seven times the number of lenses that houseflies have in one eye. If one housefly eye and one dragonfly eye together have 34,000 lenses, how many lenses do houseflies have in one eye? How many do dragonflies have in one eye?

d. Think you do not have enough room to farm? Think again. You could farm worms under your desk with a commercially available worm farm that measures 16" x 16" x 28". You can buy the worms online. At 1200 worms per pound, you could start your own business just as John did. He's not good at keeping his records, however, and he needs your help.

John buys his worms from two online stores, Worm Heaven and Wiggles R Us. John remembers that he ordered 1200 more than twice as many worms from Worm Heaven as he did from Wiggles R Us. He also knows he has 18,000 worms. How many worms did he order from each store?

Problem continues on next page. →

5-143.   *Problem continued from previous page.*

   e.   There are many kinds of animals that live in and on our bodies, called
        parasites. Some of the longest parasites live in our intestines. Two of these
        parasites are roundworms and tapeworms. Their lengths can be quite
        different, depending on how long they have been living in someone's body.

        One of the longest tapeworms ever measured was three feet less than seven
        times the length of the longest roundworm ever measured. If you laid these
        two worms end to end, they would measure an amazing 69 feet! How long
        was the tapeworm and how long was the roundworm?

   f.   Did you know that most of the states in this
        country have official state insects and
        butterflies? Out of 30 states, the three most
        common insects are Monarch butterflies,
        honeybees, and ladybugs. The number of
        states that have Monarch butterflies as their
        official insect is one more than the number
        of states that have ladybugs as their official
        insect. The number of states that have
        honeybees as their official insect is three
        times the number of states with ladybugs as their state insect minus one.
        How many states have each kind of insect as their state insect?

   g.   Mosquitoes and other biting insects can cause a great deal of discomfort.
        They can also spread diseases that threaten public health in many areas of
        the world. The seed oil of a plant commonly called the physic nut is burned
        in lamps in India and parts of Africa to repel biting insects, especially
        mosquitoes. A scientific investigation was done to identify which
        chemicals in the oil were responsible for deterring mosquitoes. Three
        chemicals in the oil, specifically palmitic, linoleic, and stearic acids, were
        tested for find their effectiveness against mosquitoes that spread two deadly
        diseases in Africa, yellow fever and dengue fever.

        In the study, palmitic acid was determined to be the most effective
        chemical, providing three times the protection of stearic acid and was ten
        percentage points higher in protection than linoleic acid. The effectiveness
        percentages of stearic acid plus linoleic acid together were five percentage
        points higher than palmitic acid. What is the effectiveness of stearic acid in
        repelling mosquitoes?

5-144.   The number of girls at Middle School
Cyber Summer Camp was six more
than twice the number of boys. There
were a total of 156 middle school
students at the camp. Use the 5-D
Process to find the number of boys
and the number of girls at camp.

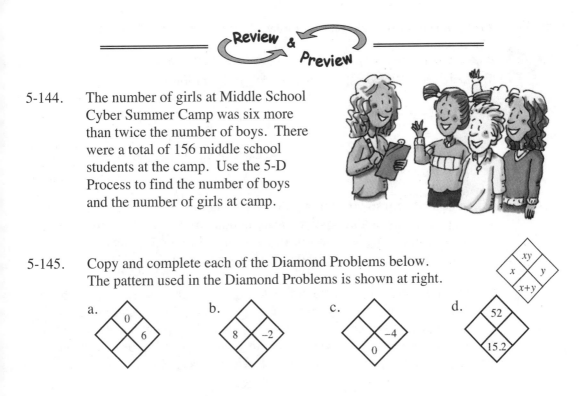

5-145.   Copy and complete each of the Diamond Problems below.
The pattern used in the Diamond Problems is shown at right.

a.   0   6

b.   8   −2

c.   −4   0

d.   52   15.2

5-146.   **Multiple Choice:** Which of the following expressions could be used to find the
average (mean) of the numbers k, m, and n?

A. $k+m+n$ B. $3(k+m+n)$ C. $\frac{k+m+n}{3}$ D. $3k+m+n$

5-147.   The Giant Prize Wheel at the county fair is evenly divided into 10 sections.
One is labeled "Large Prize," three are labeled "Small Prize," and the rest are
labeled "No Prize."

a.   If you spin once, what is the probability of winning a large prize?

b.   If you spin once, what is the probability of winning any prize?

c.   If 50 people spin the prize wheel, approximately how many people should
expect to win a prize of any kind?

5-148.   This problem is a checkpoint for Order of Operations. It will be referred to as Checkpoint 5.

Evaluate each expression using the Order of Operations.

a. $16 - 2^3 \div 8 + 5$

b. $(-2 + 6)^2 - \left(\frac{3}{2}\right) \cdot 14 + 1$

Check your answers by referring to the Checkpoint 5 materials located at the back of your book.

If you needed help solving these problems correctly, then you need more practice. Review the Checkpoint 5 materials and try the practice problems. Also, consider getting help outside of class time. From this point on, you will be expected to do problems like these quickly and easily.

Ideally, at this point you are comfortable working with these types of problems and can solve them correctly. If you feel that you need more confidence when solving these types of problems, then review the Checkpoint 5 materials and try the practice problems provided. From this point on, you will be expected to do problems like these correctly and with confidence.

Chapter 5 Closure   What have I learned?

Reflection and Synthesis

The activities below offer you a chance to reflect about
what you have learned during this chapter. As you work,
look for concepts that you feel very comfortable with, ideas
that you would like to learn more about, and topics you
need more help with.

①   WHAT HAVE I LEARNED?

Doing the problems in this section will help you to evaluate which types of
problems you feel comfortable with and which ones you need more help
with.

Solve each problem as completely as you can. The table at the end of this
closure section provides answers to these problems. It also tells you where
you can find additional help and where to find practice problems like them.

CL 5-149.   Evan is trying to save $60 to buy new parts for his bike. He has saved 45%
of what he needs so far.

a.   Draw a diagram to represent this situation.

b.   How much has Evan saved so far?

c.   How much does Evan still need to save? Write your answer as a dollar
amount and as a percent.

CL 5-150.   Julia has two children who are four years apart in age. Julia is four times
older than her youngest child. The sum of the ages of Julia and her children
is 76 years. Use the 5-D Process to find the ages of Julia and each of her
children.

CL 5-151. Erika is playing a game where the number of spaces she moves is determined by the spinner at right. Each half of the spinner—left and right—is divided into equal regions as shown.

a. What is the probability that Erika will spin an even number on her next spin?

b. If Erika spins a 4, she will land on a space that says, "Get an extra turn." If she then spins a 5, she gets 50 bonus points and will win the game. What is the probability that she can spin a 4 and then a 5?

CL 5-152. Melanie collects stickers. Her favorite stickers have unicorns on them. She has a sheet of stickers that has 2 unicorn stickers on it and 5 dragons. She would like to increase her chances of getting a unicorn sticker when she selects one randomly.

If she takes two sheets of stickers like this and combines them, will she be more likely to select a unicorn sticker? Why or why not?

CL 5-153. Identify the following events as independent or dependent.

a. Reaching into a drawer in the dark, pulling out one sock, and then reaching back in and pulling out another.

b. Selecting a dog biscuit for your dog, feeding it to her, and then getting another one.

c. Rolling a 3 on each of two dice that are tossed at the same time.

d. Spinning a 5 on a spinner and then spinning again and getting a 4.

CL 5-154. Build each collection of tiles represented below on a mat. Name the collection using a simpler algebraic expression, if possible. If it is not possible to simplify the expression, explain why not.

a. $(-x)+5-4x+x-(-3)+(-3x)$

b. Nine plus four times a number, plus three minus seven times the number

c. $3-7x^2+9x$

d. $2x+3x^2-7+(-x^2)$

CL 5-155.   Evaluate each expression below.

a. $2\frac{3}{10}-1\frac{2}{5}$

b. $\frac{9}{3}\cdot\frac{4}{5}$

c. $\frac{3}{4}+5\frac{7}{8}$

d. $\frac{2}{9}\cdot(-\frac{3}{7})\cdot(\frac{14}{5})$

e. $-\frac{9}{15}-(-\frac{26}{45})$

f. $5\frac{1}{6}\cdot(-\frac{7}{9})$

CL 5-156.   Alaska has a very low population density. It only has 655,000 people in 570,374 square miles. Find the unit rate of density in terms of people per square mile.

CL 5-157.   For each of the problems above, do the following:
- Draw a bar or number line that represents 0 to 10.

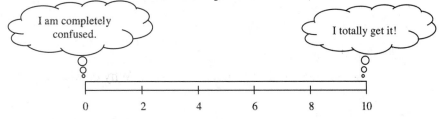

- Color or shade in a portion of the bar that represents your level of understanding and comfort with completing that problem on your own.

If any of your bars are less than a 5, choose *one* of those problems and do one of the following tasks:
- Write two questions that you would like to ask about that problem.
- Brainstorm two things that you DO know about that type of problem.

If all of your bars are a 5 or above, choose one of those problems and do one of these tasks:
- Write two questions you might ask or hints you might give to a student who was stuck on the problem.
- Make a new problem that is similar and more challenging than that problem and solve it.

WHAT TOOLS CAN I USE?

You have several tools and references available to help support your learning: your teacher, your study team, your math book, and your Toolkit, to name only a few. At the end of each chapter, you will have an opportunity to review your Toolkit for completeness. You will also revise or update it to reflect your current understanding of big ideas.

The main elements of your Toolkit should be your Learning Logs, Math Notes, and the vocabulary used in this chapter. Math words that are new appear in bold in the text. Refer to the lists provided below and follow your teacher's instructions to revise your Toolkit, which will help make it useful for you as you complete this chapter and as you work in future chapters.

Learning Log Entries

- Lesson 5.2.1 – Probability for "Either/Or" Events
- Lesson 5.2.3 – Independent and Dependent Events
- Lesson 5.2.5 – Methods to Organize Probability Outcomes
- Lesson 5.3.4 – Defining and Deciding

Math Notes

- Lesson 5.1.1 – Equivalent Ratios
- Lesson 5.1.2 – Part-to-Whole Relationships
- Lesson 5.2.3 – Independent and Dependent Events
- Lesson 5.2.4 – Probability of Compound Events
- Lesson 5.2.5 – Probability Models for Multiple Events
- Lesson 5.3.3 – Solving Problems with the 5-D Process
- Lesson 5.3.4 – Consecutive Integers

Mathematical Vocabulary

The following is a list of vocabulary found in this chapter. Some of the words have been seen in the previous chapter. The words in bold are words that are new to this chapter. Make sure that you are familiar with the terms below and know what they mean. For the words you do not know, refer to the glossary or index. You might also add these words to your Toolkit so that you can reference them in the future.

5-D Process	**consecutive integers**	**complement**
compound events	desired outcomes	**dependent events**
equivalent ratios	experimental probability	**independent events**
mutually exclusive	outcome	**partition**
percent	possible outcomes	probability
probability table	**probability tree**	proportional relationship
ratio	sample space	**scalene triangle**
simplify	**simulation**	**single event**
systematic list	theoretical probability	variable

Answers and Support for Closure Problems
What Have I Learned?

Note: MN = Math Note, LL = Learning Log

Problem	Solution	Need Help?	More Practice
CL 5-149.	a. b. $27 c. $33 dollars, or 55% of $60	Lessons 5.1.1 and 5.1.2 MN: 5.1.2	Problems 5-18, 5-19, 5-40, 5-52, 5-85, 5-86, and 5-111
CL 5-150.	Julia is 48. The children are 12 and 16.	Section 5.3 MN: 5.3.3 LL: 5.3.4	Problems 5-38 and 5-144
CL 5-151.	a. $\frac{1}{4} + \frac{1}{6} = \frac{3}{12} + \frac{2}{12} = \frac{5}{12}$ b. $\frac{1}{6} \cdot \frac{1}{4} = \frac{1}{24}$	Lesson 5.2.3 MN: 5.2.5 LL: 5.2.3	Problems 5-49, 5-52, 5-65, 5-81, and 5-83
CL 5-152.	P(unicorn, 1 sheet): $\frac{2}{7}$ P(unicorn, 2 sheets): $\frac{4}{14} = \frac{2}{7}$ They are the same.	Section 5.2 MN: 5.2.4 and 5.2.5 LL: 5.2.5	Problems 5-29, 5-30, 5-39, 5-71, 5-88, and 5-126
CL 5-153.	a. Dependent b. Dependent c. Independent d. Independent	Lesson 5.2.3 MN: 5.2.4 LL: 5.2.3	Problems 5-47 and 5-49
CL 5-154.	a. $-7x + 8$ b. $-3x + 12$ c. Fully simplified. d. $2x^2 + 2x - 7$	Lessons 4.3.1 and 4.3.3 MN: 4.3.2 LL: 4.3.3	Problems CL 4-124, 5-53, 5-113, and 5-125
CL 5-155.	a. $\frac{9}{10}$ b. $\frac{36}{15}$ or $\frac{12}{5}$ c. $6\frac{5}{8}$ d. $-\frac{84}{315}$ or $-\frac{4}{15}$ e. $-\frac{1}{45}$ f. $-\frac{217}{54}$ or $-4\frac{1}{54}$	Lessons 1.2.6, 2.2.5, and 2.2.6 MN 2.2.5 and 2.3.1 LL: 1.2.8	Problems CL 1-146, CL 2-135, CL 3-136, 5-13, 5-21, and 5-87
CL 5-156.	About 1.15 people per square mile.	Lesson 4.2.3 MN: 4.2.4	Problems CL 4-127, 5-91, and 5-139

5.4 How can I use it? What is the connection?

Mid-Course Reflection Activities

The activities in this section review several major topics you have studied so far. As you work, think about the topics and activities that you have done during the first half of this course and how they connect to each other. Also think about which concepts you are comfortable using and those with which you need more practice.

As you work on this activity, keep the questions below in mind.

What mathematical concepts have you studied in this course so far?

What do you still want to know more about?

What connections did you find?

5-ML.   MEMORY LANE

Have you ever heard someone talk about "taking a trip down memory lane?" People use this phrase to mean taking time to remember things that have happened in the past, especially events that a group of people shared.

As you follow your teacher's directions to visit your mathematical "memory lane," think about all the activities you have done and what you have learned in your math class so far this year. Your Toolkit should be a useful resource to help you with this activity.

Focus on these four areas as you remember your previous work in this course:

- Working with Signed Numbers
- Probability
- Algebraic Thinking
- Proportional Relationships

5-SH. SCAVENGER HUNT

Today your teacher will give you several clues about mathematical situations. For each clue, work with your team to find all of the situations posted around the classroom or provided on a resource page. Remember that more than one situation – up to three – may match each clue. Once you have decided which situation matches (or which situations match) a clue, justify your decision to your teacher and receive the next clue. Be sure to record your matches on paper.

Your goal is to find the match(es) for each different clue.

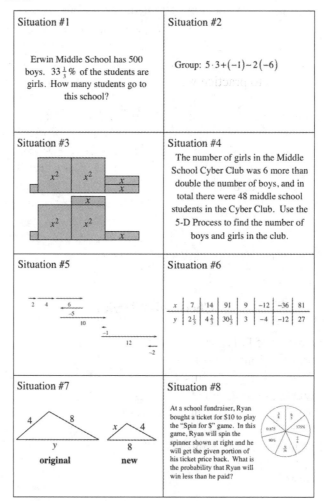

Core Connections, Course 2
Checkpoint Materials

Notes to Students (and their Teachers)

Students master different skills at different speeds. No two students learn exactly the same way at the same time. At some point you will be expected to perform certain skills accurately. Most of the Checkpoint problems incorporate skills that you should have been developing in grades 5 and 6. If you have not mastered these skills yet it does not mean that you will not be successful in this class. However, you may need to do some work outside of class to get caught up on them.

Starting in Chapter 1 and finishing in Chapter 9, there are 9 problems designed as Checkpoint problems. Each one is marked with an icon like the one above and numbered according to the chapter that it is in. After you do each of the Checkpoint problems, check your answers by referring to this section. If your answers are incorrect, you may need some extra practice to develop that skill. The practice sets are keyed to each of the Checkpoint problems in the textbook. Each has the topic clearly labeled, followed by the answers to the corresponding Checkpoint problem and then some completed examples. Next, the complete solution to the Checkpoint problem from the text is given, and there are more problems for you to practice with answers included.

Remember, looking is not the same as doing! You will never become good at any sport by just watching it, and in the same way, reading through the worked examples and understanding the steps is not the same as being able to do the problems yourself. How many of the extra practice problems do you need to try? That is really up to you. Remember that your goal is to be able to do similar problems on your own confidently and accurately. This is your responsibility. You should not expect your teacher to spend time in class going over the solutions to the Checkpoint problem sets. If you are not confident after reading the examples and trying the problems, you should get help outside of class time or talk to your teacher about working with a tutor.

Checkpoint Topics

1. Area and Perimeter of Polygons
2. Multiple Representations of Portions
3. Multiplying Fractions and Decimals
5. Order of Operations
6. Writing and Evaluating Algebraic Expressions
7A. Simplifying Expressions
7B. Displays of Data: Histograms and Box Plots
8. Solving Multi-Step Equations
9. Unit Rates and Proportions

Checkpoint 1
Problem 1-141
Area and Perimeter of Polygons

Answers to problem 1-141: a. 96 cm^2, 40 cm; b. 22 in.^{2}, 25.05 in.; c. 144 cm^2, 52 cm; d. 696.67 m^2, 114.67 m

Area is the number of square units in a flat region. The formulas to calculate the area of several kinds of polygons are:

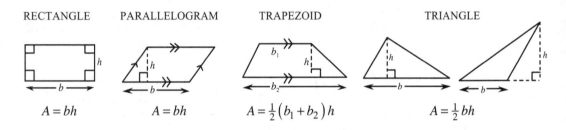

RECTANGLE	PARALLELOGRAM	TRAPEZOID	TRIANGLE
$A = bh$	$A = bh$	$A = \frac{1}{2}(b_1 + b_2)h$	$A = \frac{1}{2}bh$

Perimeter is the distance around a figure on a flat surface. To calculate the perimeter of a polygon, add together the length of each side.

Example 1:
Compute the area and perimeter.

parallelogram
$A = bh = 6 \cdot 4 = 24$ feet^2

$P = 6 + 6 + 5 + 5 = 22$ feet

Example 2:
Compute the area and perimeter.

triangle
$A = \frac{1}{2}bh = \frac{1}{2} \cdot 6 \cdot 7 = 21$ cm^2

$P = 6 + 8 + 9 = 23$ cm

Now we can go back and solve the original problem.

a. Rectangle: $A = bh = 12 \cdot 8 = 96$ cm^2; $P = 8 + 8 + 12 + 12 = 40$ cm

b. Triangle: $A = \frac{1}{2}bh = \frac{1}{2} \cdot 11 \cdot 4 = 22$ in.^{2}; $P = 11 + 9.05 + 5 = 25.05$ in.

c. Parallelogram: $A = bh = 16 \cdot 9 = 144$ cm^2; $P = 16 + 16 + 10 + 10 = 52$ cm

d. Trapezoid: $A = \frac{1}{2}(b_1 + b_2)h = \frac{1}{2}(25 + 44.67) \cdot 10 = 696.67$ m^2;
$P = 21 + 25 + 24 + 44.67 = 114.67$ m

Here are some more to try. Find the area and perimeter of each figure.

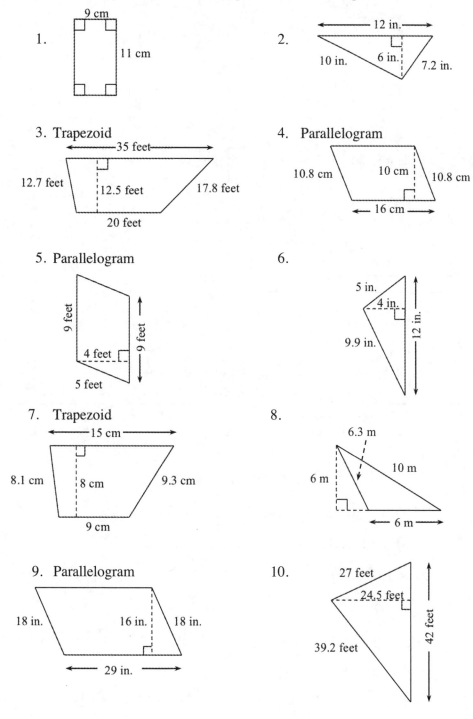

1.
9 cm
11 cm

2.
12 in.
10 in.
6 in.
7.2 in.

3. Trapezoid
35 feet
12.7 feet
12.5 feet
17.8 feet
20 feet

4. Parallelogram
10.8 cm
10 cm
10.8 cm
16 cm

5. Parallelogram
9 feet
9 feet
4 feet
5 feet

6.
5 in.
4 in.
12 in.
9.9 in.

7. Trapezoid
15 cm
8.1 cm
8 cm
9.3 cm
9 cm

8.
6.3 m
10 m
6 m
6 m

9. Parallelogram
18 in.
16 in.
18 in.
29 in.

10.
27 feet
24.5 feet
42 feet
39.2 feet

11.

$1\frac{3}{4}$ feet

2 feet

12. Trapezoid

21 in.

32.7 in.

20 in.

13 in.

24 in.

13. Trapezoid

18 feet

19.8 feet

16 feet

16.2 feet

32 feet

14.

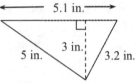

5.1 in.

3 in.

5 in.

3.2 in.

15. Parallelogram

10 cm

9 cm

10 cm

10 cm

16. Trapezoid

2.7 m

0.8 m

0.5 m

1.2 m

4.4 m

Answers:

1. 99 cm^2, 40 cm

2. 36 in.^{2}, 29.2 in.

3. 343.75 feet^2, 85.5 feet

4. 160 cm^2, 53.6 cm

5. 36 feet^2, 28 feet

6. 24 in.^{2}, 26.9 in.

7. 96 cm^2, 41.4 cm

8. 18 m^2, 22.3 m

9. 464 in.^{2}, 94 in.

10. 514.5 feet^2, 108.2 feet

11. $\frac{14}{4} = 3\frac{1}{2}$ feet^2 , $\frac{30}{4} = 7\frac{1}{2}$ feet

12. 457 in.^{2}, 90.7 in.

13. 400 feet^2, 86 feet

14. 7.65 in.^{2}, 13.3 in.

15. 90 cm^2, 40 cm

16. 1.78 m^2, 9.1 m

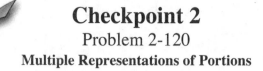

Checkpoint 2

Problem 2-120

Multiple Representations of Portions

Answers to problem 2-120: a. 43%, $\frac{43}{100}$, b. $\frac{9}{10}$, 0.9, 90% , c. $\frac{39}{100}$, 0.39 , d. 64%, 0.64

Portions of a whole may be represented in various ways as represented by this web. Percent means "per hundred" and the place value of a decimal will determine its name. Change a fraction in an equivalent fraction with 100 parts to name it as a percent.

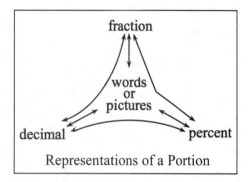

Representations of a Portion

Example 1: Name the given portion as a fraction and as a percent.   0.3

Solution: The digit 3 is in the tenths place so $0.3 =$ three tenths $= \frac{3}{10}$.

On a diagram or a hundreds grid, 3 parts out of 10 is equivalent to 30 parts out of 100 so $\frac{3}{10} = \frac{30}{100} = 30\%$.

Example 2: Name the given portion as a fraction and as a decimal.   35%

Solution: $35\% = \frac{35}{100} =$ thirty-five hundredths $= 0.35$; $\frac{35}{100} = \frac{7}{20}$

Now we can go back and solve the original problem.

a. 0.43 is forty-three hundredths or $\frac{43}{100} = 43\%$

b. nine tenths is $\frac{9}{10} = \frac{9}{10} \cdot \frac{10}{10} = \frac{90}{100} = 90\%$; $\frac{9}{10} = 0.9$

c. $39\% = \frac{39}{100} =$ thirty-nine hundredths $= 0.39$

d. $\frac{16}{25} = \frac{16}{25} \cdot \frac{4}{4} = \frac{64}{100} = 0.64 = 64\%$

Here are some more to try. For each portion of a whole, write it as a percent, fraction, and a decimal.

1. 6%	2. 0.35
3. $\frac{1}{4}$	4. $\frac{2}{5}$
5. 0.16	6. 87%
7. $\frac{13}{25}$	8. 21%
9. $\frac{7}{50}$	10. 0.050
11. 65%	12. 3.7%
13. $\frac{7}{10}$	14. 0.66
15. $\frac{19}{20}$	16. 20%
17. 0.23	18. 1.0
19. 135%	20. $\frac{77}{100}$

Answers:

1. $\frac{6}{100} = \frac{3}{50}, 0.06$
2. $35\%, \frac{35}{100} = \frac{7}{20}$
3. $25\%, 0.25$
4. $40\%, 0.4$
5. $16\%, \frac{16}{100} = \frac{4}{25}$
6. $\frac{87}{100}, 0.87$
7. $52\%, 0.52$
8. $\frac{21}{100}, 0.21$
9. $14\%, 0.14$
10. $5\%, \frac{5}{100} = \frac{1}{20}$
11. $\frac{13}{20}, 0.65$
12. $\frac{37}{1000}, 0.037$
13. $70\%, 0.7$
14. $66\%, \frac{66}{100} = \frac{33}{50}$
15. $95\%, 0.95$
16. $\frac{20}{100} = \frac{1}{5}, 0.2$
17. $23\%, \frac{23}{100}$
18. $100\%, \frac{100}{100} = \frac{1}{1}$
19. $\frac{135}{100} = 1\frac{35}{100} = 1\frac{7}{20}, 1.35$
20. $77\%, 0.77$

Checkpoint 3

Problem 3-110
Multiplying Fractions and Decimals

Answers to problem 3-110: a. $\frac{9}{20}$, b. $\frac{1}{5}$, c. $4\frac{2}{9}$, d. $7\frac{1}{5}$, e. 12.308, f. 0.000208

To multiply fractions, multiply the numerators and then multiply the denominators. To multiply mixed numbers, change each mixed number to a fraction greater than one before multiplying. In both cases, simplify by looking for factors than make "one."

To multiply decimals, multiply as with whole numbers. In the product, the number of decimal places is equal to the total number of decimal places in the multiplied numbers. Sometimes zeros need to be added to place the decimal point.

Example 1: Multiply $\frac{3}{8}\cdot\frac{4}{5}$

Solution:

$\frac{3}{8}\cdot\frac{4}{5}\Rightarrow\frac{3\cdot4}{8\cdot5}\Rightarrow\frac{3\cdot\cancel{4}}{2\cdot\cancel{4}\cdot5}\Rightarrow\frac{3}{10}$

Example 2: Multiply $3\frac{1}{3}\cdot2\frac{1}{2}$

Solution:

$3\frac{1}{3}\cdot2\frac{1}{2}\Rightarrow\frac{10}{3}\cdot\frac{5}{2}\Rightarrow\frac{10\cdot5}{3\cdot2}\Rightarrow\frac{5\cdot\cancel{2}\cdot5}{3\cdot\cancel{2}}\Rightarrow\frac{25}{3}$ or $8\frac{1}{3}$

Note that we are simplifying using Giant Ones but no longer drawing the Giant One.

Example 3: Multiply 12.5 · 0.36

Solution:

$$\begin{array}{rl} 12.5 & \text{(one decimal place)} \\ \times0.36 & \text{(two decimal places)} \\ \hline 750 & \\ 3750 & \\ \hline 4.500 & \text{(three decimal places)} \end{array}$$

Now we can go back and solve the original problem.

a. $\frac{2}{3}\cdot\frac{2}{5}\Rightarrow\frac{2\cdot2}{3\cdot5}\Rightarrow\frac{4}{15}$

b. $\frac{7}{10}\cdot\frac{2}{7}\Rightarrow\frac{\cancel{7}\cdot\cancel{2}}{5\cdot\cancel{2}\cdot\cancel{7}}\Rightarrow\frac{1}{5}$

c. $2\frac{1}{3}\cdot2\frac{1}{2}\Rightarrow\frac{7}{3}\cdot\frac{5}{2}\Rightarrow\frac{7\cdot5}{3\cdot2}\Rightarrow\frac{35}{6}$ or $5\frac{5}{6}$

d. $1\frac{1}{3}\cdot2\frac{1}{6}\Rightarrow\frac{4}{3}\cdot\frac{13}{6}\Rightarrow\frac{2\cdot\cancel{2}\cdot13}{3\cdot\cancel{2}\cdot3}\Rightarrow\frac{26}{9}$ or $2\frac{8}{9}$

e.
$$\begin{array}{r} 2.71 \\ \times4.5 \\ \hline 1355 \\ 10840 \\ \hline 12.195 \end{array}$$

f.
$$\begin{array}{r} 0.35 \\ \times0.0007 \\ \hline 0.000245 \end{array}$$

Here are some more to try. Multiply the fractions and decimals below.

1. $0.08 \cdot 4.7$

2. $0.21 \cdot 3.42$

3. $\frac{4}{7} \cdot \frac{1}{2}$

4. $\frac{5}{6} \cdot \frac{3}{8}$

5. $\frac{8}{9} \cdot \frac{3}{4}$

6. $\frac{7}{10} \cdot \frac{3}{4}$

7. $3.07 \cdot 5.4$

8. $6.57 \cdot 2.8$

9. $\frac{5}{6} \cdot \frac{3}{20}$

10. $2.9 \cdot 0.056$

11. $\frac{6}{7} \cdot \frac{4}{9}$

12. $3\frac{1}{7} \cdot 1\frac{2}{5}$

13. $\frac{2}{3} \cdot \frac{5}{9}$

14. $\frac{3}{5} \cdot \frac{9}{13}$

15. $2.34 \cdot 2.7$

16. $2\frac{1}{3} \cdot 4\frac{4}{5}$

17. $4\frac{3}{5} \cdot \frac{1}{2}$

18. $\frac{3}{8} \cdot \frac{5}{9}$

19. $0.235 \cdot 0.43$

20. $421 \cdot 0.00005$

Answers:

1. 0.376

2. 0.7182

3. $\frac{2}{7}$

4. $\frac{5}{16}$

5. $\frac{2}{3}$

6. $\frac{21}{40}$

7. 16.578

8. 18.396

9. $\frac{1}{8}$

10. 0.1624

11. $\frac{8}{21}$

12. $4\frac{2}{5}$

13. $\frac{10}{27}$

14. $\frac{27}{65}$

15. 6.318

16. $11\frac{1}{5}$

17. $2\frac{3}{10}$

18. $\frac{5}{24}$

19. 0.10105

20. 0.02105

Checkpoint 5
Problem 5-148
Order of Operations

Answers to problem 5-148: a: 20, b: –4

In general, simplify an expression by using the **Order of Operations**:

- Evaluate each exponential (for example, $5^2 = 5 \cdot 5 = 25$).
- Multiply and divide each term from left to right.
- Combine like terms by adding and subtracting from left to right.

But simplify *the expressions in parentheses* or any other expressions of grouped numbers first. Numbers above or below a "fraction bar" are considered grouped. A good way to remember is to circle the terms like in the following example. Remember that terms are separated by + and – signs.

Example 1: Simplify $12 \div 2^2 - 4 + 3(1 + 2)^3$

Simplify within the circled terms: Be sure to perform the exponent operations before dividing.
$12 \div 2^2 = 12 \div 2 \cdot 2 = 3$

Then perform the exponent operation: $3^3 = 3 \cdot 3 \cdot 3 = 27$

Next, multiply and divide left to right: $3(27) = 81$

Finally, add and subtract left to right: $3 - 4 = -1$

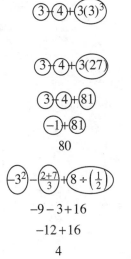

Example 2: Simplify $-3^2 - \frac{2+7}{3} + 8 \div \left(\frac{1}{2}\right)$

Simplify within the circled terms: $-3^2 = -3 \cdot 3 = -9$
$$\frac{2+7}{3} = \frac{9}{3} = 3 \qquad 8 \div \frac{1}{2} = 8 \cdot \frac{2}{1} = 16$$

Then add and subtract, left to right.

Now we can go back and solve the original problem.

a. $16 - 2^3 \div 8 + 5$
$16 - 2 \cdot 2 \cdot 2 \div 8 + 5$
$16 - 4 \cdot 2 \div 8 + 5$
$16 - 8 \div 8 + 5$
$16 - 1 + 5$
$15 + 5$
20

b. $(-2 + 6)^2 - \left(\frac{3}{2}\right) \cdot 14 + 1$
$(4)^2 - \frac{42}{2} + 1$
$16 - 21 + 1$
$-5 + 1$
-4

Here are some more to try.

1. $10 \cdot \frac{1}{2} + (-6)(-3)$

2. $\frac{-5+(-6)\left(\frac{2}{3}\right)}{-3}$

3. $(6-8)(9-10)-(4+2)(6+3)$

4. $\frac{-84}{36-12(-5)}$

5. $\frac{1}{2}(6-2)^2 - 4 \cdot 3$

6. $3\left(2(1+5)+8-3^2\right)$

7. $(8+12) \div 4 - 6$

8. $-6^2 + 4 \cdot 8$

9. $18 \cdot 3 \div 3^3$

10. $10 + 5^2 - 25$

11. $20 - (3^3 \div 9) \cdot 2$

12. $100 - (2^3 - 6) \div 2$

13. $85 - (4 \cdot 2)^2 - 3$

14. $22 + (3 \cdot 2)^2 \div 2$

15. $16 + 11(-2)^2 - 25\left(\frac{2}{5}\right)$

16. $54 \div 3^2 + \left(\frac{4}{3}\right)\left(\frac{27}{2}\right) - 1^2$

17. $2(3-1)^3 \div 8$

18. $(7^2 - 1) \div 4 + 2$

19. $-3 \cdot 2 \div (-2-4)$

20. $-3 \cdot 2 \div -2 - 4$

21. $12 + 3\left(\frac{8-2}{12-9}\right) - 2\left(\frac{9-1}{19-15}\right)$

22. $15 + 4\left(\frac{11-2}{9-6}\right) - 2\left(\frac{12-4}{18-10}\right)$

23. $32 \div 16 - 8 \cdot 25\left(\frac{1}{2}\right)^2$

24. $36 + 16 \cdot \left(\frac{1}{4}\right) - (50 \div 25)^2$

Answers:

1. 23

2. 3

3. –52

4. $-\frac{7}{8}$

5. –4

6. 33

7. –1

8. –4

9. 2

10. 10

11. 14

12. 99

13. 18

14. 40

15. 50

16. 23

17. 2

18. 14

19. 1

20. –1

21. 14

22. 25

23. –48

24. 36

Puzzle Investigator Problems

Dear Students,

Puzzle Investigator problems (PIs) present you with an opportunity to investigate complex, interesting problems. Their purpose is to focus on the process of solving complex problems. **You will be evaluated on your ability to show, explain, and justify your work and thoughts**. Save *all* of your work, including what does not work, in order to write about the processes you used to reach your answer.

Completion of a Puzzle Investigator problem includes four parts:

- **Problem Statement:** State the problem clearly in your own words so that anyone reading your paper will understand the problem you intend to solve.

- **Process and Solutions:** Describe in detail your thinking and reasoning as you work from start to finish. Explain your solution and how you know it is correct. Add diagrams when it helps your explanation. Include what you do that does not work and changes you make along the way. If you do not complete this problem, describe what you <u>do</u> know and where and why you are stuck.

- **Reflection:** Reflect about your learning and your reaction to the problem. What mathematics did you learn from it? What did you learn about your math problem solving strategies? Is this problem similar to any other problems you have done before? If yes, how?

- **Attached work:** Include <u>all</u> your work and notes. Your scratch work is important because it is a record of your thinking. Do not throw anything away.

PI-1.   LONG DISTANCE

The odometer (which measures the distance traveled) on Mario's parents' car reads 28,882 when his father fills it up. Since Mario's family is going on vacation, his father set the trip odometer to 0 so he will know how many miles long the trip is. To keep Mario and his sister busy during the trip, he gives them the following problems.

a.   Mario noticed that there are only 2 different digits in the number 28,882. How far will the car need to travel before all the digits are different? What is that number?

b.   The numbers 101, 1221, and 1357531, among many others, are all **palindromes** because their digits read the same left-to-right as they do right-to-left. When are the next five times that the digits of the car odometer will be a palindrome?

c.   When is the next time that both the car odometer and the trip odometer will be a palindrome?

PI-2.   CROSSED PATHS

Sandra left her home at 6 a.m. Saturday and hiked all day to a cottage at the top of the mountain. She arrived at 6 p.m. and spent the night in the cottage. The next morning she left the cottage at 6 a.m. and hiked home by the same trail, arriving at 6 p.m.

Both days she was on the trail for 12 hours, but sometimes stopped to eat, swim, or gather flowers. This means that she was not traveling at the same speed the entire time.

Must it be true that there is at least one point along the trail that Sandra passed at exactly the same time on each of the two days? Or is it possible that she was never at any place on Sunday at the exact same time she had been there on Saturday?

Your Task: Decide if there must be at least one point on the trail that Sandra passed at exactly the same time both days. Then explain your reasoning in a way that will convince someone else that your decision is correct.

PI-3.   CROSSING OVER

Elizabeth, Brian, Dean, and Leslie want to cross a bridge. They all begin on the same side and have only 17 minutes to get everyone across to the other side.

To complicate matters, it is nighttime and there is only one flashlight. A maximum of two people can cross at one time. Any group that crosses, either 1 or 2 people, <u>must</u> have the flashlight with them. The flashlight must be walked back and forth; it cannot be thrown.

Each student walks at a different speed. A pair must walk together at the rate of the slower student's pace.

Elizabeth:	1 minute to cross
Brian:	2 minutes to cross.
Dean:	5 minutes to cross.
Leslie:	10 minutes to cross.

For example, if Elizabeth and Leslie walk across first, 10 minutes have elapsed when they get to the other side of the bridge. If Leslie returns across the bridge with the flashlight, a total of 20 minutes has passed, and you have failed the mission.

Your Task: Find a strategy that can get everyone across in 17 minutes. Use diagrams and words to help clearly explain your strategy.

PI-4.   TOURNAMENT

Five friends decided to have a video
game competition. Each person is
scheduled to play everyone other
person.

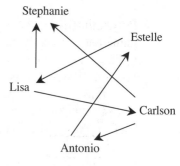

After several games, Stephanie started a
diagram to show which pairs have played and
who has won so far. The arrows in her
diagram point from the winner to the loser.
For example, when Lisa and Carlson played,
Lisa won.

a.   How many more games need to be played? Show how you know.

b.   Stephanie's diagram can help you predict the winner of future matches!
     For each pair below, who do you think will win? If you think it is equally
     likely that either player will win, explain why. Use Stephanie's diagram to
     support your answer.

     i.   Stephanie and Antonio   ii.   Estelle and Carlson

c.   Is there always a winner? For example, is it possible to have a tournament
     with five friends where everyone wins and loses two games? If it is
     possible, draw a diagram for a different tournament with five friends so that
     each person wins and loses 2 games. If it is not possible, explain why it
     cannot be done.

d.   How many games would be played in a tournament of 6 friends if each
     person played every other person exactly once? What if there were 10
     friends?

PI-5.   POLYOMINOES!

Polyominoes are shapes made of some number of unit squares. This is why a
game using rectangular pieces made with two squares is called "dominoes"
(which can be referred to as 2-ominoes). Below are all the possible 3-ominoes
and 4-ominoes.

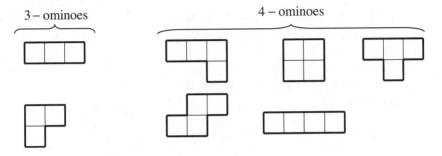

a.   It turns out there are 12 different 5-ominoes! Draw them. For two designs
     to be different, one design should not be able to be turned or flipped or slid
     onto another so that it will match exactly.

b.   It turns out that 9 of the 5-ominoes can be created by adding a single square
     to one of the 4-ominoes. Which 4-omino would that be? Use diagrams to
     show how the 5-ominoes are formed.

c.   Using the 2×2 square, four 4-ominoes can be put
     together to make a 4×4 square, as shown at right.
     Will this work for the other 4-ominoes? Form 4×4
     squares using four of the same 4-omino. Are there
     any 4-ominoes that will not form a square?

d.   The cross shape at right can be tiled using four
     copies of one 5-omino. In fact, it turns out that
     there are several different 5-ominoes that can do
     this. See how many ways you can find to do it.

PI-6. DESIGNING AN APARTMENT

Ms. Speedi wants to build her dream house and would like you to design it. According to local zoning laws, she is limited to a one-story house with a maximum area of 1,000 square feet. (This is the maximum area of the floor.) She also has some personal requirements for this house:

- There must be two bedrooms with a combined area of at least 250 square feet.

- There should be at least one bathroom near the bedrooms.

- The living room cannot be smaller than 200 square feet.

- The kitchen must be at least 220 square feet.

- The building costs are cheaper when the entire structure is rectangular. Therefore, make the overall shape of Ms. Speedi's house a rectangle.

a. Design a possible layout of Ms. Speedi's dream house. Make sure your design meets the zoning law (with a maximum area of 1,000 square feet) and Ms. Speedi's personal requirements.

b. On graph paper, draw a scaled blueprint of Ms. Speedi's house. Provide details that help others understand your design like the front door, windows, and interior doors. Add furniture if you like.

c. What are the benefits of your design over others? What are the drawbacks? What assumptions did you make for your design? Did you need to make any difficult decisions?

PI-7. SQUARES GALORE

How many squares do you see at right? Can you identify more than 4 squares? How can we know when we have found all the squares? The puzzles below will help you investigate these questions.

a. How many squares can you find on an 8×8 checkerboard, like the one shown at right? (By the way, there are more than 65 squares.) Organize your work so that you can find patterns that help you to determine how many 1×1 squares, 2×2 squares, and so on, that you can find.

b. Use your patterns from part (a) to figure out how many squares would be in a design made with square tiles if it is 30 tiles wide and 30 tiles long. Can you do this without drawing a diagram?

c. Is there a square made up of square tiles (like the checkerboard) that has only 75 squares overall? What about one that has 120 squares overall? If it is possible, show the square design and explain how you found it. If it is not possible, explain why that design cannot exist.

Glossary

5-D Process   An organized method to solve problems. The 5 D's stand for Describe/Draw, Define, Do, Decide, and Declare. This is a problem-solving strategy for which solving begins by making a prediction about the answer or one element of it (a trial), and then confirming whether the result of the trial is correct. If not, information is gained about how close the trial is to the correct value, so that adjustments to the trial value may be made. Being organized is extremely important to the success of this method, as well as writing a usable table. The 5-D Process leads to writing equations to represent word problems. (p. 295)

absolute value   The absolute value of a number is the distance of the number from zero. Since the absolute value represents a distance, without regard to direction, absolute value is always non-negative. Thus, the absolute value of a negative number is its opposite, while the absolute value of a non-negative number is just the number itself. The absolute value of x is usually written "$|x|$." For example, $|-5| = 5$ and $|22| = 22$. (p. 89)

acute angle   An angle with a measure greater than $0°$ and less than $90°$. An example is shown at right. (p. 460)

acute triangle   A triangle with all three angle measures less than $90°$.

addition $(+)$ An operation that tells how many objects there are when two sets are combined. The result is the number of objects in the two sets together which is called a sum. In arithmetic, the word "object" usually means "number."

additive identity   The number 0 is called the additive identity because adding 0 to any number does not change the number. For example, $7 + 0 = 7$. (p. 96)

Additive Identity Property   The Additive Identity Property states that adding zero to any expression leaves the expression unchanged. That is, $a + 0 = a$. For example, $-2 + 0 = -2$.

additive inverse   The number you need to add to a given number to get a sum of 0. For example, the additive inverse of -3 is 3. It is also called the opposite. (p. 96)

Additive Inverse Property   The Additive Inverse Property states that for every number a there is a number $-a$ such that $a = -a = 0$. For example, the number 5 has an additive inverse of -5; $5 + (-5) = 0$. The additive inverse of a number is often called its opposite. For example, 5 and -5 are opposites.

adjacent angles For two angles to be adjacent, they must satisfy these three conditions: (1) The two angles must have a common side; (2) They must have a common vertex; and (3) They can have no interior points in common. This means that the common side must be between the two angles; no overlap between the angles is permitted. In the example at right, $\angle ABC$ and $\angle CBD$ are adjacent angles. (p. 466)

algebra A branch of mathematics that uses variables to generalize the rules of numbers and numerical operations.

algebra tiles An algebra tile is a manipulative whose area represents a constant or variable quantity. The algebra tiles used in this course consist of large squares with dimensions x-by-x; rectangles with dimensions x-by-1; and small squares with dimensions 1-by-1. These tiles are named by their areas: x^2, x, and 1, respectively. The smallest squares are called "unit tiles." In this text, shaded tiles will represent positive quantities while unshaded tiles will represent negative quantities. (p. 220)

algebraic expression See *expression*.

algorithm A fixed rule for carrying out a mathematical procedure. For example, to find the average of a set of values, find the sum of the values and divide by the number of values.

angle Generally, an angle is formed by two rays that are joined at a common endpoint. Angles in geometric figures are usually formed by two segments that have a common endpoint (such as the angle shaded in the figure at right). Also see *acute angle*, *obtuse angle*, and *right angle*. (p. 460)

area For this course, area is the number of square units needed to fill up a region on a flat surface. In later courses, the idea will be extended to cones, spheres, and more complex surfaces. Also see *surface area*. (p. 10)

Area = 15 square units

area model An area model or diagram is one way to represent the probabilities of the outcomes for a sequence of two events. The total area is 1, and the probabilities are represented by proportional parts. In the example, P(S) and P(not S) are the dimensions of the right side of the rectangle. The probabilities that A will occur or not occur are the dimensions of the top of the rectangle. The area of each part is the probability of each possible sequence of two events. (p. 281)

	A 0.8	Not A 0.2
S 0.4	0.32	0.08
Not S 0.6	0.48	0.12

area of a triangle To find the area of a triangle, multiply the length of the base b by the height h and divide by two: $A = \frac{1}{2}bh$. (p. 10)

Associative Property of Addition The Associative Property of Addition states that if a sum contains terms that are grouped, then the sum may be grouped differently with no effect on the total, that is, $a+(b+c)=(a+b)+c$. For example, $3+(4+5)=(3+4)+5$. (p. 190)

Associative Property of Multiplication The Associative Property of Multiplication states that if a product contains terms that are grouped, then the product may be grouped differently with no effect on the result, that is, $a(bc)=(ab)c$. For example, $2\cdot(3\cdot4)=(2\cdot3)\cdot4$. (p. 190)

average The sum of given values divided by the number of values used in computing the sum. For example, the average of $1, 4$, and 10 is $(1+4+10)/3$. See *mean*. (p. 13)

axis (plural: axes) On a coordinate plane, two number lines that meet at right angles at the origin $(0,0)$. The x-axis runs horizontally and the y-axis runs vertically.

bar graph A bar graph is a set of rectangular bars that have height proportional to the number of data elements in each category. Each bar stands for all of the elements in a single distinguishable category (such as "red"). Usually all of the bars are the same width and separated from each other. Also see *histogram*.

base of a geometric figure (a) The base of a triangle: any side of a triangle to which a height is drawn. There are three possible bases in each triangle. (b) The base of a trapezoid: either of the two parallel sides. (c) The base of a parallelogram (including rectangle, rhombus, and square): any side to which a height is drawn. There are four possible bases. (d) The base of a three-dimensional figure. Also see *prism* and *pyramid*.

base of an exponent When working with an exponential expression in the form b^a, b is called the base. For example, 2 is the base in 2^5. (5 is the exponent, and 32 is the value.) See *exponent*.

bin An interval on a histogram.

boundary point The endpoint or endpoints of a ray or segment on a number line where an inequality is true, marked with a solid dot. For strict inequalities (that is, inequalities involving $<$ or $>$), the point is not part of the solution, and is marked with an open dot. Boundary points may be found by solving the equality associated with the given inequality. For example, the solution to the equation $2x=6$ is $x=3$, so the inequality $2x\geq6$ has a boundary point at 3. A boundary point is also sometimes called a "dividing point." (p. 336)

box plot   A graphic way of showing a summary of data using the median, quartiles, and extremes of the data. (p. 404)

center of a circle   On a flat surface, the fixed point from which all points on the circle are equidistant. *See* circle.

center of a data distribution   Numbers that locate or approximate the center of a data set. Two of the ways to measure the center of a data set are the mean and the median. When dealing with measures of center, it is often useful to consider the distribution of the data. For symmetric distributions with no outliers, the mean can represent the middle, or "typical" value, of the data well. However, in the presence of outliers or non-symmetrical data distributions, the median may be a better measure. *Also see* mean and median. (pp. 13, 19, 393)

certainty   When an event will definitely happen. The probability of a certain event is 1.

chord   A line segment with its endpoints on a circle. A chord that passes through the center of a circle is called a "diameter." *See* circle. (p. 471)

circle   The set of all points on a flat surface that are the same distance from a fixed point. If the fixed point (center) is O, the symbol $\odot O$ represents a circle with center O. If r is the length of a circle's radius and d is the length of its diameter, the circumference of the circle is $C = 2\pi r$ or $C = \pi d$. The area of the circle is $A = \pi r^2$. (p. 471)

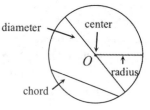

circumference   The perimeter (distance around) of a circle. (p. 498)

cluster sample   A subgroup of the population that has the similar characteristic of interest as that of the whole population. A cluster sample is one way to obtain a representative sample. (p. 450)

coefficient (numerical)   A number multiplying a variable or product of variables. For example, -7 is the coefficient of $-7x$. (p. 331)

combination histogram and box plot   A way to visually represent a distribution of data. The box plot is drawn with the same x-axis as the histogram.

combining like terms   Combining two or more like terms simplifies an expression by summing constants and summing those variable terms in which the same variables are raised to the same power. For example, combining like terms in the expression $3x + 7 + 5x - 3 + 2x^2 + 3y^2$ gives $8x + 4 + 2x^2 + 3y^2$. When working with algebra tiles, combining like terms involves putting together tiles with the same dimensions. (p. 444)

common   Shared.

common factor   A common factor is a factor that is the same for two or more terms. For example, x^2 is a common factor for $3x^2$ and $-5x^2y$.

common multiple   A number that is a multiple of the two or more numbers. For example, 24 and 48 are common multiples of 3 and 8.

Commutative Property of Addition   The Commutative Property of Addition states that if two terms are added, then the order may be reversed with no effect on the total. That is, $a + b = b + a$. For example, $7 + 12 = 12 + 7$. (p. 190)

Commutative Property of Multiplication   The Commutative Property of Multiplication states that if two expressions are multiplied, then the order may be reversed with no effect on the result. That is, $ab = ba$. For example, $5 \cdot 8 = 8 \cdot 5$. (p. 190)

comparison symbol   See *inequality symbol*.

compass   In this course, a compass is tool used to draw circles. (p. 469)

complement   The complement of an event is the set of all outcomes in the sample space that are not included in the event. (p. 265)

complementary angles   Two angles whose measures add up to 90°. Angles T and V are complementary because $m\angle T + m\angle V = 90°$. Complementary angles may also be adjacent, like $\angle ABC$ and $\angle CBD$ in the diagram at far right. (p. 466)

complex fraction   A fraction with a fraction in the numerator and/or denominator.

composite number   A number with more than two factors.

composite shape   A shape made of several simpler shapes. (p. 501)

compound event   A compound event in probability is an outcome that depends on two or more other events. For example, finding the probability that both a red ball and also a blue block are drawn from a bag in two draws. (p. 271, 277)

congruent   Two shapes are congruent if they have exactly the same shape and size. Congruent shapes are similar and have a scale factor of 1.

conjecture   An educated guess that often results from noticing a pattern.

consecutive integers   Integers that are in order without skipping any integers. For example, 8, 9, and 10 are consecutive integers. (p. 302)

constant of proportionality (k)   In a proportional relationship, equations are of the form $y = kx$, where k is the constant of proportionality. (p. 210)

constant term   A number that is not multiplied by a variable. In the expression $2x + 3(5 - 2x) + 8$, the number 8 is a constant term. The number 3 is not a constant term, because it is multiplied by a variable inside the parentheses. (p. 226, 331)

construction (geometric)   In mathematics, it is the process of using a straightedge and compass to create geometric diagrams. (p. 469)

convenience sample   A subgroup of the population for which it was easy to collect data. A convenience sample is not a random sample. (p. 450)

coordinate   The number corresponding to a point on the number line or an ordered pair (x, y) that corresponds to a point in a two-dimensional coordinate system. In an ordered pair, the x-coordinate appears first and the y-coordinate appears second. For example, the point $(3, 5)$ has an x-coordinate of 3. See *ordered pair*.

coordinate graph (system)   A system of graphing ordered pairs of numbers on a coordinate plane. An ordered pair represents a point, with the first number giving the horizontal position relative to the x-axis and the second number giving the vertical position relative to the y-axis. Also see *ordered pair*. (p. 87)

corresponding parts   Points, sides, edges, or angles in two or more figures that are images of each other with respect to a transformation. If two figures are congruent, then the corresponding parts of the figures are congruent to each other. See *ratio of similarity* and *congruent*. (p. 194)

counterexample   An example showing that a statement has at least one exception; that is, a situation in which the statement is false. For example, the number 4 is a counterexample to the statement that all even numbers are greater than 7.

cross section   The intersection of a three-dimensional solid and a plane. (p. 509)

cube   A polyhedron of six faces, each of which is a square. (p. 504)

cubic unit   A cube, each of whose edges measure 1 unit in length. Volume is measured in cubic units.

data display   A visual way for organizing information. Data displays used in this course are bar graphs, box plots, dot plots, histograms, scatter plots, stem-and-leaf plots, and Venn diagrams.

decimal point   The dot separating the whole number from the decimal portion, that is, the ones and tenths places in a decimal number.

degree   A unit for measuring angles. Usually denoted by ° (the degree symbol). There are 360° in one full rotation. (p. 457)

denominator   The lower part of a fraction, which expresses into how many equal parts the whole is divided.

dependent events   Two events are dependent if the outcome of one event affects the probability of the other event. For example, if one card is drawn out of a deck of cards, then the probability that the first card is red is $\frac{26}{52} = \frac{1}{2}$ because 26 of the 52 cards are red. However, the probability of the second card now depends on the result of the first selection. If the first card was red, then there are now 25 red cards remaining in a deck of 51 cards, and the probability that the second card is red is $\frac{25}{51}$. The second event (selecting the second card) is dependent on the first event (selecting the first card). (p. 266)

diameter   A line segment drawn through the center of a circle with both endpoints on the circle. The length of a diameter is usually denoted d. Note that the length of a circle's diameter is twice the length of its radius. *See* circle. (p. 471)

difference   The result of subtraction.

dimensions   The dimensions of a figure that is a flat region or space tell how far that the figure extends in each direction. For example, the dimensions of a rectangle might be 16 cm wide by 7 cm high. (p. 511)

Distributive Property   For any a, b, and c, $a(b+c) = ab + ac$. For example, $10(7+2) = 10 \cdot 7 + 10 \cdot 2$. (p. 116)

dividend   A quantity to be divided. (See *divisor*.)

divisible   A number is divisible by another if the remainder of the division is zero.

division ($\div$)   The inverse operation to multiplication, or the operation that creates equal groups.

divisor   The quantity by which another quantity is to be divided. dividend/divisor = quotient + remainder (if there is any).

Dot Plot

dot plot   A way of displaying data that has an order and can be placed on a number line. Dot plots are generally used when the data is discrete (separate and distinct) and numerous pieces of data fall on most values.

double-peaked   See *shape (of a data display)*.

edge   In three dimensions, a line segment formed by the intersection of two faces of a polyhedron. (p. 506)

endpoint   A point that mark the ends of a line segment or ray. (p. 460)

enlarge   To make larger. (p. 399)

enlargement ratio   The ratio of similarity comparing a figure to a similar larger figure is often called the enlargement ratio. This ratio shows by what factor the first figure is enlarged to get the second figure.

equal (=)   Two quantities are equal when they have the same value. For example, when $x = 4$, the expression $x + 8$ is equal to the expression $3x$ because the values of the expressions are the same.

equally likely   Outcomes or events are considered to be equally likely when they have the same probability.

equation   A mathematical sentence in which two expressions have an "equals" sign (=) between them indicating that they have an equal value. For example, the equation $7x + 4.2 = -8$ states that the expression $7x + 4.2$ has the value -8. In this course, an equation is often used to represent a rule relating two quantities.

Equation Mat   An Equation Mat puts two Expression Mats side-by-side to find the value(s) which make the expressions equal. Legal moves are used to find the value(s) that makes the expressions equal. For example, the Equation Mat at right represents the equation $2(x + 1) - 1 = x + 4$. The two sides of the mat are equal when $x = 3$. Also see *"legal" moves*. (p. 339)

equilateral   A polygon is equilateral if all of its sides have equal length. The word "equilateral" comes from "equi" (meaning "equal") and "lateral" (meaning "side"). Equilateral triangles not only have sides of equal length, but also angles of equal measure. However, a polygon with more than three sides may be equilateral without having congruent angles. For example, see the rhombus at right.

equivalent expressions   Two expressions are equivalent if they have the same value. For example, $2 + 3$ is equivalent to $1 + 4$. (p. 88)

equivalent fractions   Two fractions are equivalent if they have the same numerical value. For example, 3/6 and 5/10 are equivalent fractions. (p. 48)

equivalent ratios   Two ratios are equivalent if they have the same value when simplified. (p. 249)

evaluate (an expression) To find the numerical value of. To evaluate an expression, substitute the value(s) given for the variable(s) and perform the operations according to the Order of Operations. For example, evaluating $2x + y - 10$ when $x = 4$ and $y = 3$ gives the value 1. Also see *expression*. (p. 143)

event One or more results of an experiment. (p. 40)

experimental probability The probability based on data collected in experiments. The experimental probability of an event is defined to be $\frac{\text{number of successful outcomes in the experiment}}{\text{total number of outcomes in the experiment}}$. (p. 40)

exponent In an expression of the form b^a, a is called the exponent. For example, in the expression 2^5, 5 is called the exponent (2 is the base, and 32 is the value). The exponent indicates how many times to use the base as a multiplier. For example, in 2^5, 2 is used 5 times: $2^5 = 2 \cdot 2 \cdot 2 \cdot 2 \cdot 2 = 32$. For exponents of zero, the rule is: for any number $x \neq 0$, $x^0 = 1$. (p. 137)

expression An expression is a combination of individual terms separated by plus or minus signs. Numerical expressions combine numbers and operation symbols; algebraic (variable) expressions include variables. For example, $4 + (5 - 3)$ is a numerical expression. In an algebraic expression, if each of the following terms, $6xy^2$, 24, and $\frac{y-3}{4+x}$, are combined, the result may be $6xy^2 + 24 - \frac{y-3}{4+x}$. An expression does not have an "equals" sign. (p. 137, 331)

Expression Comparison Mat An Expression Comparison Mat puts two Expression Mats side-by-side so they can be compared to see which represents the greater value. For example, in the Expression Comparison Mat at right, Mat A represents −3, while Mat B represents −2. Since −2 > −3 Mat B is greater. (p. 319)

Expression Mat An organizing tool used to visually represent an expression with algebra tiles. (p. 230)

face One of the flat surfaces of a polyhedron, including the base(s). (p. 506)

factor (1) In arithmetic: when two or more integers are multiplied, each of the integers is a factor of the product. For example, 4 is a factor of 24, because $4 \cdot 6 = 24$.
(2) In algebra: when two or more algebraic expressions are multiplied together, each of the expressions is a factor of the product. For example, x^2 is a factor of $-17x^2y^3$, because $(x^2)(-17y^3) = -17x^2y^3$. (3) To factor an expression is to write it as a product. For example, the factored form of $3x - 18$ is $3(x - 6)$. (p. 331, 341)

fair game A game in which each player has an equally likely chance of winning. (p. 9)

family of fractions   All fractions that are equivalent to each other form a family of fractions. See *equivalent fractions*. (p. 249)

first quartile (Q1)   The median of the lower half of an ordered set of data is the lower quartile. (p. 387)

formula   An equation that shows a mathematical relationship.

fraction   The quotient of two quantities in the form $\frac{a}{b}$ where b is not equal to 0.

Fraction Busters   "Fraction Busting" is a method of simplifying equations involving fractions that uses the Multiplicative Property of Equality to rearrange the equation so that no fractions remain. To use this method, multiply both sides of an equation by the common denominator of all the fractions in the equation. The result will be an equivalent equation with no fractions. For example, when given the equation $\frac{x}{7}+2=\frac{x}{3}$, we can multiply both sides by the "Fraction Buster" 21. The resulting equation, $3x+42=7x$, is equivalent to the original but contains no fractions. (p. 408)

fraction greater than one   A fraction in which the numerator is greater than the denominator.

frequency   The number of times that something occurs within an interval or data set.

generic rectangle   A type of diagram used to visualize multiplying expressions without algebra tiles. Each expression to be multiplied forms a side length of the rectangle, and the product is the sum of the areas of the sections of the rectangle. For example, the generic rectangle at right may be used to multiply $(2x+5)$ by $(x+3)$. (p. 86, 190)

$$(2x+5)(x+3)=2x^2+11x+15$$

area as a product   area as a sum

Giant One   A fraction that is equal to 1. Multiplying any fraction by a Giant One will create a new fraction equivalent to the original fraction. (p. 48)

$$\frac{2}{3}\cdot\frac{2}{2}=\frac{4}{6}$$

graph   A graph represents numerical information in a visual form. The numbers may come from a table, situation (pattern), or rule (equation or inequality). Most of the graphs in this course show points, lines, and/or curves on a two-dimensional coordinate system like the one at right or on a single axis called a number line (see diagram below right).

−5 −4 −3 −2 −1 0 1 2 3 4 5 x

graphic organizer (GO)   A visual representation of concepts or ideas you have learned. It helps with brainstorming and/or organizing information. It can make connections between ideas more clear. Examples are concept maps, charts, and Venn diagrams.

greater than   One expression is greater than another if its value is larger. We indicate this relationship with the greater than symbol ">". For example, $4 + 5$ is greater than $1 + 1$. We write $4 + 5 > 1 + 1$. (p. 322)

greatest common factor (GCF)   For integers, the greatest positive integer that is a common factor of two or more integers. For example, the greatest common factor of 28 and 42 is 14. (p. 322)

height   (a) Triangle: the length of a segment that connects a vertex of the triangle to a line containing the opposite base (side) and is perpendicular to that line. (b) Trapezoid: the length of any segment that connects a point on one base of the trapezoid to the line containing the opposite base and is perpendicular to that line. (c) Parallelogram (includes rectangle, rhombus, and square): the length of any segment that connects a point on one base of the parallelogram to the line containing the opposite base and is perpendicular to that line. (d) Pyramid and cone: the length of the segment that connects the apex to a point in the plane containing the base of a figure and is perpendicular to that plane. (e) Prism or cylinder: the length of a segment that connects one base of the figure to the plane containing the other base and is perpendicular to that plane.

hexagon   A polygon with six sides. (p. 506)

histogram   A way of displaying data that is much like a bar graph in that the height of the bars is proportional to the number of elements. The difference is that each bar of a histogram represents the number of data elements in a range of values, such as the number of people who weigh from 100 pounds up to, but not including, 120 pounds. Each range of values should have the same width. Also see *bar graph*. (p. 382)

horizontal   Parallel to the horizon. The *x*-axis of a coordinate graph is the horizontal axis. (p. 121)

hundredths grid   A square with an area of 1 unit in which each side is divided into tenths. The area of each small square is $\frac{1}{10}$ by $\frac{1}{10}$ or $\frac{1}{100}$. (p. 154)

Identity Property of Addition   The Identity Property of Addition states that adding zero to any expression leaves the expression unchanged. That is, $a + 0 = a$. For example, $7 + 0 = 7$, and $-2y + 0 = -2y$.

Identity Property of Multiplication The Identity Property of Multiplication states that multiplying any expression by 1 leaves the expression unchanged. That is, $a(1) = a$. For example, $437x \cdot 1 = 437x$. (p. 46)

impossibility An event with a probability of zero.

improper fraction *See* fraction greater than one.

independent events If the outcome of a probabilistic event does not affect the probability of another event, then the events are independent. For example, assume that a normal six-sided die is being rolled twice to determine the probability of rolling a 1 twice. The result of the first roll does not affect the probability of rolling a 1 on the second roll. Since the probability of rolling a 1 on the first roll is $\frac{1}{6}$ and the probability of rolling a 1 on the second roll is also $\frac{1}{6}$, then the probability of rolling two 1s in a row is $\frac{1}{6} \cdot \frac{1}{6} = \frac{1}{36}$. (p. 266)

inequality An inequality consists of two expressions on either side of an inequality symbol. For example, the inequality $7x + 4.2 < -8$ states that the expression $7x + 4.2$ has a value less than −8. (p. 336)

inequality symbols The symbol $\leq$ read from left to right means "less than or equal to," the symbol $\geq$ read from left to right means "greater than or equal to," and the symbols $<$ and $>$ mean "less than" and "greater than," respectively. For example, "$7 < 13$" means that 7 is less than 13. (p. 322)

inference A statistical prediction. (p. 455)

integers The set of numbers $\{\ldots, -3, -2, -1, 0, 1, 2, 3, \ldots\}$. (p. 91)

interest An amount paid which is a percentage of an initial value (principal). For example, a savings account may offer 4% annual interest rate, which means they will pay $4.00 in interest for a principal of $100 kept in the account for one year. (p. 417)

interquartile range (IQR) A way to measure the spread of data. It is calculated by subtracting the first quartile from the third quartile. (p. 387)

interval A set of numbers between two given numbers. (p. 121)

inverse operation An operation that undoes another operation. For example, multiplication is the inverse operation for division.

irrational numbers The set of numbers that cannot be expressed in the form $\frac{a}{b}$, where a and b are integers and $b \neq 0$. For example, π and $\sqrt{2}$ are irrational numbers. (p. 490)

isosceles trapezoid A trapezoid with two (non-parallel) sides of equal length.

isosceles triangle   A triangle with two sides of equal length.

lateral face   A (flat) sides of a polyhedron. It is always a polygon. (p. 506)

least common multiple (LCM)   The smallest common multiple of a set of two or more integers. For example, the least common multiple of 4, 6, and 8 is 24.

"legal" moves   When working with an Equation Mat or Expression Comparison Mat, there are certain "legal" moves you can make with the algebra tiles that keep the relationship between the two sides of the mat intact. For example, removing an x tile from the positive region of each side of an equation mat is a legal move; it keeps the expressions on each side of the mat equal. The legal moves are those justified by the properties of the real numbers. (p. 340)

less than   (1) One expression is less than another if its value is not as large. This relationship is indicated with the less than symbol "$<$." For example, $1+1$ is less than $4+5$, so the comparison is written as $1+1<4+5$. (2) Sometimes the comparison is made that one amount is a certain quantity less than another amount. For example, a student movie ticket might cost two dollars *less than* an adult ticket. (p. 322)

like terms   Two or more terms that contain the same variable(s), with corresponding variables raised to the same power. For example, $5x^2$ and $2x^2$ are like terms. See *combining like terms*. (p. 226)

line   A line is an undefined term in geometry. A line is one-dimensional and continues without end in two directions. A line is made up of points and has no thickness. A line may be named with a letter (such as l), but also may be labeled using two points on the line, such as $\overleftrightarrow{AB}$ shown the right.

$$\longleftarrow\!\!\!\!\bullet\!\!-\!\!-\!\!-\!\!-\!\!\bullet\!\!\longrightarrow$$

$$A \qquad\qquad B$$

line segment   The portion of a line between two points. A line segment is named using its endpoints. For example, the line segment at right may be named either $\overline{AB}$ or $\overline{BA}$.

$$\bullet\!\!-\!\!-\!\!-\!\!-\!\!\bullet$$

$$A \qquad\qquad B$$

lowest common denominator (LCD)   The smallest common multiple of the denominators of two or more fractions. For example, the LCD of $\frac{5}{12}$ and $\frac{3}{8}$ is 24.

lowest terms of a fraction   A fraction for which the numerator and the denominator have no common factor greater than one.

mean   The mean, or average, of several numbers is one way of defining the "middle" of the numbers. To find the average of a group of numbers, add the numbers together then divide by the number of numbers in the set. For example, the average of the numbers 1, 5, and 6 is $(1+5+6)\div 3=4$. The mean is generally the best measure of central tendency when there are not outliers in the data set. See *average*. (p. 13)

measure of central tendency Mean and median are measures of central tendency, reflecting special statistical information about a set of data. See *center (of a data distribution)*. (p. 19)

measurement For the purposes of this course, a measurement is an indication of the size or magnitude of a geometric figure. For example, an appropriate measurement of a line segment would be its length. Appropriate measurements of a square would include not only the length of a side, but also its area and perimeter. The measure of an angle represents the number of degrees of rotation from one ray to the other about the vertex. (p. 511)

median The middle number of an ordered set of data. If there is no distinct middle, then the average of the two middle numbers is the median. The median is generally more accurate than the mean as a measure of central tendency when there are outliers in the data set. (p. 19)

mixed number (fraction) A number that consists of an integer and a fraction. For example, $3\frac{3}{8}$.

multiple The product of a whole number and any other (nonzero) whole number. For example, 15 is a multiple of 5.

multiple representations of a portion See *portions web*.

multiplication ($\cdot$) An operation that reflects repeated addition. For example, $3 \cdot 4 = 4 + 4 + 4$.

multiplicative identity The number 1 is called the multiplicative identity because multiplying any number by 1 does not change the number. For example, $7(1) = 7$. (p. 48)

Multiplicative Identity Property The Multiplicative Identity Property states that multiplying any expression by 1 leaves the expression unchanged. That is, $a(1) = a$. For example, $437x \cdot 1 = 437x$. (p. 175)

multiplicative inverse The multiplicative inverse for a non-zero number is the number we can multiply by to get the multiplicative identity, 1. For example, for the number 5, the multiplicative inverse is $\frac{1}{5}$; for the number $\frac{2}{3}$ the multiplicative inverse is $\frac{3}{2}$. (p. 160)

multiplier The number you can multiply by in order to increase or decrease an amount. See *scale factor*. (p. 187)

mutually exclusive Two events are mutually exclusive if they have no outcomes in common. (p. 275)

negative number A negative number is a number less than zero. Negative numbers are graphed on the negative side of a number line, which is to the left of the origin. (p. 91)

net   A drawing of each of the faces of a prism or pyramid, as if it were cut along its edges and flattened out.

number line   A diagram representing all real numbers as points on a line. All real numbers are assigned to points. The numbers are called the coordinates of the points and the point for which the number 0 is assigned is called the origin. Also see *boundary point*. (p. 91)

numerator   The number above the bar in a fraction that tells the numbers of parts in relationship to the number of parts in the whole.

obtuse angle   Any angle that measures between (but not including) 90° and 180°. (p. 460)

obtuse triangle   A triangle with one obtuse angle.

octagon   A polygon with eight sides. (p. 506)

one-dimensional   Something that does not have any width or depth. Lines and curves are one-dimensional. (p. 511)

operation   A mathematical process such as addition, subtraction, multiplication, division, raising to a power, or taking a root.

opposite (of a number)   The same number but with the opposite sign (+ or −). The additive inverse.

Order of Operations   The specific order in which certain operations are to be carried out to evaluate or simplify expressions: parentheses (or other grouping symbols), exponents (powers or roots), multiplication and division (from left to right), and addition and subtraction (from left to right). (p. 137)

ordered pair   Two numbers written in order as follows: (x, y). The primary use of ordered pairs in this course is to represent points in an xy-coordinate system. The first coordinate (x) represents the distance from the x-axis. The second coordinate (y) represents the distance from the y-axis. For example, the ordered pair $(3, 5)$ represents the point shown in bold at right.

origin   The point on a coordinate plane where the x-axis and y-axis intersect is called the origin. This point has coordinates $(0, 0)$. The point assigned to zero on a number line is also called the origin. See *axis*.

outcome   Possible result in an experiment or consequence of an action. (p. 40, 266)

outlier A number in a set of data that is much larger or much smaller than the other numbers in the set. (p. 393)

parallel Two or more straight lines on a flat surface that do not intersect (no matter how far they are extended) are parallel. The matching arrows on the parallelogram (see below) indicate that those segments are parallel.

parallel box plot A way to visually compare multiple data distributions by drawing each of their box plots on the same axis. (p. 444)

parallelogram A quadrilateral with two pairs of parallel sides. (p. 10)

pentagon A polygon with five sides. (p. 506)

percent (%) A ratio that compares a number to 100. Percents are often written using the "%" symbol. For example, 0.75 is equal to $\frac{75}{100}$ or 75%. (p. 23)

percent ruler A diagram like the one shown at right. It is used to visually aid in determining an amount that is a percent of a whole. (p. 292)

0   whole
|—+—+—+—+—+—+—+—+—+—+—+—|
0%   5   100%

perimeter The distance around a figure on a flat surface. (p. 10)

Perimeter =
$5 + 8 + 4 + 6 = 23$ units

perpendicular Two rays, line segments, or lines that meet (intersect) to form a right angle (90°) are called perpendicular. A line and a flat surface may also be perpendicular if the line does not lie on the flat surface but intersects the surface and forms a right angle with every line on the flat surface passing through the point of intersection. A small square at the point of intersection of two lines or segments indicates that the lines form a right angle and are therefore perpendicular.

pi (π) The ratio of the circumference (C) of the circle to its diameter (d). For every circle, $\pi = \frac{\text{circumference}}{\text{diameter}} = \frac{C}{d}$. Numbers such as 3.14, 3.14159, or $\frac{22}{7}$ are approximations of π. (p. 498)

place value The number assigned to each place that a digit occupies.

plane A plane is a two-dimensional flat surface that extends without end. It is made up of points and has no thickness. (p. 509)

point An exact location in space. In two dimensions, an ordered pair specifies a point on a coordinate plane. See *ordered pair*.

polygon   A two-dimensional closed figure of three or more line segments (sides) connected end to end. Each segment is a side and only intersects the endpoints of its two adjacent sides. Each point of intersection is a vertex. At right are two examples of polygons. (p. 506)

polyhedron   A three-dimensional figure with no holes for which all faces are polygons. (p. 506)

population   A collection of objects or group of people about whom information is gathered. (p. 450)

portion   A part of something; a part of a whole.

portions web   The web diagram at right illustrates that fractions, decimals, and percents are different ways to represent a portion of a number. Portions may also be represented in words, such as "four fifths" or "seven fourths," or as diagrams.

Representations of a Portion

positive numbers   Numbers that are greater than zero. (p. 91)

power   A number or variable raised to an exponent in the form x^n. See *exponent*.

prime factor   A factor that is a prime number. (p. 52)

prime factorization   The expression of a number as the product of prime factors.

prime number   A positive integer with exactly two factors. The only factors of a prime number are 1 and itself. For example, the numbers 2, 3, 17, and 31 are all prime. (p. 52)

principal   Initial investment or capital. An initial value. (p. 417)

prism   A three-dimensional figure that consists of two parallel congruent polygons (called *bases*) and a vertical surface containing segments connecting each point on each side of one base to the corresponding point on the other base. The lateral surface of a prism consists of parallelograms. (p. 506)

probability   A number that represents how likely an event is to happen. When a event has a finite number of equally-likely outcomes, the probability that one of those outcomes, called A, will occur is expressed as a ratio and written as: $P(A) = \frac{\text{number of successful outcomes}}{\text{total number of possible outcomes}}$. For example, when flipping a coin, the probability of getting tails, $P(\text{tails})$, is 1/2 because there is only one tail (successful outcome) out of the two possible equally likely outcomes (a head and a tail). Probability may be written as a ratio, decimal, or percent. A probability of 0 (or 0%) indicates that the occurrence of that outcome is impossible, while a probability of 1 (or 100%) indicates that the event must occur. Events that "might happen" will have values somewhere between 0 and 1 (or between 0% and 100%). (p. 40)

probability table *See area model.*

probability tree Tree diagrams are useful for representing possible outcomes of probability experiments. For example, the tree diagram at right represents the possible outcomes when a coin is flipped twice.

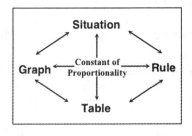

product The result of multiplying. For example, the product of 4 and 5 is 20.

proportion An equation stating that two ratios (fractions) are equal. For example, the equation at right is a proportion. A proportion is a useful type of equation to set up when solving problems involving proportional relationships. (p. 210)

$$\frac{68 \text{ votes for Mr. Mears}}{100 \text{ people surveyed}} = \frac{34 \text{ votes for Mr. Mears}}{50 \text{ people surveyed}}$$

proportional equation An equation stating that two ratios (fractions) are equal. (p. 210)

proportional relationship Two values are in a proportional relationship if a proportion may be set up that relates the values. (p. 210)

proportions web The web diagram at right illustrates the connections between different representations of the same proportional relationship. (p. 212)

```
                    Situation
                       ↑
Graph ←——Constant of——→ Rule
       Proportionality
                       ↓
                     Table
```

protractor A geometric tool used for physically measuring the number of degrees in an angle. (p. 458)

pyramid A three-dimensional figure with a base that is a polygon. The lateral faces are formed by connecting each vertex of the base to a single point (the vertex of the pyramid) that is above or below the surface that contains the base. (p. 506)

quadrants The coordinate plane is divided by its axes into four quadrants. The quadrants are numbered as shown in the first diagram at right. When graphing data that has no negative values, sometimes a graph that shows only the first quadrant is used.

4-quadrant graph:

II	I
III	IV

1st-quadrant graph:

quadrilateral A polygon with four sides. The shape at right is a quadrilateral. (p. 506)

quartile Along with the median, the quartiles divide a set of data into four groups of the same size. Also see *box plot*. (p. 387)

quotient The result of a division problem. (p. 162)

radius (plural: radii)   A line segment drawn from the center of a circle to a point on the circle. (p. 471)

random   An event is random if its result cannot be known (and can only be guessed) until the event is completed. For example, the flip of a fair coin is random because the coin can either land on heads or tails and the outcome cannot be known for certain until after the coin is flipped.

random number   A number generated by a process whose outcome does not follow any sort of pattern and thus the number cannot be predicted.

random number generator   A computational device designed to generate a set of numbers that lack any pattern. (p. 259)

random sample   A sample which was chosen as a result of a random process. A random sample can represent the whole population well. (p. 455)

range   The range of a set of data is the difference between the highest and lowest values. (p. 387)

rate   A ratio comparing two quantities, often a comparison of time. For example, miles per hour.

ratio   A ratio compares two quantities by division. A ratio may be written using a colon, but is more often written as a fraction. For example, the comparison may be made of the ratio of female students in a particular school to the total number of students in the school. This ratio could be written as 1521:2906 or as the fraction shown at right. (p. 214)

$$\frac{1521 \text{ female students}}{2906 \text{ total students}}$$

ratio of similarity   The ratio of any pair of corresponding sides of two similar figures. This means that once it is determined that two figures are similar, all of the pairs of corresponding sides of the figures have the same ratio. For example, for the similar triangles $\triangle ABC$ and $\triangle DEF$ at right, the ratio of similarity is $\frac{5}{11}$. The ratio of similarity may also be called the linear scale factor. (p. 194)

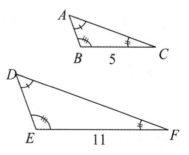

rational numbers   Numbers that may be expressed in the form $\frac{a}{b}$, where a and b are integers and $b \neq 0$. For example, 0.75 is a rational number because 0.75 may be expressed in the form $\frac{3}{4}$. (p. 70)

ray A ray is part of a line that starts at one point and extends without end in one direction. In the example at right, ray $\overrightarrow{AB}$ is part of $\overleftrightarrow{AB}$ that starts at A and contains all of the points of $\overleftrightarrow{AB}$ that are on the same side of A as point B, including A. Point A is the endpoint of $\overrightarrow{AB}$. (p. 460)

[diagram of ray with points A and B]

reciprocals The reciprocal of a nonzero number is its multiplicative inverse, that is, the reciprocal of x is $\frac{1}{x}$. For a number in the form $\frac{a}{b}$, where a and b are non-zero, the reciprocal is $\frac{b}{a}$. The product of a number and its reciprocal is 1. For example, the reciprocal of 12 is $\frac{1}{12}$, because $12 \cdot \frac{1}{12} = 1$. (p. 160)

rectangle A quadrilateral with four right angles. (p. 10)

reduce To make smaller. (p. 399)

regular polygon A polygon is regular if the polygon is a convex polygon with congruent angles and congruent sides. For example, the shape at right is a regular hexagon.

REGULAR HEXAGON

repeating decimal A repeating decimal is a decimal that repeats the same sequence of digits forever from some point onward. For example, 4.56073073073… is a decimal for which the three digits 073 continue to repeat forever. Repeating decimals are always the decimal expansions of rational numbers. (p. 81)

representative sample A subgroup of the population that has the similar characteristic of interest as that of the whole population. Representative samples are usually the result of random sampling. (p. 450)

remainder The amount left over when the divisor does not divide the dividend exactly. For example $63 \div 5$ is 12 with a remainder of 3.

rewrite To rewrite an equation or expression is to write an equivalent equation or expression. Rewriting could involve using the Distributive Property, combining like terms, or using Fraction Busters. We usually rewrite in order to change expressions or equations into more useful forms or sometimes, just simpler forms. (p. 146)

rhombus A quadrilateral with four congruent sides. Also see *equilateral*.

right angle An angle that measures 90°. A small square is used to note a right angle, as shown in the example at right.

90°

right triangle A triangle that has one right angle. The side of a right triangle opposite the right angle is called the "hypotenuse," and the two sides adjacent to the right angle are called "legs."

hypotenuse leg #2 leg #1

round (a number)   To express an approximate value of a number that is exact to a given decimal place. For example, if the number 1234.56 is 1235 when rounded to the nearest whole number and is 1200 when rounded to the nearest 100.

rule   A rule is an equation or inequality that represents the relationship between two numerical quantities. A rule is often used to represent the relationship between quantities in a table, a pattern, a real-world situation, or a graph.

sample   A subset (group) of a given population with the same characteristics as the whole population. (p. 450)

sample space   The collection of all possible outcomes of an event. (p. 400)

scale (scaling)   The ratio between a length of the representation (such as a map, model, or diagram) and the corresponding length of the actual object. For example, the map of a city may use one inch to represent one mile. (p. 36)

scale drawing   A drawing that shows a real object with accurate sizes except they have all been reduced or enlarged by a certain amount (called the scale factor). (p. 192)

scale factor   A ratio that compares the sizes of the parts of one figure or object to the sizes of the corresponding parts of a similar figure or object. In this course it is also referred to as the multiplier. (p. 194)

scale on axes   The scale on an axis tells you what number each successive tick mark on the axis represents. A complete graph has the scale marked with numbers on each axis. Each axis should be scaled so that each interval represents the same amount. (p. 121)

scalene triangle   A triangle with no congruent sides. (p. 293)

scatter plot   Two related sets of data may have the corresponding values of the sets listed as ordered pairs. If these ordered pairs are graphed in the coordinate plane, then the result is a scatter plot.

set   A collection of items.

shape (of a data display)   Statisticians use the following words to describe the overall shape of a data distribution: symmetric, skewed, single-peaked, double-peaked, and uniform. Examples are shown below. (p. 393)

symmetric   skewed   single-peaked   double-peaked   uniform

side of an angle   One of the two rays that form an angle.

similar figures Similar figures have the same shape but are not necessarily the same size. For example the two triangles at right are similar. In similar figures, the measures of corresponding angles are equal and the ratio of the corresponding sides lengths are equal. (p. 194)

simple interest Interest paid on the principal alone. (p. 417)

simplify To simplify an expression is to write a less complicated expression with the same value. A simplified expression has no parentheses and no like terms. For example, the expression $3-(2x+7)-4x$ may be simplified to $-4-6x$. When working with algebra tiles, a simplified expression uses the fewest possible tiles to represent the original expression. (p. 226)

simulation (probability) When conducting an experiment with an event that is unrealistic to perform, a simulation can be used. A simulation is a similar experiment that has the same probabilities as the original experiment. (p. 259)

single-peaked See *shape (of a data display)*. (p. 393)

skewed (data display) See *shape (of a data display)*. (p. 393)

solution The number or numbers that when substituted into an equation or inequality make the equation or inequality true. For example, $x = 4$ is a solution to the equation $3x = 12$ because $3x$ equals 12 when $x = 4$. (p. 363)

solve To find all the solutions to an equation or an inequality. The solution(s) may be number(s), variable(s), or an expression. (p. 340)

spread (data display) A measure of the amount of variability in a data set. Three ways to measure spread are the range, the mean absolute deviation, and the interquartile range. (p. 387)

square A quadrilateral with four right angles and four congruent sides.

square

square units The units used to describe the measure of an area in the form of 1×1 unit squares.

stem-and-leaf plot A frequency distribution that arranges data so that all digits except the last digit in each piece of data are in the stem, the last digit of each piece of data are the leaves, and both stems and leaves are arranged in order from least to greatest. The example at right displays the data: 49, 52, 54, 58, 61, 61, 67, 68, 72, 73, 73, 73, 78, 82, 83, 108, 112, and 117. (p. 382)

"leaf"

4	9
5	2 4 8
6	1 1 7 8
7	2 3 3 3 8
8	2 3
9	
10	8
11	2 7

"stem"

stoplight icon   The icon (shown at right) will appear periodically throughout the text. Problems that display this icon contain errors of some type. (p. 43)

straight angle   An angle that measures 180°. This occurs when the rays of the angle point in opposite directions, forming a line. (p. 460)

180°

straightedge   A tool used as a guide to draw lines, rays, and segments. (p. 469)

subproblems   A problem solving strategy that breaks a problem into smaller parts that must be solved in order to solve the original, more complex problem.

substitution   Replacing one symbol with a number, a variable, or another algebraic expression of the same value. Substitution does not change the value of the overall expression. For example, suppose that the expression $13x - 6$ must be evaluated for $x = 4$. Since x has the value 4, 4 may be substituted into the expression wherever x appears, giving the equivalent expression $13(4) - 6$. (p. 143)

subtraction (–)   An operation that gives the difference between two numbers. (p. 147)

sum   The result of adding two or more numbers. For example, the sum of 4 and 5 is 9.

Super Giant One   A Giant One in which either or both the numerator and denominator are fractions. (p. 165)

supplementary angles   Two angles a and b for which $a + b = 180°$. Each angle is called the supplement of the other. In the example at right, angles A and B are supplementary. Supplementary angles are often adjacent. For example, since $\angle LMN$ is a straight angle, then $\angle LMP$ and $\angle PMN$ are supplementary angles because $m\angle LMP + m\angle PMN = 180°$. (p. 466)

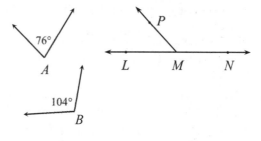

surface area   The sum of all the area(s) of the surface(s) of a three-dimensional solid. For example, the surface area of a prism is the sum of the areas of its top and bottom bases, and its vertical surfaces (lateral faces). (p. 503)

symmetric   See *shape (of a data display)*. (p. 393)

systematic list   A list created by following a system (organized process). When finding probabilities, a systematic list helps to find all outcomes of a sample space or event. (p. 277)

term A term is a single number, variable, or the product of numbers and variables, such as -45, $1.2x$, and $3xy^2$. (p. 137)

terminating decimal A terminating decimal is a decimal that has only a finite number of non-zero digits, such as 4.067. Terminating decimals are a particular kind of repeating decimal for which the repeating portion is zeros, so the example could be written 4.0670000000… but it is not necessary to write the zeros at the end. (p. 81)

theoretical probability A calculated probability based on the possible outcomes when each outcome has the same chance of occurring: (number of successful outcomes)/(total number of possible outcomes). (p. 40)

third quartile (Q3) The median of the upper half of an ordered set of data. (p. 387)

three-dimensional An object that has height, width, and depth. (p. 511)

tick mark A symbol that shows that a number line has been divided into intervals of equal length. See *number line*.

trapezoid A quadrilateral with at least one pair of parallel sides. (p. 10)

triangle A polygon with three sides. (p. 506)

triangle inequality In a triangle with side lengths a, b, and c, c must be less than the sum of a and b and greater than the difference of a and b. In the example at right, a is greater than b (that is, $a > b$), so the possible values for c are all numbers such that $c > a - b$ and $c < a + b$. (p. 476)

two-dimensional An object having length and width. (p. 511)

uniform See *shape (of a data display)*. (p. 393)

unit of measure A standard quantity (such as a centimeter, second, square foot, or gallon) that is used to measure and describe an object. A single object may be measured using different units of measure. For example, a pencil may be 80 mm long, meaning that the pencil is 80 times as long as a unit of 1 mm. However, the same pencil is 8 cm long, so that the pencil is the same length as 8 cm laid end-to-end. This is because 1 cm is the same length as 10 mm.

unit rate A rate with a denominator of one when simplified. (p. 214)

variability *See* spread.

variable A symbol used to represent one or more numbers. In this course, letters of the English alphabet are used as variables. For example, in the expression $3x - (8.6xy + z)$, the variables are x, y, and z. (p. 220)

variable expression See *expression*.

vertex (plural: vertices) (1) For a two-dimensional geometric shape, a vertex is a point where two or more line segments or rays meet to form a "corner," such as in a polygon or angle. (2) For a three-dimensional polyhedron, a vertex is a point where the edges of the solid meet. (p. 460, 506)

examples of vertices

vertical At right angles to the horizon. On a coordinate graph, the y-axis runs vertically. (p. 121)

vertical angles The two opposite (that is, non-adjacent) angles formed by two intersecting lines. "Vertical" is a relationship between pairs of angles, so one angle cannot be called vertical. Angles that form a vertical pair are always congruent. (p. 466)

volume A measurement of the size of the three-dimensional region enclosed within an object. Volume is expressed as the number of $1 \times 1 \times 1$ unit cubes (or parts of cubes) that fit inside a solid. (p. 511)

voluntary response sample A subgroup of the population that chose to respond to a survey. A voluntary response sample is not a random sample. (p. 450)

x-axis The horizontal number line on a coordinate graph. See *axis*.

x-coordinate In an ordered pair, (x, y), that represents a point in the coordinate plane, x is the value of the x-coordinate. That is, the distance from the y-axis that is needed to plot the point. (p. 87)

y-axis The vertical number line on a coordinate graph. See *axis*.

y-coordinate In an ordered pair, (x, y), that represents a point in the coordinate plane, y is the value of the y-coordinate. That is, the distance from the x-axis that is needed to plot the point. (p. 87)

zero pair Two quantities whose sum is zero. A number and its opposite make a zero pair because their sum is 0. (p. 231)

Index
Student Version

Many of the pages referenced here contain a definition or an example of the topic listed, often within the body of a Math Notes box. Others contain problems that develop or demonstrate the topic. It may be necessary to read the text on several pages to fully understand the topic. Also, some problems listed here are good examples of the topic and may not offer any explanation. The page numbers below reflect the pages in the Student Version. References to Math Notes boxes are bolded.

Rate
  interest, 415, **417**
  of change, **214**
  relationship to distance and time, 379,
    380, 381
  unit, 207, **214**
Ratio, 246, **249**
  application, 533
  equivalent, **249**
  percent, **253**
  rate of change, **214**
Rational numbers, 70, 162
  adding, 88, 93
  division, 162
Ray, **460**, 462, **466**
Reasoning
  critiquing that of others, 527
  repeated, 531
Reciprocal, **160**
  fraction division, **165**
Recorder/Reporter, 4
Rectangle
  area, **10**
Rectangular prism, 512
Reduce, 187, **399**
Removing
  balanced sets, 320, **340**
  zeros, 320, 324, **340**
Renting the Hall, 415
Repeated reasoning, 531
Repeating decimal, 22, 71, 73, 78
  as a fraction, 79, **81**
Representations of a portion
  Checkpoint 2, 118, 541
Representations of a Portion web, 23, **24**, 45,
  81
Representative sample, 447, **450**, **455**
Resource Manager, 4
Response sample, voluntary, 448, **450**
Rewriting an expression, 146
Right angle, **460**, 462
Rock-Paper-Scissors, 264, 265
Rotation, 457
Ruler
  to measure angles. *See* protractor

S
Sample, 447, **450**, *Also see* survey
  cluster, 448, **450**
  convenience, 448, **450**
  population, **450**
  random, 453, **455**
  representative, 447, **450**, **455**
  voluntary response, **450**
Sample space, 38, **40**
  complement, 255
  modifying, 38
Sampling techniques, 448, 493
Scale, 192, **399**
  graphing, 113, 114, 119, **121**
  interval, **121**
  on a map, 193
Scale drawing, 192, 193, 530
Scale factor, 187, **194**, 384, 385, 390, 391,
  397, **399**, 410, *Also see* multiplier
Scalene triangle, 293
Scaling, **36**, 384, 385, 390
  interval, **36**
  volume, 526
Scavenger Hunt, 316
Secret Code (PI-14), 570
Septagon, **506**
Shape
  of a data distribution, **393**
Shape Challenge, 236, 237
Shapes
  similar, 187, 189, 192, **194**, 384
Shell Box, The, 517
Similar, 192
Similar figures, 187, 189, **194**, 384
Simple interest, 415, **417**
Simplify, **226**
  an expression, 132, 146
    term, 132, 135
      Checkpoint 7A, 400, 549
    order of operations, **137**
  legal move, 320, 327
  removing zeros, 320, 324
  with zero, 229
Simulation
  probability, 259
Single-peaked
  data distribution, **393**
Skewed
  data distribution, **393**

Common Core State Standards for Mathematics

Mathematics | Grade 7

In Grade 7, instructional time should focus on four critical areas: (1) developing understanding of and applying proportional relationships; (2) developing understanding of operations with rational numbers and working with expressions and linear equations; (3) solving problems involving scale drawings and informal geometric constructions, and working with two- and three-dimensional shapes to solve problems involving area, surface area, and volume; and (4) drawing inferences about populations based on samples.

(1) Students extend their understanding of ratios and develop understanding of proportionality to solve single- and multi-step problems. Students use their understanding of ratios and proportionality to solve a wide variety of percent problems, including those involving discounts, interest, taxes, tips, and percent increase or decrease. Students solve problems about scale drawings by relating corresponding lengths between the objects or by using the fact that relationships of lengths within an object are preserved in similar objects. Students graph proportional relationships and understand the unit rate informally as a measure of the steepness of the related line, called the slope. They distinguish proportional relationships from other relationships.

(2) Students develop a unified understanding of number, recognizing fractions, decimals (that have a finite or a repeating decimal representation), and percents as different representations of rational numbers. Students extend addition, subtraction, multiplication, and division to all rational numbers, maintaining the properties of operations and the relationships between addition and subtraction, and multiplication and division. By applying these properties, and by viewing negative numbers in terms of everyday contexts (e.g., amounts owed or temperatures below zero), students explain and interpret the rules for adding, subtracting, multiplying, and dividing with negative numbers. They use the arithmetic of rational numbers as they formulate expressions and equations in one variable and use these equations to solve problems.

(3) Students continue their work with area from Grade 6, solving problems involving the area and circumference of a circle and surface area of three-dimensional objects. In preparation for work on congruence and similarity in Grade 8 they reason about relationships among two-dimensional figures using scale drawings and informal geometric constructions, and they gain familiarity with the relationships between angles formed by intersecting lines. Students work with three-dimensional figures, relating them to two-dimensional figures by examining cross-sections. They solve real-world and mathematical problems involving area, surface area, and volume of two- and three-dimensional objects composed of triangles, quadrilaterals, polygons, cubes, and right prisms.

(4) Students build on their previous work with single data distributions to compare two data distributions and address questions about differences between populations. They begin informal work with random sampling to generate data sets and learn about the importance of representative samples for drawing inferences.

Grade 7 Overview

Ratios and Proportional Relationships

- Analyze proportional relationships and use them to solve real-world and mathematical problems.

The Number System

- Apply and extend previous understandings of operations with fractions to add, subtract, multiply, and divide rational numbers.

- Know that there are numbers that are not rational and approximate them by rational numbers.

Expressions and Equations

- Use properties of operations to generate equivalent expressions.

- Solve real-life and mathematical problems using numerical and algebraic expressions and equations.

Geometry

- Draw, construct and describe geometrical figures and describe the relationships between them.

- Solve real-life and mathematical problems involving angle measure, area, surface area, and volume.

- Solve real-life and mathematical problems involving volume of cylinders, cones, and spheres.

Statistics and Probability

- Use random sampling to draw inferences about a population.

- Draw informal comparative inferences about two populations.

- Investigate chance processes and develop, use, and evaluate probability models.

Mathematical Practices

1. Make sense of problems and persevere in solving them.

2. Reason abstractly and quantitatively.

3. Construct viable arguments and critique the reasoning of others.

4. Model with mathematics.

5. Use appropriate tools strategically.

6. Attend to precision.

7. Look for and make use of structure.

8. Look for and express regularity in repeated reasoning.

Ratios and Proportional Relationships   7.RP

Analyze proportional relationships and use them to solve real-world and mathematical problems.

1. Compute unit rates associated with ratios of fractions, including ratios of lengths, areas and other quantities measured in like or different units. *For example, if a person walks 1/2 mile in each 1/4 hour, compute the unit rate as the complex fraction* $^{1/2}/_{1/4}$ *miles per hour, equivalently 2 miles per hour.*

2. Recognize and represent proportional relationships between quantities.
    a. Decide whether two quantities are in a proportional relationship, e.g., by testing for equivalent ratios in a table or graphing on a coordinate plane and observing whether the graph is a straight line through the origin.
    b. Identify the constant of proportionality (unit rate) in tables, graphs, equations, diagrams, and verbal descriptions of proportional relationships.
    c. Represent proportional relationships by equations. *For example, if total cost t is proportional to the number n of items purchased at a constant price p, the relationship between the total cost and the number of items can be expressed as t = pn.*
    d. Explain what a point *(x, y)* on the graph of a proportional relationship means in terms of the situation, with special attention to the points (0, 0) and (1, *r*) where *r* is the unit rate.

3. Use proportional relationships to solve multistep ratio and percent problems. *Examples: simple interest, tax, markups and markdowns, gratuities and commissions, fees, percent increase and decrease, percent error.*

The Number System   7.NS

Apply and extend previous understandings of operations with fractions to add, subtract, multiply, and divide rational numbers.

1. Apply and extend previous understandings of addition and subtraction to add and subtract rational numbers; represent addition and subtraction on a horizontal or vertical number line diagram.
    a. Describe situations in which opposite quantities combine to make 0. *For example, a hydrogen atom has 0 charge because its two constituents are oppositely charged.*
    b. Understand $p + q$ as the number located a distance $|q|$ from p, in the positive or negative direction depending on whether q is positive or negative. Show that a number and its opposite have a sum of 0 (are additive inverses). Interpret sums of rational numbers by describing real-world contexts.
    c. Understand subtraction of rational numbers as adding the additive inverse, $p - q = p + (-q)$. Show that the distance between two rational numbers on the number line is the absolute value of their difference, and apply this principle in real-world contexts.
    d. Apply properties of operations as strategies to add and subtract rational numbers.

2. Apply and extend previous understandings of multiplication and division and of fractions to multiply and divide rational numbers.
    a. Understand that multiplication is extended from fractions to rational numbers by requiring that operations continue to satisfy the properties of operations, particularly the distributive property, leading to products such as $(-1)(-1) = 1$ and the rules for multiplying signed numbers. Interpret products of rational numbers by describing real-world contexts.
    b. Understand that integers can be divided, provided that the divisor is not zero, and every quotient of integers (with non-zero divisor) is a rational number. If p and q are integers, then $-(p/q) = (-p)/q = p/(-q)$. Interpret quotients of rational numbers by describing real world contexts.

c. Apply properties of operations as strategies to multiply and divide rational numbers.

    d. Convert a rational number to a decimal using long division; know that the decimal form of a rational number terminates in 0s or eventually repeats.

3. Solve real-world and mathematical problems involving the four operations with rational numbers.[1]

Expressions and Equations   7.EE

Use properties of operations to generate equivalent expressions.

1. Apply properties of operations as strategies to add, subtract, factor, and expand linear expressions with rational coefficients.

2. Understand that rewriting an expression in different forms in a problem context can shed light on the problem and how the quantities in it are related. *For example, $a + 0.05a = 1.05a$ means that "increase by 5%" is the same as "multiply by 1.05."*

Solve real-life and mathematical problems using numerical and algebraic expressions and equations.

3. Solve multi-step real-life and mathematical problems posed with positive and negative rational numbers in any form (whole numbers, fractions, and decimals), using tools strategically. Apply properties of operations to calculate with numbers in any form; convert between forms as appropriate; and assess the reasonableness of answers using mental computation and estimation strategies. *For example: If a woman making $25 an hour gets a 10% raise, she will make an additional 1/10 of her salary an hour, or $2.50, for a new salary of $27.50. If you want to place a towel bar 9 3/4 inches long in the center of a door that is 27 1/2 inches wide, you will need to place the bar about 9 inches from each edge; this estimate can be used as a check on the exact computation.*

4. Use variables to represent quantities in a real-world or mathematical problem, and construct simple equations and inequalities to solve problems by reasoning about the quantities.

    a. Solve word problems leading to equations of the form $px + q = r$ and $p(x + q) = r$, where p, q, and r are specific rational numbers. Solve equations of these forms fluently. Compare an algebraic solution to an arithmetic solution, identifying the sequence of the operations used in each approach. *For example, the perimeter of a rectangle is 54 cm. Its length is 6 cm. What is its width?*

    b. Solve word problems leading to inequalities of the form $px + q > r$ or $px + q < r$, where p, q, and r are specific rational numbers. Graph the solution set of the inequality and interpret it in the context of the problem. *For example: As a salesperson, you are paid $50 per week plus $3 per sale. This week you want your pay to be at least $100. Write an inequality for the number of sales you need to make, and describe the solutions.*

Geometry   7.G

Draw, construct, and describe geometrical figures and describe the relationships between them.

1. Solve problems involving scale drawings of geometric figures, including computing actual lengths and areas from a scale drawing and reproducing a scale drawing at a different scale.

2. Draw (freehand, with ruler and protractor, and with technology) geometric shapes with given conditions. Focus on constructing triangles from three measures of angles or sides, noticing when the conditions determine a unique triangle, more than one triangle, or no triangle.

3. Describe the two-dimensional figures that result from slicing three-dimensional figures, as in plane sections of right rectangular prisms and right rectangular pyramids.

---

[1] Computations with rational numbers extend the rules for manipulating fractions to complex fractions.

Solve real-life and mathematical problems involving angle measure, area, surface area, and volume.

4. Know the formulas for the area and circumference of a circle and use them to solve problems; give an informal derivation of the relationship between the circumference and area of a circle.

5. Use facts about supplementary, complementary, vertical, and adjacent angles in a multi-step problem to write and solve simple equations for an unknown angle in a figure.

6. Solve real-world and mathematical problems involving area, volume and surface area of two- and three-dimensional objects composed of triangles, quadrilaterals, polygons, cubes, and right prisms.

Statistics and Probability 7.SP

Use random sampling to draw inferences about a population.

1. Understand that statistics can be used to gain information about a population by examining a sample of the population; generalizations about a population from a sample are valid only if the sample is representative of that population. Understand that random sampling tends to produce representative samples and support valid inferences.

2. Use data from a random sample to draw inferences about a population with an unknown characteristic of interest. Generate multiple samples (or simulated samples) of the same size to gauge the variation in estimates or predictions. *For example, estimate the mean word length in a book by randomly sampling words from the book; predict the winner of a school election based on randomly sampled survey data. Gauge how far off the estimate or prediction might be.*

Draw informal comparative inferences about two populations.

3. Informally assess the degree of visual overlap of two numerical data distributions with similar variabilities, measuring the difference between the centers by expressing it as a multiple of a measure of variability. *For example, the mean height of players on the basketball team is 10 cm greater than the mean height of players on the soccer team, about twice the variability (mean absolute deviation) on either team; on a dot plot, the separation between the two distributions of heights is noticeable.*

4. Use measures of center and measures of variability for numerical data from random samples to draw informal comparative inferences about two populations. *For example, decide whether the words in a chapter of a seventh-grade science book are generally longer than the words in a chapter of a fourth-grade science book.*

Investigate chance processes and develop, use, and evaluate probability models.

5. Understand that the probability of a chance event is a number between 0 and 1 that expresses the likelihood of the event occurring. Larger numbers indicate greater likelihood. A probability near 0 indicates an unlikely event, a probability around 1/2 indicates an event that is neither unlikely nor likely, and a probability near 1 indicates a likely event.

6. Approximate the probability of a chance event by collecting data on the chance process that produces it and observing its long-run relative frequency, and predict the approximate relative frequency given the probability. *For example, when rolling a number cube 600 times, predict that a 3 or 6 would be rolled roughly 200 times, but probably not exactly 200 times.*

7. Develop a probability model and use it to find probabilities of events. Compare probabilities from a model to observed frequencies; if the agreement is not good, explain possible sources of the discrepancy.

    a. Develop a uniform probability model by assigning equal probability to all outcomes, and use the model to determine probabilities of events. *For example, if a student is selected at random from a class, find the probability that Jane will be selected and the probability that a girl will be selected.*

    b. Develop a probability model (which may not be uniform) by observing frequencies in data generated from a chance process. *For example, find the approximate probability that a spinning penny will land heads up or that a tossed paper cup will land open-end down. Do the outcomes for the spinning penny appear to be equally likely based on the observed frequencies?*

8. Find probabilities of compound events using organized lists, tables, tree diagrams, and simulation.

    a. Understand that, just as with simple events, the probability of a compound event is the fraction of outcomes in the sample space for which the compound event occurs.

    b. Represent sample spaces for compound events using methods such as organized lists, tables and tree diagrams. For an event described in everyday language (e.g., "rolling double sixes"), identify the outcomes in the sample space which compose the event.

    c. Design and use a simulation to generate frequencies for compound events. *For example, use random digits as a simulation tool to approximate the answer to the question: If 40% of donors have type A blood, what is the probability that it will take at least 4 donors to find one with type A blood?*